MACHINE TRANSLATION:
Past, Present, Future

ELLIS HORWOOD SERIES IN COMPUTERS AND THEIR APPLICATIONS

Series Editor: Brian Meek, Computer Centre, King's College, University of London

Atherton, R.	**Structured Programming with COMAL**
Bailey, R.	**Functional Programming with HOPE**
Barrett, R., Ramsay, A. & Sloman, A.	**POP-11: A Practical Language for Artificial Intelligence**
Berry, R.E.	**Programming Language Translation**
Bishop, P.	**Fifth Generation Computers: Concepts, Implementations and Uses**
Brailsford, D.F. & Walker, A.N.	**Introductory ALGOL 68 Programming**
Bull, G.M.	**The Dartmouth Time Sharing System**
Burns, A.	**New Information Technology**
Burns, A.	**The Microchip: Appropriate or Inappropriate Technology**
Carberry, J.C.	**COBOL**
Chivers, I.D.	**A Practical Introduction to Standard PASCAL**
Chivers, I.D. & Clark, M.W.	**Interactive FORTRAN 77: A Hands-on Approach**
Clark, M.W.	**pc-Portable FORTRAN**
Cope, T.	**Computing using BASIC: An Interactive Approach**
Dahlstrand, I.	**Software Portability and Standards**
Davie, A.J.T. & Morrison, R.	**Recursive Descent Compiling**
de Saram, H.	**Programming in micro-PROLOG**
Deasington, R.J.	**A Practical Guide to Computer Communications and Networking, 2nd Edition**
Deasington, R.J.	**X.25 Explained: Protocols for Packet Switching Networks**
Eisenbach, S.	**Functional Programming: Languages, Tools and Architectures**
Ellis, D.	**Computers in Medical Practice**
Ennals, J.R.	**Artificial Intelligence: Applications to Logical Reasoning and Historical Research**
Fernando, C.	**Cluster Analysis on Microcomputers**
Fossum, E. *et al.*	**Computerization of Working Life**
Gray, P.M.D.	**Logic, Algebra and Databases**
Harland, D.M.	**Concurrency and Programming Languages**
Harland, D.M.	**Polymorphic Programming Languages**
Hill, I.D. & Meek, B.L.	**Programming Language Standardisation**
Hogger, C.J. & Hogger, E.I.	**PROLOG for Scientists and Engineers**
Hutchison, D.	**Fundamentals of Computer Logic**
Hutchison, D. & Silvester, P.	**Computer Logic: Principles and Technology**
Hutchins, W.J.	**Machine Tranlsation: Past, Present, Future**
Lester, C.	**Advanced Programming in PASCAL**
McKenzie, J., Elton, L. & Lewis, R.	**Interactive Computer Graphics in Science Teaching**
Matthews, J.	**FORTH**
Meek, B.L., Heath, P. & Rushby, N.	**Guide to Good Programming Practice, 2nd Edition**
Millington, D.	**Systems Analysis and Design for Computer Application**
Moore, L.	**Foundations of Programming with PASCAL**
Moseley, L., Sharp, J. & Salenieks, P.	**PASCAL in Practice**
Moylan, P.	**Assembly Language for Engineers**
Narayanan, A. & Sharkey, N.E.	**An Introduction to LISP**
Paterson, A.	**Office Systems: Planning, Procurement and Implementation**
Pemberton, S. & Daniels, M.C.	**PASCAL Implementation**
Pesaran, M.H. & Slater, L.J.	**Dynamic Regression: Theory and Algorithms**
Peter, R.	**Recursive Functions in Computer Theory**
Phillips, C. & Cornelius, B.	**Computational Numerical Methods**
Ramsden, E.	**Microcomputers in Education 2**
Ramsay, A. & Barrett, R.	**POP-11 in Practice: Examples in Artificial Intelligence**
Schirmer, G.	**Programming in C**
Sharp, J.A.	**Data Flow Computing**
Smith, I.C.H.	**Microcomputers in Education**
Späth, H.	**Cluster Analysis Algorithms**
Späth, H.	**Cluster Dissection and Analysis**
Stratford-Collins, M.J.	**ADA: A Programmer's Conversion Course**
Teskey, F.N.	**Principles of Text Processing**
Tizzard, K.	**C for Professional Programmers**
Turner, S.J.	**An Introduction to Compiler Design**
Whiddett, R.J., *et al.*	**UNIX: A Practical Introduction for Users**
Whiddett, R.J.	**Concurrent Programming: Techniques and Implementations**
Young, S.J.	**An Introduction to ADA, 2nd (Revised) Edition**
Young, S.J.	**Real Time Languages**

MACHINE TRANSLATION:

Past, Present, Future

W. J. HUTCHINS, B.A., A.L.A.
University of East Anglia

ELLIS HORWOOD LIMITED
Publishers · Chichester

Halsted Press: a division of
JOHN WILEY & SONS
New York · Chichester · Brisbane · Toronto

First published in 1986 by
ELLIS HORWOOD LIMITED
Market Cross House, Cooper Street, Chichester, West Sussex, PO19 1EB, England

The publisher's colophon is reproduced from James Gillison's drawing of the ancient Market Cross, Chichester.

Distributors:
Australia and New Zealand:
Jacaranda-Wiley Ltd., Jacaranda Press,
JOHN WILEY & SONS INC.
GPO Box 859, Brisbane, Queensland 4001, Australia
Canada:
JOHN WILEY & SONS CANADA LIMITED
22 Worcester Road, Rexdale, Ontario, Canada
Europe and Africa:
JOHN WILEY & SONS LIMITED
Baffins Lane, Chichester, West Sussex, England
North and South America and the rest of the world:
Halsted Press: a division of
JOHN WILEY & SONS
605 Third Avenue, New York, NY 10158, USA

British Library Cataloguing in Publication Data
Hutchins, W. J.
Machine translation: past, present, future. —
(Ellis Horwood series in Computer and their applications)
1. Machine translating
I. Title
418'.02 P308

Library of Congress Card No. 86–7465

ISBN 0–85312–788–3 (Ellis Horwood Limited)
ISBN 0–470–20313–7 (Halsted Press)

Phototypeset in Times by Ellis Horwood Limited
Printed in Great Britain by Unwin Brothers, Woking

Contents

Preface

When the first computers appeared at the end of the Second World War, there were great hopes of the potential benefits which the imagined powers of these 'electronic brains' might bring. One was the prospect of translating languages, to break down communication barriers and to further the cause of international peace. At first computer technology was inadequate, but from the mid-1950s research on machine translation was vigorously pursued in many countries, not least in the Soviet Union and in the United States. Early expectations were however not fulfilled, awareness of the linguistic and computational complexities grew steadily, many researchers became disillusioned, and by the mid-1960s machine translation was in disrepute; a report for US sponsors resulted in drastic reductions of funding and US research came virtually to an end. Machine translation was now widely regarded as a 'failed' ideal — an image which it has retained in many quarters. However, research and development continued and by the mid-1970s there were machine translation systems in daily operation and substantial progress had been made on more advanced systems. The installation of an operational system in the translation service of the Commission of the European Communities was a marker for the beginning of a revival which has continued to grow stronger to the present day. The last decade has witnessed many more machine translation systems in daily operation, the commercial development of interactive systems and a steady increase in research activity, in Europe, the Soviet Union, Japan, and once more in the United States. The disillusionment of the 1960s has been replaced in the 1980s by a mood of realistic optimism. Machine translation is no longer a dream, it is a reality. This book is an account of these forty years of machine translation research and development: the projects and the systems, the problems and the solutions, the methods and the techniques, the achievements of the past and the prospects for the future.

During the last two years, I have incurred debts to many colleagues and researchers in the field of machine translation. Without their assistance the writing of this book would have been incomparably more difficult. It goes without saying of course that all faults of omission and misrepresentation are my own. Nevertheless, It is my hope that there are no gross distortions and that readers unfamiliar with machine translation will be able to obtain a reasonably balanced view of the achievements and current situation in this increasingly important field.

For the earlier periods of machine translation history I must express my particular thanks to Margaret Masterman for placing at my disposal the invaluable archive of machine translation documentation at the Cambridge Language Research Unit. I am indebted also to the late Dick Richens and to Andrew D. Booth for first hand information about the earliest history of machine translation, and I must also thank the Rockefeller Foundation Archive for providing copies of documents and correspondence relating to Warren Weaver's activities.

For information on current projects the list of individuals to be acknowledged is long; all have contributed substantially either with personal information or by sending documentation about the projects they are associated with. Their names are given here in alphabetical order: Doug Arnold (Essex University), Kenneth Beesley (Edinburgh), Christian Boitet (GETA, Grenoble), Laurent Bourbeau (Ottawa), Jaime G. Carbonell (Carnegie-Mellon University), Rod Johnson (UMIST), Frank Knowles (Aston University), Heinz Dirk Luckhardt (Saarbrücken), Elliott Macklovitch (TAUM, Montreal), Matoko Nagao (Kyoto University), Hirosato Nomura (Nippon Telegraph and Telephone Corporation), Atsushi Okajima (Hitachi), Loll Rolling (CEC, Luxembourg), Juan Sager (UMIST), Jonathan Slocum (LRC, Texas), John M. Smart (Smart AI Inc.), Harry Somers (UMIST), Karen Sparck Jones (Cambridge University), Allen Tucker (Colgate University), Yorick Wilks (New Mexico University), Toon Witkam (BSO, Utrecht).

My final thanks must go to John Campbell and to the editorial staff at Ellis Horwood for their encouragement and expertise; to the University of East Anglia for granting me study leave in order to undertake the research and to complete the writing of this book; and, most important of all, to my wife and son for their sacrifices and uncomplaining tolerance during long periods of neglect. Without their encouragement and support this book would never have been finished.

November 1985 John Hutchins

Common abbreviations

(*see also Index*)

ACL	Association of Computational Linguistics
AI	artificial intelligence
ALPAC	Automatic Language Processing Advisory Committee
CEC	Commission of the European Communities
CETA	Centre d'Etudes pour la Traduction Automatique (Grenoble)
CRDSD	*Current Research and Development in Scientific Documentation*
ELT	Electro-Technical Laboratory (Tokyo)
EURATOM	European Atomic Energy Authority
GETA	Groupe d'Etudes pour la Traduction Automatique (Grenoble)
IBM	International Business Machines
IL	interlingua, intermediary language
ITVMT	Institute of Precision Mechanics and Computer Technology (Moscow)
LM	*Language Monthly*
LRC	Linguistics Research Center (Texas)
MIAN	Steklov Mathematical Institute of the USSR Academy of Sciences (Moscow)
MIT	Massachusetts Institute of Technology
MT	machine translation
MT	*Mechanical Translation*
NBS	National Bureau of Standards
NP	noun phrase
NPL	National Physical Laboratory (Teddington, Middlesex)
NSF	National Science Foundation
OCR	optical character recognition
PP	prepositional phrase
RADC	Rome Air Development Center
SL	source language
TA	*Traduction Automatique*
TAUM	Traduction Automatique de L'Université de Montréal
TL	target language
UCLA	University of California at Los Angeles
UMIST	University of Manchester Institute of Science and Technology
USAF	United States Air Force
VP	verb phrase

1 General introduction

Machine translation is the application of computers to the translation of texts from one natural language into another.

There have been many different reasons for attempting it. The principal reason is a severely practical one: scientists, technologists, engineers, economists, agriculturalists, administrators, industrialists, businessmen, and many others have to read documents and have to communicate in languages they do not know; and there are just not enough translators to cope with the ever increasing volume of material which has to be translated. Machine translation would ease the pressure. Secondly, many researchers have been motivated by idealism: the promotion of international cooperation and peace, the removal of language barriers, the transmission of technical, agricultural and medical information to the poor and developing countries of the world. Thirdly, by contrast, some sponsors of machine translation activity have seen its importance in military and intelligence contexts: to help them find out what the 'enemy' knows. Fourthly, there are 'pure research' reasons: to study the basic mechanisms of language and mind, to exploit the power of the computer and to find its limitations. Finally, there are simple commercial and economic motives: to sell a successful product, or to maintain a high standard of living in a competitive world.

At certain periods in the nearly forty years of the history of machine translation, some of these motives have been more prominent than others. In the United States during the 1950s and 1960s fear of Soviet technological prowess (particularly after the launch of the first sputnik in 1957) stimulated much governmental and military support for Russian–English translation. In the 1970s the multilingual problems of the European Communities encouraged research on translation systems to deal with administrative, economic and technical documentation within the languages of the communities. At the same time, commercial interests began to gather pace. In the 1980s the Japanese 'fifth generation' project, in which machine translation plays an important role, has been launched to establish for Japan a major position in the future world economy. Throughout, however, there have always been researchers motivated by idealism and by scientific curiosity, and there have been sponsors willing to support basic research.

Machine translation was one of the first non-numerical applications of computers. For more than a decade until the mid-1960s it was an area of intensive research activity and the focus of much public attention; but early expectations were not fulfilled, promises of imminent commercially viable systems came to nothing, and the problems and linguistic complexities became increasingly apparent and seemed to be ever more intractable. After a widely publicised report compiled for the major US sponsors, the 'notorious' ALPAC report (Ch. 8.9), machine translation was generally considered to have been a 'failure', and no longer worthy of serious scientific consideration.

Critics and sceptics have been fond of repeating alleged mistranslations, howlers which no human translator would perpetrate, in order to ridicule the whole enterprise. The most popular example has been a story involving the translation of two idioms from English into Russian and then back again from Russian into English: *Out of sight, out of mind*, and *The spirit is willing but the flesh is weak*. According to some accounts the first came back as "Invisible insanity" and the second as "The whiskey is all right but the meat has gone bad"; according to others, however, the versions were "Invisible and insane" and "The vodka is good but the meat is rotten"; and yet others have given "invisible lunatics" and "the ghost is willing but the meat is feeble". There have been various other permutations and variants; such variety is typical of hearsay, and indeed, some accounts give the languages as German and English, and others assert they were Chinese and English. Nevertheless, the supposed translations are repeated to the present day as genuine examples of the 'literal-mindedness' of machine translation.

It would seem that a likely source was an article by John A. Kouwenhoven 'The trouble with translation' in *Harper's Magazine* for August 1962:

> Our own attempts to communicate with the Russians in their language may be no more successful. Thanks to Robert E. Alexander, the architect, I can pass along this cheering bit of news. According to Colonel Vernon Walters, President Eisenhower's official interpreter, some electronic engineers invented an automatic translating machine into which they fed 1500 words of Basic English and their Russian equivalents, claiming that it would translate instantly without the risk of human error. In the first test they asked it to translate the simple phrase: "Out of sight, out of mind." Gears spun, lights blinked, and the machine typed out in Russian "Invisible Idiot."
>
> On the theory that the machine would make a better showing with a less epigrammatic passage, they fed it the scriptural saying: "The spirit is willing, but the flesh is weak." The machine instantly translated it, and came up with "The liquor is holding out all right, but the meat has spoiled."

It is a good story, but its superficial plausibility is damaged by the lack of any evidence of a US system at the time which could translate from English into Russian — for obvious reasons the Americans wanted to translate from Russian into English — and by the discovery that both examples were familiar apocrypha of translation before there were any machine translation systems in operation. For example, in April 1956, E. H. Ullrich was reported as saying:

> Perhaps the popular Press is the most attractive outlet for mechanical translations, because it does not really matter whether these are right or wrong and amusing versions such as 'the ghost wills but the meat is feeble' might make mechanical translation into a daily feature as indispensible as the cross-word puzzle. (Ullrich 1956)

From the mid-1960s research on machine translation continued at a reduced level, largely ignored and forgotten not only by the general public but even by linguists and computer scientists. In recent years, however, the situation has changed. There are now operational systems in a number of large translation bureaux and agencies; computers are producing readable translations for administrators, scientists, and technicians at ever increasing volumes; translation systems are being marketed on a commercial basis for microcomputers; many translators are now becoming familiar with machine translation systems and with machine aids; and there is growing scientific interest in machine translation within the Artificial Intelligence community in the United States, in Japan and elsewhere. Machine translation can no longer be dismissed, it is a reality.

With distant memories of the 'failure' of machine translation in the 1950s and 1960s and supported by apocryphal translation horrors, there are still many who do not believe that computers can translate. It is true that few systems would pass the 'Turing test' by producing translations which could never be distinguished from the output of fluent human translators (Turing 1950). This book contains numerous examples of translations produced by computer programs: some are clearly unacceptable texts by whatever criteria, others however are the equal of some human translations and would not be readily identified as computer renditions. The question of how good machine translation should be in order to qualify as 'true' translation is a particularly thorny one, and still not really resolved. What matters in most cases is whether the translation serves the needs of the recipient: a rough translation (human or machine produced) might be quite adequate on some occasions; on others only a 'perfect' finished version is acceptable. Judgments of quality are necessarily both subjective and highly constrained by personal needs and attitudes.

What is probably most surprising to those unfamiliar with the complexities of machine translation are examples of errors which no human translator, however inexperienced, would ever make. A genuine, not apocryphal, howler from the Systran system (12.1 and 14.1 below) is cited by Wheeler & Lawson (1982): "la Cour de Justice considère la création d'un sixième poste d'avocat général" was rendered as "the Court of Justice is considering the creation of a sixth general avocado station".

Such examples are reassuring; there is no fear of being taken over by computers — and these fears are real among some translators. This book will show that machine translation is not a threat, it is not an insidious dehumanising destructive monster, it is not (in the words of Hays 1967) "Golem astride the Tower of Babel". Machine translation should be seen as a useful tool which can relieve translators of the monotony of much technical translation and spare them the wasteful expenditure of much tedious effort on documents of ephemeral or marginal interest. Translators can then be employed where their skills are most wanted, in the translation of sensitive diplomatic and legal documents, and in the translation of cultural and literary texts.

The term 'machine translation' has now established itself as the general accepted name for any system which uses an electronic computer to transform a text in one language into some kind of text in another natural language. The related term 'machine-aided translation' to designate the use of mechanised aids for translation has likewise established itself, by and large, as the generally accepted term. Researchers and writers have commonly used also the alternative terms 'mechanical translation' and 'automatic translation', but these are now more rarely encountered. For many writers the phrase 'mechanical translation' suggests translation done in an automaton-like (i.e. uncontemplative) manner by a human translator; and this has been the primary reason for the dropping of this term. While in English-speaking countries the use of 'automatic translation' has generally been much less common than 'machine translation', this nomenclature is the only possibility for the French and Russians ('traduction automatique' and 'avtomaticheskii perevod') There is no straight equivalent for 'machine translation'. German, however, is like English: both 'maschinelle' and 'automatische' are acceptable qualifiers of 'Sprachübersetzung' (language translation), and both forms are encountered. In the earlier periods there was often talk of 'translating machines' (French: 'machine à traduire'), but since the realisation that computers do not have to be designed specifically to function as translators this usage has died away. In recent years there has been increasing use of the terms 'computer translation' and 'computer-aided translation' — terms which are certainly more accurate than 'machine translation' and 'machine-aided translation' — but in this book the traditional, long established, and still most common term 'machine translation' will be used, abbreviated throughout in the customary way as MT.

A number of other common terms need also to be defined at the outset. Firstly, it has now become accepted practice to refer to the language from which a text is being translated as the 'source language' (abbreviated as SL), and the language into which the text is being translated as the 'target language' (TL). Secondly, there are now commonly accepted terms for the processes involved: 'analysis' procedures accept source language texts as input and derive representations from which 'synthesis' procedures produce or generate texts in the target language as output. These processes may involve various aspects of language structure: 'morphology' is concerned with the inflectional forms and derivational variants of words or lexical items, 'syntax' is concerned with the ways in which words combine in sentence structures, and 'semantics' is concerned with meaning relationships among sentences and texts. Other terms will be introduced and defined as they arise.

Between fully automatic translation on the one hand and human translation on the other there are a number of intermediate possibilities where there are various kinds of collaboration between man and machine. The intervention can take place before, during or after the machine processes. There can be human preparation of input, or 'pre-editing' in the MT jargon; there can be (as there usually has to be) human revision of the output, or 'post-editing'. There can be collaboration during the translation processes, when a human assistant (usually a translator but not necessarily) may be asked by the computer to resolve problems which it cannot deal with. Finally, a translator may do most of the work alone and call upon the machine to assist with problems of terminology. We may then refer to: MT proper (fully automatic), MT with post-editing, MT with edited or restricted input, human-aided MT (interactive MT), machine-aided human translation, and human translation with no machine aids. This book is not concerned with the last two; it is concerned only with systems where a substantial portion of the translation process is carried out by machine. The dividing line between some interactive MT systems and machine-aided translation is blurred on occasions, but in most cases there is little dispute.

This book is a history and assessment of efforts to mechanise processes of translating from one natural language into another. Although it includes some details about the development of mechanised aids for translating, i.e. primarily automatic dictionaries of various kinds, it does not include aspects of natural language processing which are not directly concerned with the translation problem. Hence, although nearly all computational linguistics, natural language processing in Artificial Intelligence and certain approaches to automatic indexing and abstracting have their origins in MT research, these 'offshoots' of MT will not be covered (except for passing references in the early stages of MT research). Obviously, the field has to be restricted in some way. The consequence of this restriction is that methods of potential relevance to MT problems will not be dealt with in any detail if they have not in fact been applied in any MT system. Likewise research which may have been seen at one time as of potential relevance to MT but which in fact did not lead to any kind of MT system will be ignored by and large. Another area which must be excluded for obvious reasons is the development of computer technology and programming, except where these developments have direct bearing on particular features of MT systems or MT research methodology. In brief, this book aims to be restricted exclusively to developments in machine translation.

Inevitably, this account has been written from a 'Western' perspective. An attempt has been made to be as comprehensive as possible and to be as balanced as possible in the evaluation of the contributions of the many MT projects in the forty years' history of MT research. However, the literature is both voluminous and multilingual; access to documentation is frequently difficult, and for personal reasons some foreign language material is inaccessible. For those aspects which have been less well treated than they might have been in a truly comprehensive account of MT and its history, the bibliography should guide the interested reader to the relevant literature. Basic sources are given in sections 3.11 and 9.7 below.

The next chapter deals with the earliest history of MT from its beginnings just after the Second World War to the mid-1950s. Chapter 3 outlines some basic methods and strategies found in MT systems. The following four chapters describe individually the MT projects up to the mid-1960s when much of the impetus of MT research was halted by the notorious ALPAC report. The circumstances leading up to this event and its subsequent effects are dealt with in chapters 8 and 9. The following chapters describe the MT projects from the mid-1960s to the present day. The final chapter includes a brief summary of the present scene and considers some future possibilities.

2

The precursors and the pioneers

2.1 BEFORE THE COMPUTER

The use of mechanical devices to overcome language barriers was suggested first in the seventeenth century. There were two stimulants: the demise of Latin as a universal language for scientific communication, and the supposed inadequacy of natural languages to express thought succinctly and unambiguously. The idea of universal languages arose from a desire both to improve international communication and to create a 'rational' or 'logical' means of scientific communication.

Suggestions for numerical codes to mediate among languages were common. Leibniz's proposals in the context of his monadic theory are perhaps the best known. Another proposal was made by Descartes in comments on the sixteenth proposition of his famous correspondent Anonymous. In a letter to Pierre Mersenne on 20 November 1629 (Mounin 1964:16) Descartes described a proposed universal language in the form of a cipher where the lexical equivalents of all known languages would be given the same code number. Descartes wrote: "Mettant en son dictionnaire un seul chiffre qui se rapporte a *aymer, amare, philein*, et tous les synonymes [of *aimer* in all languages] le livre qui sera écrit avec ces caractères [i.e. the code numbers] pourra être interprété par tous ceux qui auront ce dictionnaire". Actual examples of such mechanical dictionaries were published by Cave Beck in 1657, by Athanasius Kircher in 1663, and by Johann Joachim Becher in 1661. At the height of enthusiasm about machine translation in the early 1960s some writers saw these seventeenth century proposals as genuine forerunners of machine translation. Becher's book, for example, was republished under the title *Zur mechanischen Sprachübersetzung: ein Programmierungsversuch aus dem Jahre 1661* (Becher 1962), indicating the conviction of its editor that Becher's ideas foreshadowed certain principles of machine translation. Apart from an ingenious script, Becher's book is distinguished from others of this kind only by the size of the dictionary: 10,000 Latin words (stems and endings) were provided with codings. Like others, however, Becher failed to tackle the real difficulties of providing equivalent entries in other languages (Greek, Hebrew, German, French, Slav, and Arabic were proposed) and the necessary means to cope with syntactic differences.

The vast work by John Wilkins, *An Essay towards a Real Character and a Philosophical Language* (1668), was a more genuine attempt at a universal language in that it sought to provide a logical or rational basis for the establishment of inter-language equivalencies. Wilkins' aim was "a regular enumeration and description of all those things and notions, to which marks or names ought to be assigned according to their respective natures", i.e. a codification which embodied a universal classification of concepts and entities, a genuine interlingua.

All these writers recognised the problems of genuine differences between languages that could not be captured completely in dictionaries, however 'logically' constructed. Many of them, like Kircher, advised their fellows to write in a simple style and avoid rhetorical flourishes.

Suggestions for mechanical dictionaries on numerical bases continued to be made throughout the following centuries until the middle of the present century. Couturat and Leau in their *Histoire de la langue universelle* (1903) list numerous examples, including one by W. Rieger entitled *Zifferngrammatik, welche mit Hilfe der Wörterbücher ein mechanisches Uebersetzen aus einer Sprache in alle anderen ermöglicht* (Code-grammar, which with the help of dictionaries enables the mechanical translation from one language into all others); a title which links the present mechanical age to the seventeenth century.

As the reference to Couturat and Leau implies, all these apparent precursors of MT should be regarded more accurately as contributions to the ideal of a 'universal language' and to the development of international auxiliary languages (Large 1985), of which the best known is now Esperanto. Both concepts have in fact inspired many of those engaged in machine translation.

None of these proposals involved the construction of machines; all required the human translator to use the tools provided in a 'mechanical' fashion, i.e. for man to simulate a machine. It was not until the invention of mechanical calculators in the nineteenth and twentieth centuries (starting with the pioneer activities of George Boole) that an automatic device could be envisaged which could perform some translating processes. In fact, the first explicit proposals for 'translating machines' did not appear until 1933, when two patents were issued independently in France and Russia. In both cases, the patents were for mechanical dictionaries.

A French engineer of Armenian extraction, Georges Artsrouni was issued a patent on 22 July 1933 for a translation machine which he called a "Mechanical Brain" (Corbé 1960). The invention consisted of a mechanical device worked by electric motor for recording and retrieving information on a broad band of paper which passed behind a keyboard. The storage device was capable of several thousand characters, and was envisaged by its inventor in use for railway timetables, bank accounts, commercial records of all sorts, and in particular as a mechanical dictionary. Each line of the broad tape would contain the entry word (SL word) and equivalents in several other languages (TL equivalents); corresponding to each entry were coded perforations on a second band, either paper or metal, which functioned as the selector mechanism. The required entry was punched at the keyboard, the perforations located and the full entry retrieved within, it was claimed, 10 to 15 seconds. A prototype machine was exhibited and demonstrated in 1937; the French railway administration and the post and telegraph services showed considerable interest, and only the start of the Second World War in 1940 prevented installation of Artsrouni's invention.

More important in retrospect was the patent issued in Moscow on 5 September 1933 to Petr Petrovich Smirnov-Troyanskii for the construction of a "machine for the selection and printing of words while translating from one language into another or into several others simultaneously." (quoted from Panov 1960). A brief account by Troyanskii himself written in February 1947 was published in 1959 (Troyanskii 1959). Troyanskii envisaged three stages in the translation process; the machine was involved only in the second stage, performing as an automated dictionary. In the first stage a human editor knowing only the source language was to analyse the input text into a particular 'logical' form: all inflected words were to be replaced by their base forms (e.g. the nominative form of a noun, the infinitive form of a verb) and ascribed their syntactic functions in the sentence. For this process Troyanskii had devised his own 'logical analysis symbols'. In the second stage the machine was designed to transform sequences of base forms and 'logical symbols' of source texts into sequences of base forms and symbols of target languages. In the third stage an editor knowing only the target language was to convert this sequence into the normal forms of his own language. Troyanskii envisaged both bilingual translation and multilingual translation. Although the machine was assigned the task only of automating the dictionary, it is interesting to note that Troyanskii believed that "the process of logical analysis could itself be mechanised, by means of a machine specially constructed for the purpose" (quoted by Panov 1960a). It was this vision of the next steps beyond a simple mechanical dictionary that marks Troyanskii's proposal as a genuine precursor of machine translation.

In the 1933 patent, the technical implementation proposed was a purely mechanical device, a table over which passed a tape listing in vertical columns equivalent words from various languages (not dissimilar to Artsrouni's machine). But, by 1939 he had added an improved 'memory' device operating with photo-elements (Delavenay 1960; Mounin 1964), and by May 1941 it appears that an experimental machine was operational. Troyanskii in fact went further towards the electronic computer; in 1948 he had a project for an electro-mechanical machine similar to the Harvard Mark I machine developed between 1938 and 1942, and which is regarded as a forerunner of the ENIAC computer (Augarten 1984).

Troyanskii was clearly ahead of his time; Soviet scientists and linguists failed to respond to his proposal when he sought their support in 1939, and later "the Institute of Automation and Telemechanics of the Academy of

Sciences was equally unforthcoming in 1944" (Delavenay 1960). In retrospect, there seems to be no doubt that Troyanskii would have been the father of machine translation if the electronic digital calculator had been available and the necessary computer facilities had been ready (Mounin 1964; Panov 1960). History, however, has reserved for Troyanskii the fate of being an unrecognised precursor; his proposal was neglected in Russia and his ideas had no direct influence on later developments; it is only in hindsight that his vision has been recognised.

2.2 THE FIRST BEGINNINGS (1946-1949)

The electronic digital computer was a creation of the Second World War: the ENIAC machine at the Moore School of Electrical Engineering in the University of Pennsylvania was built to calculate ballistic firing tables; the Colossus machine at Bletchley Park in England was built to decipher German military communications. Immediately after the war, projects to develop the new calculating machines were established at numerous centres in the United States and Great Britain (Augarten 1984). The first applications were naturally in the fields of mathematics and physics, but soon the enormous wider potential of the "electronic brain" were realised and non-numeric applications began to be contemplated.

The first suggestion that electronic computers could be used to translate from one language into another seems to have been made during conversations in New York between Andrew D. Booth and Warren Weaver.

Warren Weaver was at this time vice president of the Rockefeller Foundation. During the war Weaver had served on a scientific mission to investigate Britain's weapons development, and at the Rockefeller Foundation he was closely involved in the sponsorship of computer research and development. Booth had become interested in automatic digital calculation while working at the British Rubber Producers' Association in Welwyn Garden City, and had started to build a machine for crystallographic calculations. In 1945 he was appointed a Nuffield Fellow in the Physics Department at Birkbeck College in the University of London under Professor J. D. Bernal, where he constructed a relay calculator during 1945 and 1946 and initiated plans for computational facilities in the University of London. As a consequence of this work and the efforts of Bernal he obtained funds to visit the United States in 1946 under the auspices of the Rockefeller Foundation. There he visited all the laboratories engaged in computer research and development, at Princeton, MIT, Harvard, and Pennsylvania (Booth 1980).

While he was in the United States he met Weaver for the first time on 20 June 1946 at the Rockefeller Foundation in New York (Weaver 1946). According to Booth (1985): "At that time neither they nor I had any interest in machine translation. The discussions that I had with Warren Weaver were entirely on the subject of coming over to look into the question of acquiring the techniques for building a machine for the University of London based on American experience."

At the end of his US visit in July Booth submitted a report on computer development with particular reference to X-ray crystallography, and he was offered a Rockefeller fellowship to enable him to work at an institution of his own choice in the United States the following year. Booth selected the von Neumann group at the Institute for Advanced Study, Princeton University, recognised then and now as doing the most advanced research on computers at the time. On his return to the United Kingdom, Booth stopped work on the X-ray calculator and, together with Kathleen Britten, devoted himself to the problem of von Neumann type computers, and in particular to problems of large-scale storage (Booth 1980).

Booth met Weaver again at the Rockefeller Centre in New York on 6 March 1947. According to Booth (1985): "The discussion then was entirely on the question of the Rockefeller Foundation financing a computer for the University of London, and Weaver pointed out that there was very little hope that the Americans would fund a British computer to do number crunching, although they might be interested if we had any additional ideas for using the machine in a non-numerical context, and he suggested I thought about things of that type. I had already thought about non-numerical applications from conversations with A. M. Turing in the mid-1940s . . . One of these was in fact translation, although at that time I had thought only of using the machine as a dictionary." Weaver suggested treating translation as a cryptography problem.

Weaver had in fact already on 4 March 1947, just before this meeting with Booth, written to Norbert Wiener of the Massachusetts Institute of Technology, one of the pioneers in the mathematical theory of communication, about the possibility of MT. In his letter (Weaver 1947, quoted in Weaver 1949), after commenting on the problem of translation in the post-war world Weaver wrote:

> Recognizing fully, even though necessarily vaguely, the semantic difficulties because of multiple meanings, etc., I have wondered if it were unthinkable to design a computer which would translate. Even if it would translate only scientific material (where the semantic difficulties are very notably less), and even if it did produce an inelegant (but intelligible) result, it would seem to me worth while . . . Also knowing nothing official about, but having guessed and inferred considerable about, powerful new mechanized methods in cryptography . . . one naturally wonders if the problem of translation could conceivably be treated as a problem in cryptography. When I look at an article in Russian, I say: "This is really written in English, but it has been coded in some strange symbols. I will now proceed to decode." . . . As a linguist and expert on computers, do you think it is worth thinking about?

Wiener's response on the 30 April disappointed Weaver: "I frankly am afraid the boundaries of words in different laguages are too vague and the emotional and international connotations are too extensive to make any quasi mechanical translation scheme very hopeful." (Wiener 1947). Weaver wrote again on 9 May but failed to interest Wiener in the possibilities. He also tried to interest Ivor Richards, the literary critic and linguist, who collaborated with C. K. Ogden on the development of Basic English (Richards 1943, Ogden 1968), and who at this time was professor at Harvard University (Marshall 1947); but with equal lack of success it would appear.

At the Institute for Advanced Study, between March and September 1947, Booth worked with his assistant Kathleen Britten on many tentative ideas for the new London computer, including the recognition of sounds and of printed characters and also the details of a code, which would enable information from a dictionary stored in a computer memory to be retrieved from standard teletype input (Booth *et al.* 1958:1).

This work was reported in a memorandum sent to the Rockefeller Foundation early the next year, on 12 February 1948. In it, Booth mentioned as "a possible application of the electronic computer . . . that of translating from one language into another", adding that "We have considered this problem in some detail . . ." (Booth 1948). Booth admitted later (Booth *et al.* 1958:2) that the program written in Princeton would probably have been of little practical use, nevertheless it was obviously of sufficient encouragement for him to continue to develop his ideas on dictionary lookup procedures.

It is evident that the first serious discussions and investigations of the possibilities of machine translation took place during 1947, beginning with Weaver's letter to Wiener and his meeting with Booth in early March. However, at a later date in 1955 when writing the 'Historical introduction' to the MT collection he edited with Locke (Booth & Locke 1955), Booth recollected the first mention of MT as having occurred during his 1946 visit. This has been generally accepted as the 'birth' date of MT; however, in other later publications Booth gives the date 1947 (e.g. Booth 1956, 1958), and he has now confirmed the March 1947 meeting as the one when the MT discussion with Weaver occurred (Booth 1985). On the other hand, in a letter to Bernal on 20 May 1948, written in acknowledgement of Booth's February report, Weaver himself stated: "I think I may have been the first to suggest this possible use. At any rate I did discuss it two or three years ago, and talked with both you and Booth about it, I believe." (Weaver 1948).

Booth and Weaver were not, however, the only ones at this time with thoughts of using computers for translation. Booth mentioned discussions with Turing. Alan Turing's influence in the development of computers and in their possibilities as 'intelligent machines' is now well known, and he may legitimately be regarded as the pioneer of what is now known as Artificial Intelligence. In a report for the National Physical Laboratory written during July and August 1948 but containing ideas stemming from his wartime activites at Bletchley Park in cryptanalysis using the Colossus machines (Hodges 1983), he mentions a number of possible ways in which the new computers could demonstrate their 'intelligence': "(i) Various games, e.g. chess, noughts and crosses, bridge, poker; (ii) The learning of languages;

(iii) Translation of languages; (iv) Cryptography; (v) Mathematics." (Turing 1948). Like Weaver, it would seem that Turing saw translation as similar to cryptanalysis, but unlike Weaver, he was not to take his ideas any further.

As there were no facilities available at Birkbeck College, Booth began construction of a small computer at the laboratories of the British Rubber Producers' Research Association in Welwyn Garden City near London. The machine was operational by 12 May 1948 and a demonstration was given on 25 May to Warren Weaver and Gerard Pomerat, also of the Rockefeller Foundation (Booth 1980 Weaver 1949). On this occasion Weaver met Richard H. Richens, with whom Booth had been collaborating in experiments on mechanical dictionaries.

Richens had first met Booth on 11 November 1947. His interest in mechanical translation had arisen independently out of experiments with punched cards for storing information at the Commonwealth Bureau of Plant Breeding and Genetics, where he was Assistant Director. "The idea of using punched cards for automatic translation arose as a spin-off, fuelled by my realisation as editor of an abstract journal (*Plant Breeding Abstracts*) that linguists conversant with the grammar of a foreign language and ignorant of the subject matter provided much worse translations than scientists conversant with the subject matter but hazy about the grammar." (Richens 1984). Richens is to be credited with the first suggestion of the automatic grammatical analysis of word-endings (Delavenay 1960:28). He proposed the segmenting of words into their stems (or base forms) and endings (e.g. inflections), both to reduce the size of dictionaries and to introduce grammatical information into a dictionary translation system. For example, in the case of the Latin verb *amat* a search is made for the longest matching stem, i.e. 'am-', and for the ending '-at'. The stem provides the English translation *love* and the ending gives the grammatical information '3rd person singular'. In this way grammatical annotations augment a strict word-by-word dictionary 'translation'. The validity of the approach was tested by hand and by using punched card machinery on a wide variety of languages; the texts were taken from abstracts in plant genetics. The result of this collaboration with Booth was a memorandum written during 1948.

From a later version of this memorandum, presented at the MIT conference in 1952 (see below), some idea of these early efforts in 'dictionary translation' can be gleaned (Richens & Booth 1955).
From the French text:

> Il n'est pas étonn*ant de constat*er que les hormone*s de croissance ag*issent sur certain*es espèce*s, alors qu'elles sont in*opér*antes sur d'autre*s, si l'on song*e à la grand*e spécificité de ces substance*s.
>
> (Where the stars (*) indicate automatic segmentations.)

The 'English translation':

> *v* not is not/step astonish *v* of establish *v* that/which? *v* hormone *m* of growth act *m* on certain *m* species *m*, then that/which? *v* not operate *m*

on of other *m* if *v* one dream/consider *z* to *v* great *v* specificity of those substance *m*.

(Where *v* indicates a French word not translated, *m* "multiple, plural or dual", *z* "unspecific", and slashes alternative translations.)

These tentative experiments by Booth and Richens were known to very few. Brief mention was made during the International Conference on Science Abstracting held in Paris, June 1949, when R. B. Reid of Unesco told some delegates about what he had heard of their work from Professor Bernal (Reid 1949). Shortly afterwards, a short account was given by Holmstrom in a report on scientific and technical dictionaries which was submitted to Unesco and circulated in mimeograph form in July 1949 (Holmstrom 1951). However, it was undoubtedly the memorandum which Warren Weaver wrote on 15 July 1949 that had most widespread and profound influence (Weaver 1949). The memorandum was distributed to some 200 of Weaver's acquaintances who, it was thought, might have potential interest in the concept of machine translation (Weaver 1949). For probably all recipients this memorandum was literally the first suggestion they had seen that the new electronic computers could be used as translating machines. In effect this memorandum launched machine translation as a scientific enterprise in the United States and subsequently elsewhere. Its historic impact is unquestionable; and it was later published in the Locke & Booth collection (1955) of early contributions to MT.

In his memorandum Weaver dates the origin of his speculations about MT to his wartime experience with electronic computers and to stories of startling achievements in cryptanalysis using computers. Weaver remarks that "it was very natural . . . to think, several years ago, of the possibility that such computers be used for translation." He then reproduces the correspondence with Wiener, and refers to Booth's mention of MT in his 1948 memorandum as being the "first instance known to W. W. subsequent to his own notion about it", and outlines the experiments by Richens.

Weaver knew of one other MT experiment at the time of his memorandum. Newspapers had recently reported the use of one of the California computers in a primitive kind of word-for-word translation. These reports had prompted a letter in the *Herald Tribune* of 13 June 1949 from a Max Zeldner demonstrating how ridiculous would be word-for-word translations of literary texts. Mounin (1964: 20) speculated that these reports referred probably to the very tentative experiments mentioned by Olaf Helmer of the RAND Corporation at the 1952 MIT conference (see below).

2.3 WEAVER'S MEMORANDUM (1949)

Weaver's memorandum concentrated more on the general strategies and long-term objectives of MT than on the more technical problems Booth and Richens had been tackling. Because of its historic importance it is worth enumerating in some detail the issues and problems raised by Weaver. He raised four points: the problem of multiple meaning, the logical basis of language, the application of communication theory and cryptographic techniques, and the possibilities of language universals.

The problem of deciding which specific meaning an ambiguous word may have in a particular text was, he suggested, solvable in principle if a sufficient amount of the immediate context is taken into account. The practical question of how much context is necessary could be answered by a statistical study of different types of texts on a variety of subject matters. Weaver explicitly rejected the idea of actually storing in dictionaries long sequences of words for this purpose, but did suggest that "some reasonable way could be found of using the micro context to settle the difficult cases of ambiguity."

He expressed optimism about finding logical aspects in languages. In connection with a remark by Hans Reichenbach that he "was amazed to discover that, for (apparently) widely varying languages, the basic logical structures have important common features," Weaver commented that Reichenbach's observation seemed to be confirmed in the linguistics literature and he mentioned work by Erwin Reifler (below) on the comparative semantics of Chinese and English. Secondly, Weaver expressed the conviction that "insofar as written language is an expression of logical character" then the theorem of McCulloch and Pitts (1943) on the mathematical possibility of computing logical proofs appeared to offer a demonstration of the logical possibility of implementing the translation process on a computer, i.e. that the problem of translating with a computer is formally solvable.

On the applicability of communication theory Weaver pointed to the important work of Shannon (which he was instrumental in popularising, e.g. Shannon & Weaver 1949) and its relation to cryptography. The success of computers in cryptanalysis had prompted Weaver's speculations about MT, as the letter to Wiener in 1947 illustrates. In the memorandum he recounted an anecdote about the deciphering of a short 100-word coded text in Turkish. The cryptographer did not know Turkish, nor did he know that the message was in Turkish. (Before distributing his memorandum, Weaver checked the veracity of the story with his informant, Professor W. Prager of Brown University: the decipherment had been done by R. E. Gilman of the Mathematic Department (Prager 1948).) For Weaver this achievement was sufficient demonstration of the power of cryptanalytic techniques independent of the languages involved. Allied to the probabilistic foundation of communication theory, Weaver believed that the translation problem could be largely solved by "statistical semantic studies".

For Weaver the "most promising approach of all" was the investigation of language invariants or universals. He linked this again with logical structures of language and with probabilistic uniformities. The analogy he suggested was "of individuals living in a series of tall closed towers, all erected over a common foundation. When they try to communicate with one another, they shout back and forth, each from his own closed tower . . . communication proceeds very poorly indeed. But, when an individual goes down his tower, he finds himself in a great open basement, common to all the towers. Here he establishes easy and useful communication . . . Thus may it be true that the way to translate . . . is not to attempt the direct route, shouting from tower to tower. Perhaps the way is to descend, from each language, down to the common base of human communication — the real but as yet undiscovered universal language . . ."

2.4 FROM WEAVER TO THE FIRST MT CONFERENCE (1950–1952)

Weaver's memorandum brought to the attention of a wide circle the possibilities of a new and exciting application of the computers whose potentialities were being discovered and proclaimed with enthusiasm and optimism at this time. But, it did more. It indicated potentially fruitful lines of research in statistical analyses of language, on the logical bases of language, and on semantic universals of language. In addition, it pointed to some actual, even if tentative, achievements in the work of Booth and Richens. It was, however, received with considerable scepticism by many linguists who rejected it for its naivety in linguistic matters and for its unfounded assumptions on the 'logicality' of language, and they were naturally sceptical about the possibility of formalising language and translation processes.

The memorandum had also been noticed by the press. An account appeared in *Scientific American* in December 1949, which reported on the experiment by Booth and Richens. This in turn was picked up by the British newspaper the *News Chronicle* in the spring of 1950, and so appeared the first of what in coming years were to be frequent misunderstandings and exaggerations. Booth's APEXC computer program was described as an "electronic translator", at which an operator "could select which of a dozen or more languages he desired to translate. As fast as he could type the words, say, in French, the equivalent in Hungarian or Russian would issue on the tape."

2.4.1 First MT studies.

Weaver's own favoured approach, the application of cryptanalytic techniques, was immediately recognised as mistaken (see Mounin 1964: 31–39) for a detailed discussion). Confusion between the activities of deciphering and translation arise whenever the same person does both. Obviously, no translating is involved when an English message is deciphered into English by an English-speaking recipient. Likewise, the decipherment of the highly complex Enigma code used by Germany in the Second World War, with its immensely complex sequences of manipulations and transpositions, was not translation; it was only after the German texts had been deciphered that they were translated. The Colossus computers at Bletchley Park were applied to cracking the cipher, not to translating the German text into English. In practice, the cryptanalyst generally knows what the language is of the texts to be deciphered and often what their content is likely to be and the circumstances in which the message was transmitted. All this helps him to guess which letters and words are likely to be most frequent in the text. In the case cited by Weaver, the decipherment was based on "the frequencies of the letters, pairs of letters, etc., in English" (Prager 1948); fortunately they were much the same in Turkish and the original could be interpreted.

Though the cryptanalytic approach was mistaken, there were sufficient stimulating ideas in Weaver's paper to launch MT as a serious line of research in the United States. During the next two years, individuals and groups began MT studies at a number of locations, the Massachusetts Institute of Technology (MIT), the University of Washington in Seattle, the University of California at Los Angeles (UCLA), the National Bureau of Standards (NBS) also in Los Angeles and the RAND Corporation nearby at Santa Monica.

On 10 January 1950, Erwin Reifler circulated privately the first of a series of studies on MT (Reifler 1950). Reifler was a sinologist of German origin, head of the Department of Far Eastern and Slavic Languages and Literature at the University of Washington in Seattle. Recognising the problem of multiple meanings as an obstacle to word-for-word translation of the kind attempted by Booth and Richens, Reifler introduced the concepts of 'pre-editor' and 'post-editor'. The human 'pre-editor' would prepare the text for input to the computer and the 'post-editor' would resolve residual problems and tidy up the style of the translation. One suggestion was that the pre-editor should indicate the grammatical category of each word in the source language (SL) text by adding symbols or diacritic marks, e.g. to distinguish between the noun *co'nvict* and the verb *convi'ct*. The post-editor's role was to select the correct translation from the possibilities found by the computer dictionary and to rearrange the word order to suit the target language. As we shall see, the concepts of pre-editor and post-editor recur in one form or another throughout the development of MT research.

Following Weaver's suggestion for statistical studies of micro context for resolving problems of multiple meaning, Abraham Kaplan at the RAND Corporation investigated polysemy in mathematics texts. (The study was completed on 30 November 1950.) A group of test subjects were presented with a set of words, each with a number of possible meanings, and asked to select the most applicable sense. Kaplan limited the test to nouns, verbs, and adjectives on the assumption that "these are the major carriers of the content of any discourse, and probably more markedly exhibit ambiguities". Each word was presented first in isolation, then together with preceding and following words (up to two before and after), and finally the whole sentence. It was found that the "most practical context is . . . one word on each side, increased to two if one of the context words is a particle", i.e. an article, preposition, or conjunction (Kaplan 1955). Despite its limitations and deficiencies (Kaplan excluded homographs: words of different grammatical categories having the same form) and the tentativeness of the conclusions, this study encouraged hopes that problems of ambiguity were tractable and that statistical analyses could contribute useful linguistic data for MT.

In the latter half of 1950, a survey was conducted by W. F. Loomis on behalf of Weaver to find out all those who were interested in MT and what research was underway. The survey revealed a surprising amount of activity already (Loomis 1951): apart from Booth, Richens, and Reifler, two groups had been set up in California. One was at the RAND Corporation in Santa Monica under J. D. Williams, and Kaplan's paper was to be the first of a series of MT studies. The other had been formed by Harry D. Huskey of the National Bureau of Standards in Los Angeles, with the intention of using the SWAC (Standards Western Automatic Computer) for MT research. The group included Victor A. Oswald of the German Department at UCLA and William E. Bull of the UCLA Spanish Department, and was soon joined by Kenneth E. Harper of the UCLA Slavic Languages Department. In support of its work, the group received some funds from the Rockefeller Foundation in July 1951.

From this group appeared during 1951 the first published journal article devoted to MT (Oswald and Fletcher 1951). Up to this time papers on MT had been mimeographed memoranda and reports of limited circulation. (It is true to say that to the present day information about MT research is largely contained in report literature of limited distribution; journal and book publication has on the whole been considered secondary.) The article by Victor Oswald and Stuart L. Fletcher, of UCLA and NBS respectively, was also the first attempt to investigate syntactic aspects of MT. Arguing that word-for-word translation of a language like German would produce obviously unsatisfactory results, Oswald and Fletcher proposed a detailed grammatical coding of German sentences indicating syntactic functions of nouns and verb forms in clauses and enabling the identification of 'noun blocks' and 'verb blocks'. On the basis of the codes, certain sequences were identifiable as candidates for rearrangement when the output was to be in English. The procedures were framed as 'instructions' for the SWAC computer at NBS, but were not in fact implemented in any way. In an appendix, the authors illustrated how a mathematics text by Cantor would be coded, reordered and then translated word by word into English, e.g. the original:

> Bevor wir diese Definition im Einzelnen zergliedern, wollen wir einige Beispiele von Mengen betrachten, die uns anschauliches Material zum Verständnis der Definition liefern sollen.

reordered:

> Bevor wir zergliedern diese Definition im Einzelnen, wir wollen betrachten einige Beispiele von Mengen, die sollen liefern uns anschauliches Material zum Verständnis der Definition.

English:

> Before we analyse this definition in detail we want-to regard some examples of sets, which shall furnish us perceptible material for-the understanding of-the definition.

Oswald and Fletcher concluded that syntax "does not constitute, as had been thought by some, a barrier to mechanical translations"; they stressed the problems of solving the "lexicographic difficulties" of MT.

2.4.2 Bar-Hillel's survey (1951)

At the Massachusetts Institute of Technology a meeting on MT was held soon after the appearance of Weaver's memorandum. According to Locke and Yngve (1958: 511): "In January 1950 Dr Weaver met at MIT with a dozen men from nearly as many different fields, including the heads of our Research Laboratory of Electronics, of our Digital Computer Laboratory, and of the Department of Modern Languages . . . The conclusion was cautious: the possibility of translation by machine was worth examining". In the next year, 1951, Yehoshua Bar-Hillel became the first person to be appointed full-time specifically for research on MT; the appointment in the Research Laboratory of Electronics was made possible by a grant from the National Science Foundation (quite possibly with the influence of Weaver who was a director of NSF at the time.) Bar-Hillel's task was to study the possibilities of MT and to plan future research at MIT.

At the end of 1951 he produced a survey of the current position (Bar-Hillel 1951). The paper raised many of the issues which dominated discussion of MT in the following years: the feasibility of fully automatic MT, the role of post-editing, the objectives of syntactic analysis, the role of statistical information, the possibility of universal grammar, the logical foundations of language, and restricted vocabularies.

Bar-Hillel argued that since problems of semantic ambiguities could not be resolved at present, "high-accuracy, fully-automatic MT is not achievable in the foreseeable future". This fact, however, should not discourage MT research: a less ambitious target is feasible, "a mixed MT . . . in which a human brain intervenes . . . either at the beginning of the translation process or the end, perhaps at both, but preferably not somewhere in the midst of it." Bar-Hillel saw no alternative to the post-editor whose task would be the "elimination of semantical ambiguities, in addition, of course, to stylistic smoothing".

As for the machine processes, Bar-Hillel saw these as comprising the morphological analysis of each word into its stem and grammatical category, the "mechanical identification of small syntactical units" and the "transformation of the given sentence into another that is logically equivalent to it". The second stage required what Bar-Hillel called an "operational syntax", an explicit programmable method for syntactic analysis, the rudiments of which Bar-Hillel recognised in Oswald and Fletcher's paper.

While recognising some value in statistical analyses, he was sceptical of proposals to include only high frequency vocabulary in dictionaries since the residue are likely to be those "highly loaded with information" in a given text. In any case, he felt that the current limitations of computer storage would be solved by hardware developments.

At the end of the paper he considered the possibilities of constructing a "universal, or at least general grammar, perhaps even . . . a whole artificial exchange-language" on the basis of work by logicians such as Ajdukiewicz, Carnap, Reichenbach, and himself, and by the linguist Zellig S. Harris (cf. Ch. 3.4-5 below), or, less ambitiously, "transfer-grammars . . . in which the grammar of one language is stated in categories appropriate to some other language". Finally, he proposed the application of MT to situations where restricted vocabularies are used, e.g. by pilots and meteorologists, and where "the theoretical difficulties of such a type of MT are clearly less formidable". To these he added regularised languages such as Basic English and auxiliary languages such as Esperanto and Interlingua.

As we shall see, not only had Bar-Hillel raised many of the major MT issues recurring in the following years and to some extent to the present day, but he also stated views which he was to repeat at greater length and with great impact in the early 1960s (Ch. 8.3).

2.4.3: First MT conference (1952)

By 1952 interest in MT had grown enough for the Rockefeller Foundation to sponsor the first conference on MT. It was held at the Massachusetts Institute of Technology from 17 to 20 June 1952, and was organised by Bar-Hillel. Eighteen individuals interested in MT attended. As might be expected, MIT was well represented, by seven participants: Yehoshua Bar-Hillel; Jay W. Forrester, head of the Computer Laboratory; William N. Locke, Dept. of Modern Languages; James W. Perry, Center of International Studies; Vernon Tate, Director of Libraries; Jerome B. Wiesner, director of the Research Laboratory of Electronics; and Dudley A. Buck, Electrical Engineering Dept. The Los Angeles area was represented by four participants: Victor Oswald and William E. Bull from UCLA; Olaf Helmer from RAND; and Harry D. Huskey from NBS. Erwin Reifler came from the University of Washington, as did Stuart C. Dodd, the director of the Washington Public Opinion Laboratory. The remainder were: Andrew D. Booth from Birkbeck College (the sole British participant), Leon Dostert from the Institute of Languages and Linguistics of Georgetown University, Duncan Harkin from the Department of Defense, Victor H. Yngve from the University of Chicago, and A. Craig Reynolds from the Endicott Laboratories of IBM. The backgrounds of participants reflect already some of the principal sources of interest in MT: electronic engineering and computing, linguistics, librarianship and information science, military and governmental bodies. Although the proceedings were not published at the time, accounts of the conference appeared subsequently by Reynolds (1954) and

Reifler (1954), both compiled immediately after the conference; and, somewhat later, a number of the papers were printed in the collection by Locke and Booth (1955).

The conference opened with a public session. Bar-Hillel enunciated the need and possibilities for MT, particularly to cover the immense and growing volume of scientific research and popular periodical literature of a country. Leon Dostert spoke on his experience in setting up the simultaneous translation systems at the Nuremburg trials, at the United Nations and other international conferences. He was sceptical of the contribution of MT except for the processing of material currently not touched in specialised fields. Olaf Helmer mentioned the tentative experiments at RAND, and Perry spoke of the relationship of MT to automatic indexing and retrieval systems.

The presentations on the following days included Reifler and Bar-Hillel on pre-editing and post-editing respectively, and Booth on his work with Richens on mechanising a dictionary. For Reifler (1954) the low intelligibility of the output from the latter supported his argument for pre- and post-editing. Oswald presented his proposals for treating German syntax, and then with Bull suggested that problems of ambiguity could be overcome by constructing micro-glossaries for particular subject fields; the glossaries could be established from statistical analyses of the relevant literature, and an investigation of the vocabulary of brain surgery had already been undertaken (later published in Oswald and Lawson, 1953). Bull warned that no scientific vocabulary constituted a closed domain and the lexical ambiguities in general vocabulary would still remain. Dodd outlined his ideas of regularising English syntax and morphology for use in MT, e.g. "I will send he to she", "he have", "she did be loved" (Dodd 1955); and Reifler suggested encouraging writers to write with MT in mind (i.e. to write in MTese, as later researchers put it). Dostert put forward the advantages of a "pivot language" in the context of multilingual MT. Reifler (1954) thought this would most likely be English and he also thought that MT output should be regularised on the lines suggested by Dodd; studies of language universals could contribute to this regularization in the MT context.

According to Reynolds (1954), Bar-Hillel's operational syntax was "a completely new concept to the linguists of the conference who had intuitively felt that such a structure did exist but without the tools of symbolic logic had been unable to isolate the essential features that lead to the exceedingly simple arithmetic operations." There was naturally some discussion on the problems of writing computer programs for MT, on computer costing, and on the use of punched card machinery. The conference concluded with statements from participants about what research they hoped to do. The most challenging proposal came from Dostert, who had been converted from his original scepticism in the course of the conference. He suggested "the early creation of a pilot machine or of pilot machines proving to the world not only the possibility, but also the practicality of MT" (Reifler 1954).

2.5 FROM THE MIT CONFERENCE TO THE GEORGETOWN-IBM DEMONSTRATION (1952–1954).

The conference was an undoubted success, the participants were enthusiastic about the prospects and the general public had been made aware of the possibilities. Although no formal conclusions were drawn, it seems there was general agreement on what the next stages of MT research should be (Booth & Locke 1955: 6–7): "word frequency and word translation studies" on micro-glossaries, and investigation of suitable storage, input and output methods for "an operating automatic dictionary at the end of approximately 12 months"; immediate studies on "operational analysis of syntax"; later longer-term work would come on multilingual MT, universal grammar and interlinguas. In retrospect, the expectations were far too optimistic, but they provided a stimulating framework for further MT research.

In the following year, articles presenting MT to the general public began to appear, e.g. Booth (1953) and Bar-Hillel (1953) in *Computers and Automation*, and MT appeared in a textbook for the first time, in a chapter on 'Some applications of computing machines' in the book by Booth and his wife, the former Kathleen Britten (Booth & Booth 1953).

During 1953 Bar-Hillel left MIT to return to the Hebrew University of Jerusalem; he was replaced by Victor Yngve, who had participated at the 1952 conference. At this time, Yngve shared the view that since "word-for-word translations are surprisingly good, it seems reasonable to accept a word-for-word translation as a first approximation and then see what can be done to improve it" (Yngve 1955). A partial translation of a German mathematics text was simulated in which function words and endings were left untranslated:

> Die CONVINCINGe CRITIQUE des CLASSICALen IDEA-OF-PROBABILITY IS eine der REMARKABLEen WORKS des AUTH-ORs. Er HAS BOTHen LAWe der GREATen NUMBERen ein DOUBLEes TO SHOWen: (1) wie sie IN seinem SYSTEM TO INTERPRETen ARE, (2) THAT sie THROUGH THISe INTER-PRETATION NOT den CHARACTER von NOT-TRIVIALen DEMONSTRABLE PROPOSITIONen LOSEen . . .

Although readers with some familiarity with German could work out the general drift it was clear to Yngve that syntactic analysis was essential for better MT output, and this was to be the central emphasis of the MIT group which he formed in the coming years (Ch. 4.7 below).

One of the most significant outcomes of the 1952 conference was the establishment of a MT research team at Georgetown University by Leon Dostert to start work towards the pilot experiment he had advocated to demonstrate the practical feasibility of machine translation. Dostert was fully aware of the considerable linguistic problems of MT but had concluded that "rather than attempt to resolve theoretically a rather vast segment of the problem, it would be more fruitful to make an actual experiment, limited in scope but significant in terms of broader implications" and that the test should serve as the basis for a series of progressively larger and more complex tests. In brief, Dostert advocated what was later to be generally known as the 'empirical' approach to MT research. Collaboration was agreed with IBM, under the aegis of the company's programme of endowed research in computation; Paul Garvin was appointed at Georgetown to work on the linguistic procedures for the trial translation of Russian texts, and Peter Sheridan of the IBM Scientific Computing Service was given the task of implementing the procedures on the IBM 701 machine.

The program was ready by the end of 1953 and on 7 January 1954 a public demonstration of the Georgetown-IBM experiment took place at IBM's Technical Computing Bureau in New York. This small-scale experiment in Russian–English translation was one of the most important events in the early history of MT. It was the first real demonstration of MT on a computer; earlier experiments had either been hand simulations or had used punched card machinery. No pre-editing of text was required and the output appeared to be fully intelligible. Furthermore, it was the first implementation which went beyond word-for-word translation. Nevertheless, its limitations were clearly recognised: a vocabulary of just 250 Russian words, only six rules of grammar and a carefully selected sample of Russian sentences (Ch. 4.3 below). For the general public and the scientific community at large, however, the experiment showed that MT was a feasible objective, and it undoubtedly helped to stimulate the funding of MT research by US governmental agencies in the following decade.

The demonstration received wide publicity; Sheridan and Dostert lectured widely on the system and the potential future of MT. Further demonstrations were given during the year, for example on the 14 September at a New York meeting of the American Chemical Society (*MT* 1(3) Dec. 1954). Another demonstration was given to D. Y. Panov from the USSR Academy of Sciences, who was visiting computer installations in the United States. On his return, research on MT began in the Soviet Union.

2.6 FROM THE GEORGETOWN-IBM EXPERIMENT TO THE FIRST INTERNATIONAL CONFERENCE (1954–1956)

During 1954 two further MT groups were founded, an informal group at Cambridge in Great Britain by Margaret Masterman, and a research team at Harvard University by Anthony Oettinger, who also in the same year presented the first doctoral dissertation on MT (Ch. 4.9 below). In March appeared the first number of the journal *Mechanical Translation* issued from MIT under the editorship of Victor Yngve and supported by a grant from the Rockefeller Foundation. This journal was to carry in subsequent years many of the most important articles on MT.

During 1955 the first news of Russian activity became known. As a result of his visit to the demonstration at IBM, Professor Panov began MT experiments in January 1955 on the BESM computer at the Institute of Precision Mechanics and Computer Technology in Moscow. Within the next two years other MT groups were formed in the USSR at the Steklov Mathematical Institute, at the Institute of Linguistics and at the Laboratory of Electrical Modelling, all in Moscow, and at the University of Leningrad (Ch. 6 below).

In August 1955 the Cambridge Language Research Group held a meeting at King's College, Cambridge. Participants included R. H. Richens, the mathematicians A. F. Parker-Rhodes and E. W. Bastin, and the linguists J. R. Firth, M. A. K. Halliday, and R. A. Crossland. Already in the abstracts of the proceedings (CLRU 1956) there is evidence of the distinctive emphasis of CLRU on interlinguas, pidgin languages, logical and semantic foundations, and lattice theory (Ch. 5.2 below). At about this time also, Silvio Ceccato started a MT project in Milan, adopting a distinctive 'philosophical' approach to MT grammar and semantics (Ch. 5.3 below).

Publications on MT were now beginning to appear in larger numbers, shortly voluminous. A major publication of 1955 was the collection of articles edited by Locke and Booth (1955), the first book to be published devoted entirely to MT research. In it appear many of the most significant papers of the period up to 1955, including Weaver's memorandum, the report by Richens and Booth on their early work, and contributions to the 1952 conference. It includes also a valuable 'Historical introduction' and early papers by Oettinger (1955) on automatic dictionaries (predating his dissertation), by Yngve (1955) on syntactic analysis, by Booth (1955) on available computer hardware, and by Bar-Hillel (1955) on the problems of idiomatic usage.

It was clear that MT research was growing fast. In October 1956 the first international conference was organised by MIT attended by 30 workers from the United States, Great Britain, and Canada, and papers were received from the Soviet Union. The presentations by MT groups of their current research activity revealed the general pattern of approaches which was to dominate the next five years or so. On the one hand there was the emphasis on dictionary, lexicographic, and semantic problems, e.g. at Washington University, at Los Angeles (UCLA and RAND), at Michigan, at Harvard, and at Cambridge; and on the other hand, there was the greater emphasis on syntactic problems at Georgetown and MIT. Another major division was between the 'empirical' approach, typified by RAND and Georgetown, and the 'theoretical' approach, typified by MIT and Cambridge. A third division was between those groups aiming to produce operational systems in the near future, however limited (e.g. Birkbeck, Washington, and to some extent Georgetown), and those with the longer term objective of producing a good quality product (e.g. Harvard and MIT).

From 1956 research on MT was pursued with great vigour all over the world by numerous groups. In the United States MT research received increasingly large grants from governmental, military, and private sources. By 1964, however, the promise of operational MT systems still seemed distant and the sponsors set up a committee, which recommended in 1966 that funding of MT should be reduced. It brought to an end a decade of intensive MT research activity. The work of the various groups during these years will be described in chapters 4 to 7, after a preliminary chapter outlining some of the basic MT methods and strategies.

3

Problems, methods, and strategies

3.1 MECHANICAL DICTIONARIES

The creation of an automatic dictionary is the first and most obvious task of an MT system. Mechanical dictionaries were the central concern of all the earliest MT researchers and they are still crucial for the efficient operation of present MT systems. Like Artsrouni and Troyanskii, many early researchers tended to see the translation process almost exclusively in terms of consulting dictionaries for finding words in a target language (TL) equivalent to words of a source language (SL). The resulting 'dictionary translations' presented the TL output in the same word sequence as the SL input, i.e. 'word-for-word' translations. They knew that this would not produce good translations; they expected the results to be very poor and in need of considerable editing. Before any 'word-for-word' translations had been seen, Reifler suggested a pre-editor and a post-editor (Ch. 2.4), and the unintelligibility of the results of Richens and Booth's attempts (Ch. 2.2) confirmed the need for, at the least, post-editing. Nevertheless, the ability of many readers to make some sense of these dictionary translations encouraged MT researchers to believe that with suitable modifications the 'word-for-word' approach could in the end produce reasonable output. As we have seen, Yngve considered that they were "surprisingly good" and worth taking as first approximations to be worked on.

The mechanisation of dictionary procedures posed problems of a technical nature. Research on MT began at a time when computers were limited in their storage capacities and slow in access times. There was much discussion of storage devices and mechanisms for improving access times. Booth (1955) and Stout (1954), for example, assessed the relative merits of paper tape, punched cards and magnetic tape as external storage means and the various possibilities for internal 'memory' storage, cathode-ray-tube dielectric stores, vacuum tubes, magnetic drums, photographic drums, etc. Since the external storage could only be searched serially, the most efficient method of dictionary lookup was to sort all the words of the SL text into alphabetical order and to match them one by one against the dictionary entries. Once found, entries could often be stored internally where faster access was possible. Various proposals were made for efficient searching of internal stores, including the sequencing of items by frequency, the 'binary cut' method first put forward by Booth (1955a), and the letter-tree approach of Lamb (Ch. 4.10).

A popular method for reducing dictionary size was the division of words into stems and endings. In languages like German and Russian it was obviously wasteful to include every inflected form of nouns and verbs. The familiar regularities of noun and verb paradigms encouraged researchers to investigate methods of morphological analysis to identify stems and endings. However, there are so many peculiarities and irregularities in the morphology of languages that procedures turned out to be more complex than expected; as a result, when larger storage mechanisms with fast access times became available many MT researchers went back to the older system of storing full forms in dictionaries.

Obviously, dictionaries cannot always include all the words occurring in SL texts. A problem for all MT systems is to establish acceptable methods for dealing with missing words; basically, there are two approaches, either to attempt some kind of analysis and translation, or to print out the original unlocated SL form. In both cases, there is a further problem with the rest of the sentence; whether to attempt an incomplete translation or to give up and produce no translation. In experimental MT systems it is obviously reasonable to admit failure, but in operational systems it is desirable, on the whole, to produce some kind of translation.

3.2 POLYSEMY AND SEMANTICS

The most obvious deficiency of any word-for-word translation, whether mechanised or not, is that the order of words in the resulting TL text is more often wrong than correct. As we have seen, it was clear to Oswald and Fletcher (Ch. 2.4.1) that translation of German texts into English demanded some kind of structural analysis of the German sentences. At the simplest level, such analysis may take into account morphological features, such as the endings of nouns, adjectives and verbs, or basic syntactic sequences, such as noun–adjective and subject–verb relations. As we shall see, it is possible to use this kind of information to devise procedures for rearrangement in basically 'word-for-word' systems. But, in order to go beyond the inherent limitations of the word-for-word approach, the analysis of syntactic structures must involve the identification of phrase and clause relationships. Methods of syntactic analysis will be the subject of the next section.

The second obvious problem is that there are rarely one-to-one correspondences in the vocabularies of natural languages. In most cases, a particular SL word may correspond to a number of different TL words, so that either the MT system prints out all the possibilities or it attempts to select the one which is most appropriate for the specific text in question. The first option was adopted by many systems, as we shall see, often as an intermediate stop-gap; the selection of the right TL equivalent was left to the post-editor. Attempts to deal with the problem took a number of approaches.

The difficulty occurs usually because the SL word has what Weaver and many after him called 'multiple meanings'. Linguists distinguish between homonyms and polysemes; homonyms are words like *bank* which have two or more distinct and unrelated meanings ('geological feature' or 'financial institution'); polysemes are words like *face* which reflect different shades of meaning according to context. They distinguish also between homophones (words which sound the same but have different meanings) such as *pear*, *pair*, and *pare*, and homographs (words which are spelled the same but have different meanings) such as *tear* ('crying' versus 'ripping'). Fortunately, the homophone problem is irrelevant since MT deals only with written texts. For practical purposes it is also immaterial whether the SL word is a homograph or a polyseme: the problem for MT is the same, the relevant meaning for the context must be identified and the appropriate TL form must be selected. Consequently, it is now common in MT research to refer to methods of 'homograph resolution', whether the words concerned are strictly homographs or not.

Sometimes the TL vocabulary makes finer sense distinctions than the SL. There are familiar examples in translating from English into French or German: the verb *know* may be conveyed by *savoir* or *connaître* in French and by *wissen* or *kennen* in German; likewise the English *river* may be either *rivière* or *fleuve* in French and either *Fluss* or *Strom* in German. In neither case can we say that the English words have more than one meaning; it is just that French and German make distinctions which English does not. Nevertheless, in the context of a MT system the problem of selecting the correct TL form is much the same as when the SL form is a genuine homograph or polyseme. MT systems do, however, differ according to whether this type of SL–TL difference is tackled at the same stage as SL homograph resolution or not (see Ch. 3.9 below on MT strategies).

The difficulties are further compounded in languages like English where many words may function as nouns, verbs, or adjectives without any formal distinctions; e.g. *control* can be a verb or noun, *green* can be an adjective or a noun. The fact that there can be stress differences, e.g. between the verb *permit* and the noun *permit*, is of no assistance. For practical purposes these forms are also treated as homographs and much the same procedures for 'homograph resolution' are applied.

Various methods for tackling such SL–TL lexical differences have been proposed. One has already been mentioned, the identification of grammatical category either by morphological clues or by syntactic analysis. For example, the endings '*-ed*' and '*-ing*' generally indicate participal forms of English verbs (although they may be functioning as adjectives). Similarly, if in a two word sequence the first is definitely an adjective the second is probably a noun. Therefore, homographs which happen to belong to different syntactic categories may sometimes be distinguished in this way.

Another method is to reduce the incidence of homography in the MT dictionaries. The concept of the 'micro-glossary' was proposed (Ch. 2.4.3) not only to keep the size of dictionaries reasonably small but also to minimize problems of 'multiple meanings'. It was maintained, for example, that the Russian *vid* was to be translated usually as *species* in biological contexts and not as *view*, *shape*, or *aspect*. A micro-glossary for Russian–English translation in biology could, therefore, include just one of the English equivalents. In many cases the entry has to be the equivalent which is most often correct. In physics, for example, Russian *izmenenie* is usually equated with *change*; although in some contexts other translations may be better, the one which fits best most frequently should be selected.

The suggestion by Weaver was to examine the immediate context of a word. As we have seen, Kaplan concluded that a five word sequence was in general sufficient 'micro context' for disambiguation, i.e. for identifying the particular meaning of a polyseme. There are two ways in which immediate context can be implemented: one by expanding dictionary entries to include sequences of two or more words, i.e. phrases, the other by testing for the occurrence of specific words. For example, if the word *obrazovanie* is modified by *kristallicheskoe* then it is to be translated *formation* (rather than *education*); either the dictionary includes the whole phrase or the analysis procedure tests for the particular adjective. The dictionary solution obviously requires storage facilities of sufficient capacity, and it is also more appropriate when phrases are 'idiomatic', i.e. when the meaning (translation) of the phrase as a whole cannot be deduced (or constructed) from its individual words. Apart from familiar idioms such as *hold one's tongue, not move a finger, red herring* and *blue blood*, it could include verbal phrases such as *make away with, draw forth, look up*, and *pass off*, and noun phrases such as *full speed, upper class*, and *brute force*.

A more fundamental use of contextual information is the search for semantic features which are common to or prominent in the sentence or text as a whole, and to use this information to decide on the most fitting translation for SL words. This method involves the investigation of semantic 'invariants' or semantic regularities in vocabulary and texts, and necessarily goes far beyond the examination of lexical equivalents between languages. It involves, for example, the investigation of synonymy and paraphrase, of semantic 'universals' or 'primitive' elements (e.g. features such as 'human', 'animate', 'liquid', etc.), and of semantic relations within sentences and texts (e.g. agent-action, cause-effect, etc.).

Finally, the problem of polysemy may simply be avoided completely by insisting that texts input to a MT system are written in a regularised and normalised fashion. In other words, writers are encouraged not to be ambiguous, or rather not to include words and phrases which the MT system in use has difficulty in disambiguating. The obverse of this is to 'solve' polysemy by using a highly restricted form of TL as output, a kind of 'pidgin' language with its own idiosyncratic vocabulary usages. As we have seen, the first suggestion of this approach was made by Dodd (Ch. 2.4.3 above); the groups at the University of Washington and at Cambridge were particularly interested in MT pidgin and methods of improving output of this kind.

In theory, any of these methods can be used in any MT system; in practice, particular MT systems have emphasised one or two approaches, they have concentrated on exploiting their full potentialities and have generally neglected the alternatives. Concentration on the contextual and micro-glossary approaches was characteristic of the MT groups at RAND and Michigan. Concentration on the dictionary and lexicographic approaches was characteristic of the groups at Harvard, at the University of Washington and at IBM. Concentration on text semantics was pursued most strongly by the Milan group with its 'correlational analysis' approach and by the Cambridge group with its 'thesaurus' approach.

3.3 MORPHOLOGICAL ANALYSIS

In order to perform any kind of syntactic analysis the grammatical categories (noun, verb, adjective, adverb, etc.) of the words of sentences must be determined. The first step of analysis in any MT system is, however, the identification of the words in the SL text. This is relatively easy in English and most European languages, since words are separated by spaces in written text, but it is not for example in languages such as Chinese and Japanese where there are no external markers of word boundaries.

Obviously, dictionary entries could indicate the grammatical categories ('word class' or 'part of speech') of all SL words. However, it was clearly unnecessary to include every inflected form of a noun or a verb, particularly in languages such as Russian and German. The familiar regularities of noun and verb paradigms encouraged researchers to investigate methods of morphological analysis which would identify stems and endings. To give an English example, the words *analyses*, *analysed*, and *analysing* might all be recognised as having the same stem *analys-* and the common endings *-s*, *-ed*, *-ing*. At the same time, identification of endings was a first step towards the determination of grammatical categories, e.g. to continue the example: *-s* indicates a plural noun form or a third person singular present verb form, *-ed* indicates a past verb form, and *-ing* a present participle or adjectival form, etc. As these examples demonstrate, however, many (perhaps most) endings are ambiguous, even in Russian, and the final establishment of the grammatical category of particular words in text takes place during syntactic analysis. Morphological analysis deals necessarily with regular paradigms; irregular forms, such as the conjugation of verbs such as *be* and *have*, and the plural forms of nouns such as *geese* and *analyses*, are generally dealt with by inclusion of the irregularities in full forms in the dictionary.

3.4 SYNTACTIC ANALYSIS

The first step beyond the basic word-by-word approach is the inclusion of a few rearrangement rules, such as the inversion of 'noun–adjective' to 'adjective–noun', e.g. in French–English translation. In many early MT systems rearrangement rules were often initiated by codes attached to specific dictionary entries. Examples are to be found in the 1954 Georgetown-IBM experiment (Ch. 4.3), and in the experiment by Panov and his colleagues shortly afterwards in the Soviet Union (Ch. 6.1). When there were differences of syntactic structure more complex than inversion, the solution was often the inclusion of phrases in the dictionary, i.e. rather like idiomatic expressions. This approach was expanded and refined as the 'lexicographic' approach of the University of Washington (Ch. 4.1).

Rearrangement rules may take into account fairly long sequences of grammatical categories, but they do not imply any analysis of syntactic structure, e.g. the identification of a noun phrase. The next step beyond the basic word-for-word approach is therefore the establishment of syntagmas, such as noun phrases (nouns and modifiers, compound nouns, etc.), verbal complexes (e.g. auxiliaries and modals in conjunction with infinitives or participle forms), and coordinate structures. This level of analysis is to be seen in the later 'Georgetown system' (Ch. 4.3). Complete syntactic analysis involves the identification of relationships among phrases and clauses within sentences.

Syntactic analysis aims to identify three basic types of information about sentence structure:

(1) the sequence of grammatical elements, e.g. sequences of word classes: art(icle) + n(oun) + v(erb) + prep(osition) . . ., or of functional elements: subject + predicate. These are linear (or precedence) relations.

(2) the grouping of grammatical elements, e.g. nominal phrases consisting of nouns, articles, adjectives and other modifiers, prepositional phrases consisting of prepositions and nominal phrases, etc., up to the sentence level. These are constituency relations.

(3) the recognition of dependency relations, e.g. the head noun determines the form of its dependent adjectives in inflected languages such as French, German, and Russian. These are hierarchical (or dominance) relations.

Included among the basic objectives of any method of syntactic analysis must be at least the resolution of homographs (by identification of grammatical categories, e.g. whether *watch* is a noun or a verb), and the identification of sequences or structures which can be handled as units in SL–TL transfer, e.g. nouns and their associated adjectives.

Various models of syntactic structure and methods of parsing have been adopted in MT systems and are described in more detail in connection with particular MT projects in the following chapters. At this point, the main approaches will be outlined, illustrated in the most part by analyses (whole or partial) of the sentence *The gold watch and chain were sold by the jeweller to a man with a red beard*. This is a passive sentence (the grammatical subject is the object of the verb), containing a homograph (*watch*), an ambiguous coordinate structure (are both the watch and the chain modified by *gold*?) and three prepositional phrases each of which could in theory modify the verb or their preceding noun phrase.

An example of an analysis program (parsing program) to identify sequential (linear) information was the Predictive Syntactic Analyser developed at the National Bureau of Standards and at Harvard University (Ch. 4.8 and 4.9). The premise was that on the basis of an identified grammatical category (article, adjective, noun, etc.) the following category or sequences of categories could be anticipated with an empirically determinable measure of probability. The system had the following characteristics: under the general control of a push-down store (i.e. last in first out) a sentence was parsed one word at a time left to right, the action taken for each word being determined by a set of predictions associated with the grammatical category to which the word had been assigned. At the beginning of the analysis certain sentence types were predicted in terms of sequences of grammatical categories. Examination of each word was in two stages: first to test whether its category 'fulfilled' one of the predictions, starting from the most probable one, then either to alter existing predictions or to add further predictions. Formally, the system was an implementation of a finite state grammar (Fig. 1). The analysis of a sentence was completed if a terminal state had been reached and all categories had been accounted for. Initially, only the single most probable path through the series of predictions was taken during parsing, but in later models all possible predictions were pursued. The method did not in principle need to recognise phrase structures or dependency relations, although these could be derived from the identification of specific category sequences. (This 'building' facility was employed in a later development, the ATN parser, Ch. 9.13).

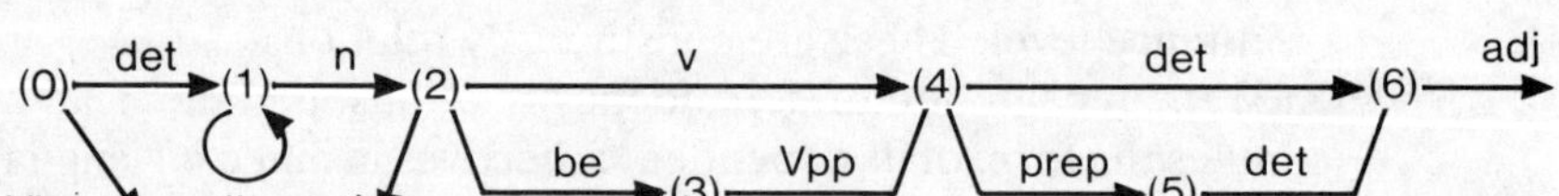

Fig. 1 — Finite state grammar.

The second approach, analysis of dependency relations, is based on the identification of 'governors', e.g. the 'head' noun in a noun phrase, and their dependents or 'modifiers', e.g. adjectives. The governor of the sentence as a whole is generally taken to be the finite verb since this specifies the number and nature of dependent nouns (Fig. 2). A verb such as *buy*, for example, can have four dependents (purchaser, object purchased, price, seller) — a concept referred to as 'valency': a transitive verb such as *see* has a valency of two, an intransitive such as *go* has a valency of one, etc. (If the valency relationships are themselves specified as, e.g. 'agency', 'instrumentality', then we have a 'case frame' analysis, Ch. 9.16 below.)

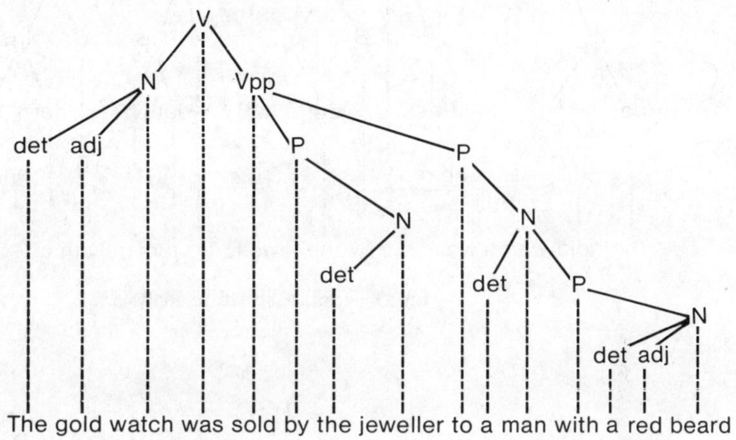

Fig. 2 — Dependency structure analysis.

The parsing of dependency structure can operate either top-down (identification first of governors and then dependents) or bottom-up (determination of governors by a process of substitution). The top-down approach was most common, and can be illustrated by Garvin's fulcrum parser (Ch. 4.6): in a series of passes the algorithm identified first the key elements of the sentence, e.g. main finite verb, subject and object nouns, prepositional phrases, then the relationships between sentence components and finally the structure of the sentence as a whole. An example of bottom-up parsing may be seen in the 'set-theoretic' approach of Kulagina (Ch. 6.2).

The third approach, that of phrase structure analysis (Fig. 3), provides labels for constituent groups in sentences: noun phrase (NP), verb phrase (VP), prepositional phrase (PP), etc. The phrase structure approach is associated most closely in the early period of MT research with the MIT project (Ch. 4.7). Parsing can be either bottom-up or top-down. In the former, structures are built up in a series of analyses from immediate constituents, e.g. first noun phrases, then prepositional structures, then verb relationships and finally the sentence structure as a whole. In top-down parsing, the algorithm seeks the fulfilment of expected constituents NP, VP, etc., by appropriate sets and sequences of grammatical categories. The bottom-up parsing strategy was the most common approach in the early MT system, but at MIT some investigation was made into the top-down strategy ('analysis by synthesis'). In systems since the mid-1960s this strategy is now probably more common.

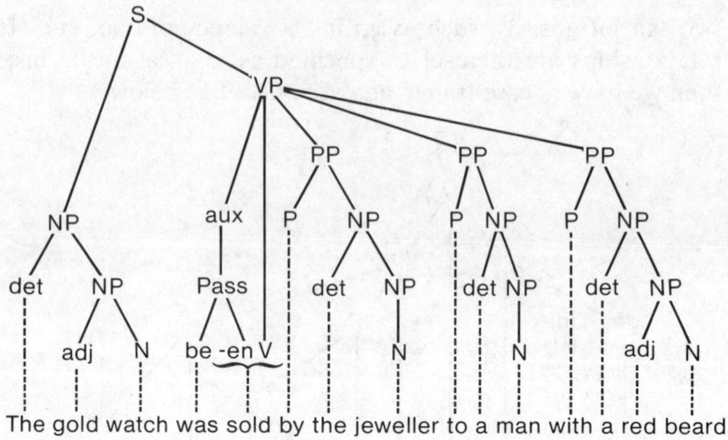

Fig. 3 — Phrase structure analysis.

It may be noted that categorial grammar developed by Bar-Hillel (1960, app. II), which was one of the first attempts at formal syntax, is a version of constituency grammar. In a categorial grammar, there are just two fundamental categories, sentence s and nominal n; the other grammatical categories (verb, adjective, adverb, etc.) are defined in terms of their potentiality to combine with one another or with one of the fundamental categories in constituent structures. Thus a transitive verb is defined as n\s because it combines with a nominal (to its left) to form sentences; and an adjective is defined as n/n because in combination with a nominal n to its right it forms a (higher-order) nominal n. In other words, the category symbols themselves define how they are to combine with other categories. Combination operates by two simple 'cancellation' rules: x/y, y → x, and y, y\x → x.

3.5 FORMAL SYNTAX AND TRANSFORMATIONAL GRAMMAR

Research in MT helped to stimulate much interest in formal linguistics. An early result of this mathematisation of syntax and linguistic theory was the demonstration that all phrase structure and dependency grammars are formally (i.e. mathematically) equivalent and that since they can be implemented on push-down automata, they are equivalent also to the so-called finite state grammars (Gross & Lentin 1967). All these grammars belong to the class of 'context-free' grammars. A context-free grammar consists of a set of rewriting rules (or production rules) of the form A → a, where A belongs to a set of 'non-terminal' symbols and a is a string of non-terminal and/or terminal symbols. Non-terminal symbols are grammatical categories

(S, NP, VP, N, Adj, etc.) and terminal symbols are lexical items of the language. Context-free grammars are important not only as the basis for formal grammars of natural languages but as the basis for computer programming, since the standard algorithmic methods used in compilers rely on finding only context-free structures in programming languages.

However, Noam Chomsky (1957) demonstrated the inherent inadequacies of finite state grammars, phrase structure grammars and the formally equivalent dependency grammars for the representation and description of the syntax of natural languages. Context-free grammars are unable, for example, to relate different structures having the same functional relationships, e.g. where discontinuous constituents are involved: *He looked up the address* and *He looked the address up*; or where there are differences of voice, e.g. the active: *The jeweller sold the watch to the man yesterday* and the passive: *Yesterday the man was sold the watch by the jeweller*. Chomsky proposed a transformational-generative model which derived 'surface' phrase structures from 'deep' phrase structures by transformational rules. Thus a passive construction in a 'surface' representation is related to an underlying active construction in a 'deep' representation, where the 'surface' subject noun appears as the 'deep' logical object (Fig. 4). Deep

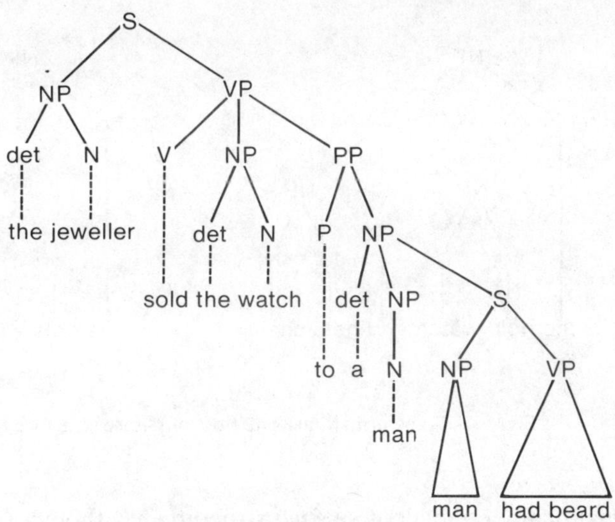

Fig. 4 — 'Deep' structure analysis.

structures are generated from an initial symbol S by 'context-free' rewriting rules. An essential feature of the Chomskyan model is that syntactic structures are generated top-down from initial symbol S, to 'deep' structure trees and then by transformational rules to 'surface' structure trees. In the case of a coordinate phrase such as *gold watch and chain* the base 'deep' structure would make explicit the fact that both watch and chain are gold (Fig. 5a). To produce the elliptical 'surface' form (Fig. 5b) a transformation rule would delete the repeated adjective. The model is not intended to provide the basis for a recognition grammar (e.g. a parser), but only to define mathematically the set of well-formed sentences, and to assign "a structural description indicating how the sentence is understood by the ideal speaker-hearer" (Chomsky 1965: 5). The implications of this approach became clearer when researchers attempted to develop 'transformational parsers' (Ch. 9.11).

Chomsky's notion of transformational rules derived formally from the work of Zellig Harris (1957). Harris' concern was the development of a symbolism for representing structural relationships. Grammatical categories were established primarily on the basis of distributional analysis. Thus, the subject of a sentence can be a (single) noun (*The man* . . .), a clause (*His leaving home* . . .), a gerundive (*The barking of dogs* . . .), an infinitive clause (*To go there* . . .), etc. In order to function as subjects, clauses have to undergo transformations from 'kernel' (atomic sentence-like) forms: e.g. *He left home* → *His leaving home, Dogs bark* → *The barking of dogs*. For Harris, transformations were a descriptive mechanism for relating surface structures, while in Chomsky's model, transformational rules derive surface structures from 'deeper' structures. By the mid-1960s (Chomsky 1965) an additional requirement of transformational rules was that they should be 'meaning-preserving', i.e. from a 'deep' structure should be generated

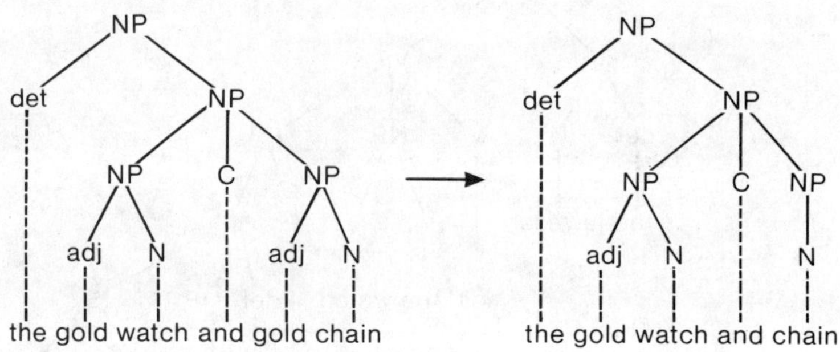

Fig. 5 — Transformational rule (loss of phrase structure relationship).

semantically equivalent surface structures. Although Chomsky's syntactic theory has undoubtedly had most influence, the formalisation of transformations by Harris had considerable impact in MT research, particularly in the representation of SL–TL structural transfer rules.

3.6 SYNTACTIC AMBIGUITY AND DISCOURSE RELATIONS

Although the identification of grammatical categories and of sentence structures is clearly important in linguistic analysis, there are inherent limitations in syntactic analysis which were recognised before even efficient parsers had been developed. A familiar example is the problem of multiple analyses of prepositional phrases. Since a prepositional phrase may modify either a verb or a preceding noun phrase a sequence such as $V + NP_1 + P + NP_2 + P + NP_3$ must have parsings which relate NP_2 and V, NP_2 and NP_1, NP_3 and V, NP_3 and NP_2 in all possible combinations. Syntactic analysis alone cannot decide which relationship is correct in a particular case. For example take the sentences:

> *The coastguard observed the yacht in the harbour with binoculars.*
> *The gold watch was sold by the jeweller to a man with a beard.*

In the first case, it was the coastguard who had the binoculars; therefore the PP *with the binoculars* modifies the verb. But in the second case, the PP *with a beard* modifies the preceding noun *man*. Only semantic information can assist the analysis by assigning semantic codes allowing *binoculars* as 'instruments' to be associated with 'perceptual' verbs such as *observe* but prohibiting *beards* to be interpreted as 'instruments' of verbs such as *sell*

Such solutions have been applied in many MT systems since the mid-1960s (as the following descriptions of systems will show). However, semantic features cannot deal with all problems of syntactical ambiguity. As Bar-Hillel argued in 1960 (Bar-Hillel 1964), human translators frequently use background knowledge to resolve syntactical ambiguities. His example was the phrase *slow neutrons and protons*. Whether *slow* modifies *protons* as well as *neutrons* can be decided only with subject knowledge of the physics involved. Similarly, in the case of the *gold watch and chain* our assumption that both objects are gold is based on past experience. On the other hand, in the case of the phrase *old men and women* the decision would probably rest on information conveyed in previous or following sentences in the particular text being analysed.

The most frequent occasions on which recourse is made to 'real world' knowledge involve the reference of pronouns. Examples are the two sentence pairs:

> The men murdered the women. They were caught three days later.
> The men murdered the women. They were buried three days later.

The correct attribution of the pronoun *they* to the men in the first pair and to the women in the second depends entirely on our knowledge that only dead people are buried, that murder implies death, that murder is a criminal act, and that criminals ought to be apprehended. This knowledge is non-linguistic, but it has linguistic implications in, for example, translation of these sentences into French where a choice of *ils* or *elles* must be made.

Of course, it is not only in cases of syntactic ambiguity that we use 'real world' knowledge to help in understanding text. Homographs can, as indicated earlier, be resolved by identification of grammatical categories, e.g. whether *watch* is a noun or a verb. However, the resolution of some homographs require, as in the physics example, knowledge of the objects referred to. There is, for example, a third sense of *watch* in the sentence: *The watch included two new recruits that night*. It can be distinguished from the other noun only by recognition that time-pieces do not usually include animate beings. It was from such instances that Bar-Hillel was to argue in an influential paper (Bar-Hillel 1960) that fully automatic translation of a high quality was never going to be feasible (Ch. 8.3 below). In practice this type of problem can be lessened if texts for translation are restricted to a more or less narrow scientific field, and so dictionaries and grammars can concentrate on a specific 'sublanguage' (and this was the argument for 'micro-glossaries'). Nevertheless, similar examples recur regularly, and the argument that MT requires 'language understanding' based on encyclopaedic knowledge and complicated inference procedures has convinced many researchers that the only way forward is the development of 'interactive' and Artificial Intelligence approaches to MT (Ch. 15 and 17).

In general, semantic analysis has developed, by and large, as an adjunct of syntactic analysis in MT systems. (Exceptions are those MT systems with an explicitly semantic orientation, cf. 9.17 below.) In most MT systems semantic analysis goes no further than necessary for the resolution of homographs. In such cases, all that is generally needed is the assignment of such features as 'human', 'animate', 'concrete', 'male', etc., and some simple feature matching procedures. For example, *crook* can only be animate in *The crook escaped from the police*, because the verb *escape* demands an animate subject noun (as in a case frame specification, Ch. 9.16 below). The 'shepherd's staff' sense of *crook* is thus excluded. In many systems semantic features have been assigned as 'selection restrictions' in an *ad hoc* manner, as the demands of the analysis of a particular group of lexical items seem to require them, and also somewhat too rigidly. There are difficulties, for example, if the verb *sell* is defined as always having inanimate objects; the sentence *The men were sold at a slave market* would not be correctly parsed. One answer suggested has been to make such 'selection restrictions' define not obligatory features but preferences (Ch. 15.1).

True semantic analysis should include some decomposition of lexical items according a set of semantic 'primitives' or putative 'universals'. Only by such means is it possible to derive common semantic representations for a pair of sentences such as *The teacher paid no attention to the pupil* and *The pupil was ignored by the teacher*. In general, the majority of MT systems have avoided or held back from the intricacies and complexities, and no doubt pitfalls, of this kind of semantics. It is found therefore only in those MT groups which have investigated interlinguas (e.g. the Cambridge group, Ch. 5.2, and the Soviet group around Mel'chuk, Ch. 10.2), and in some of those recent (since mid-1970s) groups with an interest in AI methods (Ch. 15).

3.7 SENTENCES AND TEXTS

The difficulties with pronominal reference described above stem also from the exclusive concentration on syntax-based analysis of sentences. The need for text-based analysis can be illustrated by the following two German sentences:

> In der Strasse sahen wir einen Polizist, der einem Mann nachlief. Dem Polizist folgte ein grosser Hund.

Translation into English sentence by sentence would normally retain the active verb forms producing:

> In the street we saw a policeman running after a man. A large dog followed the policeman.

Text cohesion would be improved if the second sentence were passivised as:

> The policeman was followed by a large dog.

This inversion requires that a MT system adheres as far as possible to the information structure of the original, i.e. in this case retains the *policeman* as the head (or topic) of the sentence.The problems of topicalisation and text cohesion are of course far more complex than this example. Scarcely any MT projects have even considered how they might be tackled.

3.8 TRANSFER AND SYNTHESIS

The production of output text in the target language (TL) is based on the information provided from dictionaries and from the results of analysis. In general the synthesis of TL sentences is less complex than the analysis of SL input. The process involves nearly always the derivation of correct morphological forms for TL words (unless dictionaries contain only full TL forms). Thus, for example, TL synthesis must produce the right forms of verbs, e.g. for English simple past forms it is not a matter of just adding -ed as in *picked* (from *pick*), since sometimes endings must be deleted or altered as in *lived* (not: *liveed*) and *tried* (not: *tryed*), etc. Irregular forms are generally handled by the dictionary (e.g. *went* would be coded directly as the past form of *go*).

If analysis has included the establishment of syntactic structure (e.g. a phrase structure) then synthesis must convert this structure into an appropriate TL structure and produce a linear representation, i.e. it must invert the analysis process in some way. However, it should be stressed that inversion does not imply that the rules devised for the analysis of structures for a particular language (as SL) can be simply reversed to obtain rules for synthesis of that language (as TL).

At some point in many systems (the exceptions being interlingual systems, cf. next section), the syntactic structures of SL texts are transformed into TL structures. Whether such transformations apply to only short segments (as in word-for-word systems) or to whole sentences, the process involves the specification of transformation rules. For example, a rule for changing a German construction with final past participle (*Er hat das Buch gestern gelesen*) into an English construction with a simple past form (*He read the book yesterday*) might be in this form:

$$\text{NP} + \text{aux} + \ldots + \text{Vpp} \rightarrow \text{NP} + \text{Vpst} + \ldots$$

Clearly, such transformation rules have much in common with the transformation rules which Harris devised for relating structures within the same language.

3.9 SYSTEM DESIGNS AND STRATEGIES

In broad terms, there have been three types of overall strategy adopted in MT systems.

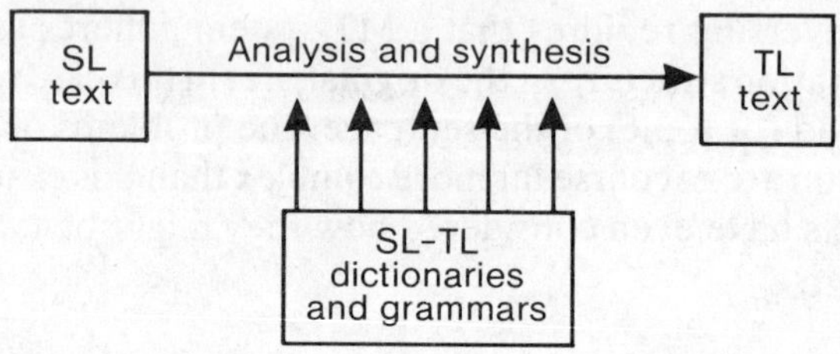

Fig. 6 — 'Direct translation' system.

The first approach is the 'direct translation' approach (Fig. 6). Systems are designed in all details specifically for one particular pair of languages. The basic assumption is that the vocabulary and syntax of SL texts need not be analysed any more than strictly necessary for the resolution of ambiguities, the correct identification of appropriate TL expressions and the specification of TL word order. Thus if the sequence of SL words is sufficiently close to an acceptable sequence of TL words, then there is no need to identify the syntactic structure of the SL text. The majority of MT systems of the 1950s and 1960s were based on this approach. They differed in the amount of analysis and/or restructuring incorporated. There was none at all in the straight 'dictionary translation' experiment of Richens and Booth (Ch. 2.2); there was just a minimum of local restructuring in the 'word-for-word' systems of the University of Washington and IBM (Ch. 4.1 and 4.2); there was partial analysis of SL structure in the Georgetown system (Ch. 4.3); and there was full sentence analysis in the systems at Ramo-Wooldridge, Harvard, and Wayne State University (Ch. 4.6, 4.9, 4.12). A primary characteristic of 'direct translation' systems of the earlier period was that no clear distinctions were made between stages of SL analysis and TL synthesis (cf. particularly the account of the Georgetown system below). In more recent (post-1970) examples of 'direct' systems there is a greater degree of 'modular' structure in the systems (cf. Ch. 9.10 below).

The second basic MT strategy is the 'interlingual' approach, which assumes that it is possible to convert SL texts into semantico-syntactic representations common to more than one language. From such 'interlingual' representations texts would be generated into other languages (Fig. 7). The common argument for translation via an interlingua is one of economy of effort in a multilingual environment (Andreev 1967). If there

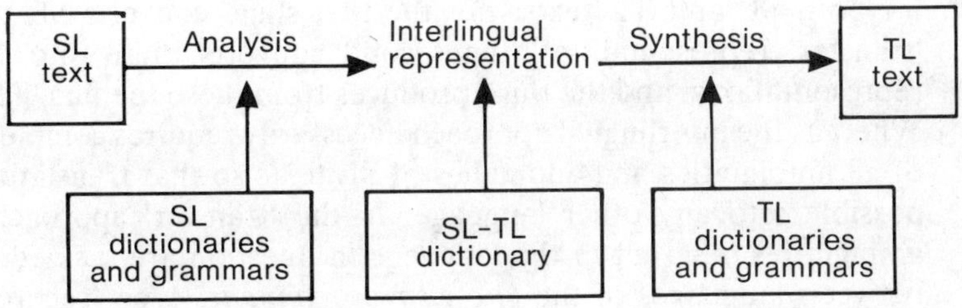

Fig. 7 — 'Interlingual' system.

are n languages involved and translation is to be from and into each of them, then a system would need $n(n\text{-}1)$ binary 'direct translation' programs. However, if translation is via an interlingua the system would need just $2n$ 'interlingual' programs. As soon as the number of languages exceeds 3, then the interlingual approach is more economic.

In interlingual systems translation from SL to TL is in two distinct and independent stages: in the first stage SL texts are fully analysed into interlingual representations, and in the second stage interlingual forms are the sources for producing (synthesising) TL texts. Procedures for SL analysis are intended to be SL-specific and not devised for any particular TL in the system; likewise, TL synthesis is intended to be TL-specific. Interlingual systems differ in their conceptions of an interlingual language: a 'logical' artificial language, or a 'natural' auxiliary language such as Esperanto; a set of semantic primitives common to all languages, or a 'universal' vocabulary, etc. Interlingual MT projects have also differed according to the emphasis on lexical (semantic) aspects and on syntactic aspects. Some concentrated on the construction of interlingual lexica (e.g. the Cambridge and the Leningrad groups); others have concentrated on interlingual 'syntax' (e.g. the Grenoble and Texas groups).

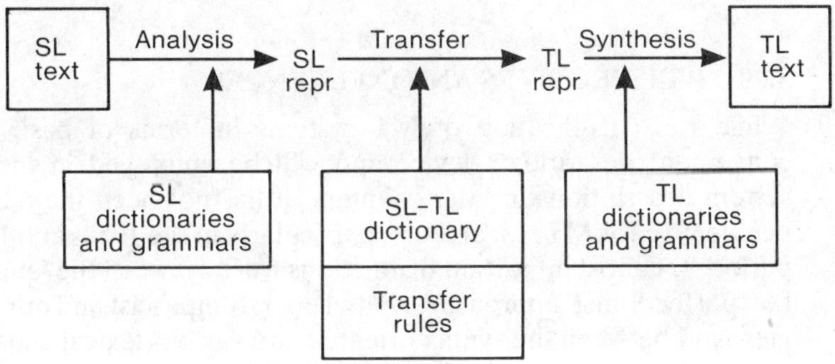

Fig. 8 — 'Transfer' system.

The third approach to overall MT strategy is the 'transfer' approach (Fig. 8). Rather than operating in two stages through a single interlingual representation, there are three stages involving underlying representations for both SL and TL texts; i.e. the first stage converts SL texts into SL 'transfer' representations, the second converts these into TL 'transfer' representations, and the third produces from these the final TL text forms. Whereas the interlingual approach necessarily requires complete resolution of all ambiguities and anomalies of SL texts so that translation should be possible into any other language, in the 'transfer' approach only those ambiguities inherent in the language in question are tackled. Differences between languages of the *know-savoir/connaître* type (section 3.2 above) would be handled during transfer. In English analysis, *know* is treated as unambiguous, there is no need to determine which kind of 'knowing' is involved. Whereas the 'interlingual' approach would require such analysis, the 'transfer' approach does not; problems of mismatch between SL and TL lexical ranges are resolved in the transfer component. Systems differ according to the 'depth' of analysis and the abstractness of SL and TL transfer representations. In the earliest systems (for which the MIT system (Ch. 4.7) is the exemplar), analysis went no further than 'surface' syntactic structures, with therefore structural transfer taking place at this depth of abstraction. Later (post-1970) transfer systems have taken analysis to 'deep' semantico-syntactic structures (of various kinds), with correspondingly more abstract transfer representations and transfer rules (cf. Ch. 13 on TAUM, GETA, etc.)

The basic difference between these two 'indirect' approaches and the (generally earlier) 'direct' approach lies in the configuration of dictionary and grammar data. In 'direct' systems the main component is a single SL–TL bilingual dictionary incorporating not only information on lexical equivalents but also all data necessary for morphological and syntactic analysis, transfer and synthesis. In 'indirect' systems, this information is dispersed among separate SL and TL dictionaries, separate SL and TL grammars, and either the interlingua vocabulary and syntax, or the SL–TL 'transfer' dictionary (of lexical equivalences) and a 'grammar' of SL–TL structure transfer rules (see Figs. 6 to 8).

3.10 PERSPECTIVES AND INFLUENCES

While the classification of MT systems in terms of basic strategy is a convenient descriptive device and will be employed in the grouping of system descriptions in later chapters, it has not been the most prominent perspective for MT researchers, particularly in the 1950s and 1960s. For this period, the most important distinctions were between the 'engineering' and the 'perfectionist' approaches, between the empiricist and other methodologies, and between the syntax oriented and various lexical and word-centred approaches.

The most immediate point of dispute was between those groups who agreed with Dostert and Booth on the importance of developing operational systems as quickly as possible (Ch. 2.4.3) and those who argued for more fundamental research before such attempts. The engineering approach held basically that all systems can be improved and that the poor quality early word-for-word systems represent a good starting point. There were differences between what Garvin (1967) dubbed the 'brute force' approach, which assumed that the basic need was larger storage capacity (e.g. the IBM solution, Ch. 4.2), and the gradualist approach which believed that algorithmic improvements based on reliable methods of (linguistic) analysis could lead to better quality (the Georgetown, ITMVT, Ramo-Wooldridge projects). The 'perfectionists' included all those groups which concentrated on basic linguistic research with 'high quality' systems as the objective (MIT, Harvard, RAND, Berkeley, MIAN, etc.). The latter differed considerably in both theories and methods. Disputes between the 'perfectionists' and the 'engineers' recurred frequently until the mid-1960s (cf. Ch. 8.2).

On questions of methodology the main point of difference concerned the 'empiricist' approach, exemplified by the RAND group (Ch. 4.4). The approach emphasised the need to base procedures on actual linguistic data; it was distrustful of existing grammars and dictionaries; it believed it was necessary to establish from scratch the data required and to use the computer as an aid for gathering data. The approach stressed statistical and distributional analyses of texts, and a 'cyclic' method of system development: i.e. routines devised for one corpus were tested on another, improved, tested on a third corpus, improved again, and so forth. The empirical approach was in fact fully in accord with the dominant linguistic methodology of the 1940s and 1950s in the United States, the descriptivist and structuralist 'tradition' associated particularly with Leonard Bloomfield (1933). The descriptivists adopted the behaviourist and positivistic method which insisted that only interpersonally observed phenomena should be considered 'scientific' data, and which rejected introspections and intuitions. They distrusted theorising, stressed data collection, and concentrated on methods of discovery and analysis. Traditional grammars were suspect: Charles Fries (1952), for example, undertook a distributional analysis of telephone conversations which resulted in new grammatical categories for English. Most descriptivists worked, however, on phonetics and phonology. Only in the mid-1950s did some descriptivists such as Zellig Harris start work on syntax. It was therefore not surprising that the empiricists regarded their research within MT as extending the range of descriptive linguistics.

The 'empiricist' emphasis on probabilistic and statistical methods, however, has perhaps a different origin. It is likely to be the considerable influence of the statistical theory of communication associated with Claude Shannon, i.e. 'information theory', and to which Warren Weaver made a substantial contribution (Shannon & Weaver 1949). The theory had great impact on the anti-metaphysical inclinations of most American linguists, since it seemed to provide a basis for developing mechanical methods for 'discovering' grammars. It may be noted that when Yngve first presented his ideas on 'syntactic transfer' (Yngve 1957), he related his tripartite model to the information-theoretic triple of sender, channel, and receiver (Ch. 4.7).

A third area of difference in early MT groups was the question of what should be taken as the central unit of language. The majority assumed the centrality of the sentence; their approach was sentence-oriented (as was and still is, in essence, that of most linguists and logicians), and so there was an emphasis on syntactic relations and problems. A minority upheld the centrality of the word. They emphasised lexical and semantic relations and problems. They included the 'lexicographic' approach of Reifler and King, the 'thesaural' approach of the Cambridge group, the 'word-centred' theories of Lamb at Berkeley, and the dictionary-centred aspects of Mel'chuk's 'meaning-text' approach. It should be stressed that these are 'differences' only of general orientation; the 'syntax-oriented' groups did not neglect lexical and semantic issues, and the 'lexis-oriented' groups did not by any means neglect syntax. Indeed, in the case of Lamb and Mel'chuk it is very much an open question whether their models can be said to be oriented one way or the other.

In the descriptions above of various aspects of MT system design and methods of analysis, it may well have been implied, at a number of points, that language systems are intrinsically multi-levelled; that is to say, that linguistic description is necessarily couched in terms of phonetics, phonology, morphology (word formation), syntax, and semantics; and furthermore, that analysis proceeds through each of these levels in turn: first morphological analysis, then syntactic analysis, then semantic analysis. (The most extensive 'stratificationalist' models were in fact developed within the MT context, by Lamb and Mel'chuk.) Although undoubtedly a 'stratal' view of language systems is dominant in linguistics and has been since the time of Saussure, the founder of modern (structuralist) linguistics, it has not been the conception of some MT project teams. Indeed, many (particularly in the earliest period) would have rejected such a stratal view of language both for being too rigid and for not conforming to reality. For them, all aspects of language (lexical, semantic, structural) interact inextricably in all linguistic phenomena. There is no doubt that among the most linguistics-oriented MT groups there has been sometimes an excessive rigidity in the application of the stratal approach to analysis (e.g. in parsing systems); and it has led to failures of various kinds (cf. Ch. 9.2 and 9.12). Nevertheless, the basic validity of the approach has not been disproved, and most modern (linguistics-oriented) MT systems retain this basic conception (e.g. the GETA and Eurotra systems).

3.11 MT RESEARCH IN THE PERIOD 1956–66

In the years immediately after the 1954 Georgetown-IBM demonstration, MT research began to receive massive funding in the United States, and to a lesser extent elsewhere. The level of support from military and intelligence sources can be explained partly by the prevailing political climate and by US fears of being overtaken by the Soviet Union in technology and science. However, it can be explained also as a reflection of the often exaggerated visions of computers as 'thinking machines'. Of all the possible tasks which these 'electronic brains' could be expected to do in the future, one of the most useful and practicable appeared to be translation. MT research became in consequence the pioneer field for work in 'artificial intelligence' (although the term was not to be coined until 1956 (McCorduck 1979)).

Much of the research in the 1950s and 1960s which was undertaken by MT groups would now be rightly regarded as belonging to other disciplines and fields. A number of projects, for example, were equally interested in problems of information retrieval and automatic indexing and abstracting, which were seen as closely linked to MT in so far as they involved complex linguistic analysis.

MT projects made major contributions to linguistic theory, principally formal grammar and mathematical linguistics. The work on syntactic analysis and parsing stimulated interest in the mathematical foundations of 'context-free' grammars (section 3.4 above). Theoretical linguistics was the focus of much of the research at MIT, where a number of prominent linguists and transformational grammarians (beginning with Chomsky himself) were engaged in basic linguistic research. Elsewhere, at RAND, the foundations of dependency grammar were elaborated by Hays (1964) on earlier work by Tesnière (1959), and at Berkeley, Lamb developed his theory of stratificational grammar (Lamb 1966). Other centres with substantial contributions to linguistic research were Harvard, Texas, and MIAN in the Soviet Union.

Above all, MT was for many years the focus for all research in what is now called computational linguistics. Much of the activity at RAND was concerned with general applications of the computer to linguistic analysis and to linguistic data processing. From the mid-1960s MT became a peripheral activity at RAND, as indeed it did at Harvard and MIT. Computational linguistics grew from MT research and the two were regularly equated. The original name of the Association for Computational Linguistics was the Association for Machine Translation and Computational Linguistics (Ch. 8.2). A further indication of close links is the fact that the University of Pennsylvania group under Zellig Harris was regularly included in accounts of MT research during the 1960s, e.g. in the surveys by Bar-Hillel (1960) and Josselson (1971). Yet it is quite clear even from contemporary reports that Harris was engaged on basic syntactic research of English and had no intention of developing an experimental MT system (even in theory).

To a significant degree, in the 1950s and 1960s MT was the current most popular 'bandwagon'; a fact which contributed to its later downfall (Ch. 8.9). The major sponsors in the US were the National Science Foundation, the Central Intelligence Agency, and the US military forces. For obvious reasons, their main interest was in Russian–English translation and this was the predominant language pair studied by MT groups during this period. In the Soviet Union the main concentration was on English–Russian, but in general the MT research effort was more diversified than in the US. In the course of time, many countries had MT research activities of some kind; the major centres outside the US and the Soviet Union were Great Britain, Italy, and France.

In the following chapters the research groups will be discussed individually. The next chapter deals with the US projects, first projects which eventually produced operational systems: University of Washington, IBM, Georgetown (4.1–3), then the 'empiricist' projects at RAND, Michigan and the associated Ramo-Wooldridge project (4.4–6), then the more 'theoretical' groups at MIT, Harvard, Berkeley, and Texas (4.7, 4.9, 4.10, 4.11). Also treated are the NBS and Wayne State and other 'minor' US projects (4.8, 4.12, 4.13). This long chapter is followed by one devoted to the groups in the United Kingdom, Birkbeck College (5.1), Cambridge (5.2), and the National Physical Laboratory (5.4); to the Milan group (5.3); and to the French, and other Western European groups (5.5–8). The next chapter covers research in the Soviet Union and in Eastern Europe. Finally, chapter 7 deals with projects and research groups in Japan (7.1), China (7.2), and Mexico (7.3).

Major information sources for this period of MT research (apart from the accounts of individual projects) are the important surveys by Bar-Hillel (1960), Delavenay (1960), Josselson (1971), Mounin (1964), Pendergraft (1967), primarily for US research; and by Harper (1963), Ljudskanov (1972), Mel'chuk (1963), and Mukhin (1963) for Soviet research. Also invaluable are news items in the journals *Mechanical Translation* (1954–65), and *Traduction Automatique* (1960–64), and the project descriptions in the National Science Foundation's biannual *Current Research and Development in Scientific Documentation* (1957–66); these sources are abbreviated *MT*, *TA* and *CRDSD* respectively in the following chapters. Representative collections of articles are to be found in conference proceedings (Edmundson 1961, NATO 1966, NPL 1962) and in collections by Booth (1967) and Bruderer (1982). Bibliographic sources are the major survey articles and Delavenay (1960a), Van Hoof (1973: 464–504), Kent (1960a), Klein (1971) and, in particular, the critical bibliography by Mel'chuk & Ravich (1967).

4

Groups and projects in the United States 1950–66

4.1 UNIVERSITY OF WASHINGTON (1949–1962)

This MT research team was one of the earliest and biggest of those set up during the 1950s. As we have seen (Ch. 2.4), Erwin Reifler, who was Professor of Chinese at Washington, was one of the pioneers of MT. Stimulated by Weaver's memorandum, he embarked on a number of studies principally concerned with German–English translation. He was supported between 1952 and 1953 by grants from the Rockefeller Foundation, enabling him to investigate general problems of MT (such as post-editing and dictionary construction) as well as more specific research on German compounds. The problem, as Reifler saw, was that it is simply impossible to provide dictionary entries for German nouns since so many compounds can be freely formed; automatic procedures are needed to divide compounds into those components which may appear in the dictionary, thus enabling plausible attempts at their translation. From his investigation Reifler (1955a) concluded that automatic procedures were feasible; the only problem was that some compounds could be split in two different ways (e.g. *Wachtraum* as *Wach/traum* (day dream) or *Wacht/raum* (guard room)); although most of these dissections would produce nonsense translations (e.g. *Literat/urkunde* (man of letters' document) instead of the correct *Literatur/kunde* (literary studies)) Reifler did not elaborate on how these components were to be translated.

Shortly afterwards Reifler began a collaborative project with members of the Department of Electrical Engineering at Washington (T. M. Stout, R. E. Wall, Professor W. R. Hill, and R. S. Wagner) on the development of a pilot MT model system for German–English translation. At the 1952 MIT conference, Reifler had agreed with Dostert of Georgetown University that what MT research needed next was to produce some prototype MT systems. The Washington prototype constructed during 1954 was extremely limited, just 60 German words with English equivalents, and none longer than 7 letters (*MT* 2(2) Nov. 1955), but it provided the foundation for a MT project, later joined by Lew R. Micklesen (a Russian expert) and David L. Johnson (a computer expert). In this group Hill concentrated on the development of large-capacity, rapid-access storage while Micklesen investigated Russian compounds and problems of grammatical information.

In June 1956 the Washington MT group received a grant from the US Air Force (Rome Air Development Center) to study the lexicographical, linguistic, and engineering prerequisites for the automatic translation of scientific Russian into English, based on the photoscopic disc memory device being developed by Gilbert W. King at the International Telemeter Corporation in Los Angeles. It was charged specifically with the preparation of the Russian–English lexicon for the USAF system. At this time, according to Reifler (1958), the "US Air Force (was) primarily not interested in machine translation, but in an efficient information retrieval system permitting quick access to the enormous amount of information stored in its files." In the initial project (1956–57) the team analysed 111 Russian texts covering 40 scientific fields, building up a database of more than 14,000 Russian–English dictionary entries of technical and general-language vocabulary. An expanded project began in March 1957 to supplement this initial collection by adding all the inflected forms for this vocabulary (i.e. complete paradigms of nouns and verbs). This lexicographic phase concluded in June 1959 with a Russian–English MT lexicon of 170,563 entries stored on over half a million IBM punch cards. Further grants were received from the US Air Force until March 1960 to enable the Washington group to investigate other aspects of Russian–English translation.

The emphasis of the Washington group's MT research was determined both by Reifler's conviction of the essential validity of the basic word-for-word approach (at least for intermediary working systems) and by the physical capacities of the photoscopic disc. At a time when existing electronic computers had limited storage capacities, grossly inadequate for MT dictionaries and translation procedures, the impressive capacity of the photoscopic disc was very attractive. Many researchers had suggested that MT required purpose-built machines, and a translation machine including the photoscopic memory seemed a practical objective.

What had been developed at the International Telemeter Corporation under Gilbert King was a memory device consisting of a rotating glass disc, together with various mechanical, optical, and electronic components. Information was stored photographically on the glass disc in binary coding in 600 concentric rows with 50,000 bits of information in each row, making possible the storage of large amounts of information in a limited space (30 million bits). Information was read by shining a light through the disc, rotating at 20 revolutions per second, and converting the resulting alternations of light and dark to electric signals by the use of a photocell; and these signals were then processed by computer (King *et al.* 1953, *MT* 3(2) Nov. 1956, King 1959, Wall 1960).

In an investigation of the dictionary requirements for the Russian–English project, Wall (1960) estimated that the storage capacity needed was 130–180 million bits. The advanced model of the disc was intended to have a capacity of 100 million bits and a random access time of 1/20 seconds, so two photoscopic discs were considered easily sufficient for a large-scale translation system.

The distinctive features of MT research at Washington (Reifler 1961a) were its particular emphasis on lexicographic approaches rather than structural linguistic approaches, its emphasis on devising a system which could deal with the vocabulary of many fields of science rather than just one field or sub-field, and its emphasis on 'free-form' dictionary entries (i.e. all paradigmatic forms of words) rather separate entries of stems and endings. A major factor in adopting the lexicographic approach was that "since Dr King's automatic system did not yet include logical equipment for linguistic purposes, it was decided to attempt to solve as many bilingual linguistic problems as possible by purely lexicographical means." However, it was discovered that many grammatical problems could also be solved by lexicography alone, without the necessity of syntactic analysis. Having been explicitly charged by their sponsors with the creation of a Russian–English lexicon it was, therefore, decided to aim for an "optimum of lexicography", leaving unsolved problems to be dealt with later (Reifler 1960, 1961a).

The emphasis on a wide range of scientific vocabulary was also mainly determined by the large capacity of the photoscopic disc. It was believed that the earlier arguments for concentrating MT systems to scientific fields had lost their force: "If specialised glossaries, idio-glossaries, for one field or sub-field of science will still be used in MT in the future, it will not be because of any limitations in the storage capacity of the permanent memory device." (Reifler 1961a). However, Reifler claimed there were also good linguistic reasons: there were believed to be considerable overlaps in scientific vocabularies and it was held that the semantic problems of scientific texts were caused mainly by the general non-scientific vocabulary and by the specifically scientific vocabulary which was shared by a number of different fields. Therefore, the Washington group set about the compilation of a general scientific vocabulary and worked out procedures in order to pinpoint the intended meaning of those (homographic) terms occurring in more than one scientific field.

For this they took two approaches: classification and cover terms. Detailed statistical analyses of multiple meanings were conducted in order to establish a general classification of scientific vocabulary fields, with the intention of assigning these classes to items of Russian and English vocabulary. In the case of overlapping vocabularies, e.g. medicine and biology, and applied science and technology, a good deal of redundancy had to be tolerated (Micklesen 1960). In the other line which was pursued, the groups sought 'cover forms', single English equivalents which would give acceptable versions for Russian terms whatever the scientific field.

Although larger storage seemed also to make procedures for dividing entries into stems and endings less necessary (Reifler 1961b), this was not the principal argument used by Reifler in favour of 'free-form' entries. A stems-ending approach requires morphological analysis, often of some complexity and certainly of considerable programming size. Furthermore, the problem of recognising homographs is increased because information carried by full forms has been lost (e.g. noun/verb homographs can be distinguished by their different inflections).

However, Reifler's goal of a MT system employing the "optimum of lexicography" went further. It meant not only an emphasis on a general-language vocabulary for all fields of science and the 'free-form approach', but also the treatment of many difficult phrases as if they were idioms. As Reifler (1961c) explained, any MT system has to cope with genuine 'bilingual' idioms, i.e. expressions which cannot be translated word-for-word (Reifler's example was that while *The man is an ass* could be translated word for word into German *Der Mann ist ein Esel*, it cannot be so translated into Chinese). But in addition, MT systems can use the same technique for non-idiomatic cases. For example, while English *league* could be German *Liga, Bund,* or *Bündnis*, and *nations* could be *Nationen* or *Völker*, the 'League of Nations' should be treated as an idiom: *Völkerbund*. Likewise, compounds in which an element may have different translations according to its context (e.g. in *Denkarbeit, Denkart, Denkmünze*, etc. where 'Denk-' can be 'thinking', 'thought', 'commemorative', etc.); these too can be treated as idiomatic terms.

The system developed under the USAF contract until 1960 was, therefore, an elaborated word-for-word system using the photoscopic store. The system had no problem with idioms, could cope with compounds and with some homographic problems by examination of immediate context. But it had no means of resolving syntactic ambiguities or of reordering the output to conform to English usage. An example translation from Micklesen (1958) shows the kind of results achieved:

> Infection/corruption (by/with/as) nodular (by/with/as) bacteria comes/advances/treads especially/peculiarly (it)(is)light/easy(ly) at/by/with/from (of) plants, (of) weakened/loosened (to/for)(by/with/as) nitrogen/nitrous (by/with/as) starvation, and/even/too (is)considerable/significant(ly) (is/are)more-difficult(ly) happens/comes-from at/by/with/from (of) plants, (is)energetic(ally) (of)growing on/in/at/to/for/by/with (of) rich(of)nitrogen/nitrous soils.

It was obvious to all that such 'translations' were, as members of the group admitted, "far from clear and far from being readily intelligible" (Wall 1960).

However, the project had always been seen as a two-stage operation with the intention after the lexicographic work of developing 'logical procedures' to deal with divergencies between source and target languages. This research began in June 1959 after the completion of the supplemented lexicon of 170,000 entries, and continued until the termination of the project in March 1960. Micklesen (1960) investigated a number of problems. One was the possibility of resolving verb homographs by a classification of object nouns (e.g. as animate, human, concrete, metals, plants, etc.) and a selection algorithm. For example, *dokhodyat*: (they)reach/ripen/are-done can only be 'ripen' if the following noun is classified as a 'fruit/vegetable'. Another problem was the practice of providing equivalents in the form of a 'minimum correlation-specification' (e.g. Russian *izmeneniya*: English (of)-change(s)), with the result that the output included a clutter of superfluous grammatical information, as in the example above. It was the object of subsequent research to reduce this clutter substantially and, if possible, to reduce the number of English alternatives provided.

In the initial stages of the project 'translations' had been manually simulated; the availability of an IBM 650 enabled some testing of the algorithms. The output from the dictionary search (still manually simulated, the IBM 650's capacity being only 2000 words) was processed in four stages (Micklesen & Wall 1961; Wall 1960). The first three resolved homographs by the identification of agreement relations (e.g. within noun phrases) and government relations (e.g. substantive and verb), and by the elimination of superfluous information (e.g. if a substantive had a preceding agreeing adjective the English preposition was eliminated: 'nervous (of) . . . impotence' became 'nervous . . . impotence'). The fourth stage inserted English equivalents for Russian case relations and translated Russian prepositions. An example of the 'improvement' given by Wall was:

> about/against/with treatment (of)(to/for)(by/with/as)nerve/nervous (of)(to/for)impotence (by/with/as)novocain

which became:

> about/against/with treatment of nerve/nervous impotence (by/with/as)novocain

As it transpired this work was the nearest the Washington team approached an actual MT system; the final stage, in which attention was to be paid to problems of producing acceptable word order in TL output, was not reached. There had been expressed some interest in transformational grammar for investigating problems of syntax but this could not be pursued. The Washington approach was throughout pragmatic: the aim was to produce something which, however inadequate, could be progressively refined. Although their own results were relatively meagre, they shared with others a general mood of optimism about MT: typical is Reifler's conviction that ". . . it will not be very long before the remaining linguistic problems in machine translation will be solved for a number of important languages" (Reifler 1958).

Although most work was done on Russian–English translation, it is no surprise that Reifler did not neglect Chinese. A particular problem with Chinese is the identification of lexical units, since word boundaries are not indicated in written Chinese; for Reifler, then, the basic approach in Chinese MT had to be lexicographic. As in the USAF project, what was needed first was a study of the general-language vocabulary of Chinese scientific texts, the aim again being the establishment of a bilingual lexicon making possible idiomatic translations with least recourse to 'logical operations' for solving problems of ambiguity and differences in syntactic structures. However, because of the "much greater morphological and syntactic agreement between Chinese and English" than between Russian and English, Reifler expected word-for-word translations from Chinese to be more intelligible than those from Russian. On the other hand, the number of English alternatives for Chinese characters is on average much higher than in the case of Russian–English translation. As in the USAF project, the Chinese vocabulary was classified according to scientific fields, in order to assist homograph resolution and selection of English equivalents. Reifler (1967) gave an example of a simulated MT from Chinese, with simulated improvements of the purely lexicographic output.

By 1959 research on the development of the photoscopic store and with it, research on the USAF Russian–English translation system had been transferred to the IBM Research Center at Yorktown Heights, New York. Apart from individual important contributions by Reifler, Wall, and Micklesen, the principal achievement of the Washington MT research group was its single-minded pursuit of the lexicographic approach and its demonstration of what could be achieved with bilingual (direct) word-for-word translation. Above all, from a historical perspective, it laid the foundations for the earliest operational MT system.

4.2 IBM RESEARCH CENTER (1958–66)

During 1958–59 the research project on the photoscopic store was transferred to the IBM Corporation's T. J. Watson Research Center at Yorktown Heights, New York. As before in Los Angeles, the research was sponsored by the Rome Air Development Center at Griffiss Air Force Base, New York, and was directed towards the establishment of a Russian–English MT system for the US Air Force. Considerable modifications of the equipment were introduced at IBM, particularly in respect of dictionary creation, Russian text input, and graphical output of English text.

Although called the USAF Automatic Translator Mark I (Shiner 1958), it could scarcely be called a MT system since it still comprised little more than the large bilingual dictionary created by the Washington MT group. It is evident, however, that the Washington entries were being amended at IBM. King (1959) remarked that "we are now incorporating useful lexicon entries by modifying lists which have only recently been made available to IBM by the Rome Air Development Center". Differences of approach were evident even before King moved to IBM in 1958.

King shared an empirical (engineering) approach to MT: "The program at IBM Research has been to examine the question . . . from an operational point of view" (King 1961). He believed that a basically word-for-word approach could be made quite acceptable, if problems of multiple meaning are solved by contextual information and if choices of 'best' equivalents are based on probabilistic criteria (King 1956).

Improvements to the Mark I system were made by the use of local context in the form of 'stuffing' procedures (King 1961). For example, the word *coping* can be either a verbal form or a noun (part of a wall). In *I shall be coping with . . .* it is identified as a verb by the preceding *be*. In the IBM system information in the dictionary attached to *be* causes the modification of *coping* as *a-coping*, thus signalling treatment as a present participle. The same 'stuffing' procedure could be applied to semantic problems. The example given by King is: "*The curfew tolls the knell of parting day*, where a class of words of which *day* is a member stuffs 'de-' in front of *parting* to form *departing*, thus resolving the many interpretations of *parting*" Furthermore, stuffing could improve English output; a simple example is the formation of verb forms: *drag* plus '-ed' becomes *dragged* after a prefix 'g' is stuffed in front of the ending ('prefix' is King's term.)

A major departure from the Washington 'lexicographic' approach was the decision to adopt the 'stems and endings' approach for dictionary entries. The arguments were presented by Micklesen, a member of the Washington team who joined IBM in 1960. Despite the large-capacity storage, it was practical on economic grounds not to require dictionary compilers to enter all paradigmatic forms, both because many may never actually occur and because errors from human fallibility were increased. Micklesen (1962) argued, therefore, that Russian words should be entered as stems as far as possible, the only exceptions being made for homographic stems, e.g. *dn* (either *day* or *bottom*), where differences conveyed by their full forms would be lost.

From June 1959 the Mark I version was translating Russian newspapers (Macdonald 1960); according to King (1963) about 10,000 words were translated daily and "were found . . . to be quite useful by the Government". As an example of a Mark I translation there is a passage from a Russian newspaper article (*Izvestia*, 14 August 1960) about the IBM system itself:

> Shakespeare Overspat/outdid . . .
>
> Begin one should from that that in United States appeared new translation immortal novel L. N. Tolstogo "War and World/peace". Truth, not all novel, but only several fragments out of it, even so few/little, that they occupy all one typewritten page. But nonetheless this achievement. Nevertheless culture not stands/costs on place . . .

Unlike some other MT researchers, King did not conceal some of the poor results of the IBM system; he never made high claims for his system and was always prepared to acknowledge its deficiencies. King (1961) admitted lack of syntactic parsing, and considerable problems of semantics. He thought, however, that improvements could be achieved by exploiting statistical procedures given the "50% redundancy in meaning content" in texts. He advocated also the production of 'pidgin' translations, output including constructed words of multiple meaning which could be learnt as if a dialect of English by recipients of translations (i.e. a variant of the notion of MTese, ch 2.4.3 above); and related to the ideas of the Cambridge group on 'pidgin' translations (5.2 below). Evidently, King was content to produce something however deficient; he thought there was no point in worrying about difficult problems, such as the translation of pronouns and the insertion of articles, if the text was 'readable' and conveyed the basic information.

Although there were some developments on the linguistic aspects of the system, the main improvements were technical, in particular a considerably improved photoscopic store (a large-capacity 10 in glass disk, which revolving at 2400 rpm was considerably faster than the Mark I version at 23 rpm). In 1964 the IBM system was demonstrated at the New York World's Fair (Bowers & Fisk 1965). In the same year this 'Mark II' version was installed in the USAF's Foreign Technology Division at the Wright-Patterson Air Force Base, Dayton, Ohio, where it remained in daily operation until 1970 (when it was replaced by Systran, see Ch. 12.1 below). The central feature was still the vast Russian–English dictionary on the photoscopic disk, updated periodically by new disks. The logical capabilities of the system remained, however, rudimentary (Kay, 1973; Bowers & Fisk 1965). Each Russian item (either stem or ending) in the dictionary was accompanied by its English equivalent and grammatical codes indicating the classes of stems and affixes that could occur before and after it. Translation was word by word, with occasional backtracking, e.g. in *s gruppami* the identification of the ending *ami* as 'instrumental' would determine the selection of *with* to translate *c*. But in general, the selection of English output for a given Russian item was determined solely by the choices made for the immediately preceding item. Prepositions, copulas and auxiliary verbs were inserted in well-defined circumstances only; but there was no insertion of English articles (Roberts & Zarechnak 1974).

In addition to lexical entries, processing instructions were also intermixed in the dictionary: 'control entries' relating to grammatical proceses (forward and backward skips), and also instructions relating to loading and printing routines. There were some 25,000 such 'control entries' included in the dictionary. This contained 150,000 entries at the World's Fair demonstration, and 180,000 in the USAF version. A small store of 3500 high-frequency entries was located in core memory, the remainder was on the photoscopic disk. A third of the entries were phrases, and there was also an extensive system of microglossaries. An average translation speed of 20 words per second was claimed (Bowers & Fisk 1965; Roberts & Zarechnak 1974).

The examples of Russian–English translations at the World's Fair were reasonably impressive, e.g. the one cited by Bowers & Fisk (1965):

> All this page is machine translation of Russian text, which is printed on preceding page. This page of translation from Russian into English is not perfect due to unsolved problems of grammar. Before machine can translate from one language into another, linguists have to introduce in memory unit of machine large quantity of grammatical rules, which increase intelligibility of given translation. But because in languages

> exists significant variety and complexity, all grammatical rules of any language are not developed completely at present time for use by computers.

However, this level of quality was not normally achieved. The limitations of word-by-word translation are more evident in other examples of Mark II output, e.g. the one cited by ALPAC (1966):

> Biological experiments, conducted on different space aircraft/vehicles, astrophysical space research and flights of Soviet and American astronauts with/from sufficient convincingness showed that short-term orbital flights lower than radiation belts of earth in the absence of heightened solar activity in radiation ratio are safe. Obtained by astronauts of dose of radiation at the expense of primary cosmic radiation and radiation of external radiation belt are so small that cannot render harmful influence on organism of person.

The Russian-English translations produced by Mark II were often rather crude and sometimes far from satisfactory. An evaluation in 1965 by Pfafflin (1965) tested the 'comprehensibility' and 'clarity' of MT versions of Russian electrical engineering texts and their human versions. Although ratings for comprehension were only marginally less for the IBM versions, the clarity of meaning was significantly lower. The general conclusion of participants was that MT versions were adequate only as a guide to determine whether a human translation was necessary. A later evaluation by Orr & Small (1967) also tested the comprehensibility of IBM translations, and this time included post-edited versions as well as 'raw' output in comparisons with human versions. There was no doubt about the result: "With a clear and remarkable consistency from discipline to discipline and from subtest to subtest, the post-edited translation group scores were significantly lower statistically than the hand-translation group scores; and the machine-translation group scores were significantly lower than the post-edited translation group scores." Nevertheless, it was noted that "a great deal of information was obtainable through the machine translations."

As one of the first operational MT systems the IBM Russian–English system has a firm place in the history of MT. But its historical significance goes further, since it was partly on the basis of Mark II translations that the members of ALPAC came to their controversial conclusions (Ch. 8.9).

Research on MT at IBM was not restricted exclusively to Russian. Macdonald (1960) gave a brief example of French–English translation by Mark I (based on a dictionary of 23,000 French words):

> The algebraic logic which is the subject of this course/s is conceived here as the part the most elementary (of) the mathematical logic. Later we/us will specify what we/us hear/mean signify by the word "algebraic". But one needs indicate immediately in what consists the mathematical logic whose algebraic logic constitutes the first part.

At this stage, the French–English system could evidently not cope with certain noun–adjective inversions or distinguish subject and object forms of pronouns. Bowers & Fisk (1965) mention that "considerable progress" had been made (presumably with a Mark II photoscopic disk) but it is not known what operational capability was achieved. This research was possibly done by Ascher Opler at the Computer Usage Company Inc. in New York under contract from IBM (Ch. 4.13). Bowers & Fisk (1965) also mentioned work on German, but information on this research is lacking.

Evidently more substantial progress seems to have been achieved with Chinese. From 1960 the IBM Research Center experimented with a Chinese–English system, operating on the same principles as the Russian–English system and also using the photoscopic storage device (King & Chang 1963). Some of the work on Chinese was done at Yale University with IBM sponsorship by Fang Yu Wang (Ch. 4.13). For the input of Chinese characters a special machine, the Sinowriter, was developed jointly with the Mergenthaler Linotype Company. Operators were required to break up characters into combinations of typical strokes and identify 'families' of characters. As in the Russian–English system, searches in the dictionary were made for the longest matching sequence of lexical items (characters). The system evidently included a certain amount of syntactic analysis (particularly for the identification of discontinuous structures) and re-arrangement of the word order for English output. An example translation was cited by King & Chang (1963):

> MODERN GUIDED-MISSILE ALREADY POSSIBLE CARRY WITH WAR HEAD OF HYDROGEN BOMB AND ATOMIC BOMB. THEREFORE IT IS ONE KIND WEAPON WITH VERY BIG POWER OF DESTRUCTION.

It was accepted that, with the IBM approach, "real translation is impossible." But "the translation can nonetheless be good enough to convey as much information as the original . . ." (King & Chang 1963). There is evidence that research on this system continued after King had moved in 1963 to the Itek Corporation (Chai 1967); however, it is not clear how much progress was made towards a viable operational system.

After 1964 research at IBM was led by Micklesen, Tarnawsky, and Chang. Attention turned to general linguistic problems and to the possible application of transformational grammar in Russian–English translation (*CRDSD* 13 (1964)). MT research at the IBM Research Center ceased in 1966 (Roberts & Zarechnak 1974).

4.3 GEORGETOWN UNIVERSITY (1952–1963)

Research on MT began on Leon Dostert's return from the MIT conference in June 1952. His consultations with linguists and engineers at Georgetown led to the setting up of the experimental system in collaboration with IBM, which was designed to demonstrate the technical feasibility of MT. As we have seen (Ch. 2.5 above), the demonstration of this small trial Russian–English system in January 1954 was one of the most significant events of early MT history, arousing a great deal of interest and helping to stimulate US government funding in subsequent years.

Dostert did not believe in the need for Reifler's pre-editor; his aim was to show that suitable codes assigned to dictionary entries could signal both grammatical and semantic contexts. The theoretical justification was a model of translation involving two basic types of decision processes: selection and manipulation (Dostert 1955). Selection deals primarily with lexical data, "choosing the item in the output language corresponding correctly to the item in the input language". Manipulation deals mainly with syntactic structure, "the modification of the sequence of items in the input text to fit into the structural pattern of the output language". All MT groups, of course, recognised the need for some rearrangement of TL texts, but Dostert was perhaps the first to give syntactic analysis an importance equal to that of lexical procedures in MT systems.

The participants in the Georgetown-IBM experiment were, on the IBM side, Cuthbert Hurd and Peter Sheridan, and on the Georgetown side, Leon Dostert and Paul Garvin. The computational aspects were the work of Sheridan, a programmer in the IBM Division of Applied Science, and the linguistic aspects were primarily the work of Garvin, a linguist who had attended the public opening meeting of the MIT conference (Bar-Hillel 1960). A detailed account of the programming of the IBM 701 was given by Sheridan (1955), and a full retrospective account of the linguistic basis of the experiment was later given by Garvin (1967a). Other accounts were given by Dostert (1955), and briefly by N. Macdonald (1954).

Forty–nine sentences in the field of chemistry were carefully selected for the experiment to illustrate a variety of different constructions and problems. From an analysis of the sentences it was concluded that translation of this small corpus could be effected with a dictionary of 250 Russian words and just six rules of grammar.

The words included in the dictionary were divided into two classes: those which could be split into stems and endings, and those which could not. Stems and endings were entered separately. Each Russian word was given one or two English equivalents, and a set of codes indicating the selection rules to be applied and defining the context required for choosing the correct English output.

The selection rules of the Georgetown-IBM system were restricted to the immediate environment of the SL text, no more than one word on either side of the word being currently translated. The six rules were numbered 0 to 5 as follows (Macdonald 1963; Dostert 1955; Pendergraft 1967; Garvin 1967a):

0. The order of the original text is to be followed.
1. There is to be a difference of order in the translation from the order in the original, and an inversion is necessary.
2. There is a problem of choice; the choice depends on an indication which follows the word under consideration.

3. There is a problem of choice; the choice depends on an indication which precedes the word under consideration.
4. A word appearing in the original text is to be dropped, and no equivalent will appear in the translation.
5. At a point where there is no equivalent word in the original text, a word is to be introduced into the translation.

The English sentences produced in the demonstration were impressively idiomatic (Macdonald 1954):

> Starch is produced by mechanical methods from potatoes
> Magnitude of angle is determined by the relation of length of arc to radius
> Processing improves the quality of crude oil

However, this idiomaticity had been achieved by the incorporation of many *ad hoc* decisions, particularly on the insertion and omission of lexical items (rules 4 and 5) in order to deal with 'idiomatic' usages. The restriction of the rearrangement rules to information from the immediate context was accepted solely for the purposes of the demonstration. It was realised that they would be quite insufficient in a larger-scale system. Nevertheless it was believed that the principal operations necessary for MT had been demonstrated. After the experiment, Dostert summarised what had been achieved: (i) authentic MT had been shown to be possible, (ii) results showed that neither pre-editing nor post-editing were necessary, (iii) the problem of MT was primarily that of linguistic analysis, (iv) systematic MT dictionaries must include semantic feature codes as well as grammatical codes, (v) there was a need for specialised dictionaries for dealing with problems of polysemy, (vi) the development of intermediate languages for multilingual systems seemed feasible.

Although the Georgetown-IBM experiment aroused considerable public interest it did not result immediately in any official support for further research at Georgetown. From 1954 until early 1956, work was continued by a small team under Dostert. About this time, the Institute of Precision Mechanics and Computer Technology of the USSR Academy of Sciences announced that research on English–Russian translation had been started on the basis of the approach adopted in the Georgetown-IBM experiment (a demonstration of which had been seen by Panov, cf. 2.5 above). A substantial grant was awarded to Georgetown University in June 1956 by the National Science Foundation. In fact most of the grant had come from the Central Intelligence Agency, as did most of the later support for the Georgetown MT research team. In late 1956 the full-scale project started, with Dostert as director and more than twenty researchers, on work towards a Russian–English MT system in the field of organic chemistry (Macdonald 1963).

The project team was organised in two research groups: one for 'translation analysis', the other for 'linguistic analysis'. The translation analysis group was concerned with the transfer operations by which the English output would be produced, i.e. primarily with the preparation of translation equivalences as a basis for the Russian–English dictionary. As far as possible, stylistic variety was excluded; the aim was to find the best single translation which would be satisfactory in most instances. The linguistic analysis group (later called the 'experimental group') was concerned with operations for the recognition of Russian input. It began with a detailed analysis of the Georgetown-IBM experiment. As a result, it was decided: (a) that input was to be in the Cyrillic alphabet, (b) that dictionary entries were not to be split into base and ending forms, (c) that the coding method was to be expanded, (d) that the six selection rules were to be recast and subdivided, and (e) that a corpus of 80 sentences was to be selected for study.

Initially problems were to be solved one at a time and solved completely, while other known problems were to be ignored until later; however, this piecemeal approach was soon found to be impractical as the linguistic problems were closely interrelated. An overall strategy was necessary. There were, however, considerable divergences of viewpoint within the linguistic analysis group and so, by January 1957, Dostert decided to set up four groups each to pursue their own ideas. The resulting methods were to be tested in 'open competition' on a prepared text taken from the Soviet *Journal of General Chemistry* and on a randomly selected text from the same source. The understanding was that the method "which responded best in a practical situation would be favored over the others." (Macdonald 1963). A tentative date for the test was set for early 1958. Some idea of these early approaches to Russian syntax can be found in the papers of a conference at Georgetown in April 1957 (Dostert 1957), e.g. Garvin (1957) on coding of cases and agreement, Pyne (1957) on rudiments of structural relations, and Zarechnak (1957) on a typology of sentences.

The four methods to be tested were a 'code-matching' method proposed by Ariadne Lukjanow, a 'syntactic analysis' method by Paul Garvin, a 'sentence-by-sentence' method by A. F. R. Brown, and a method of 'general analysis' by Michael Zarechnak. The methods differed primarily in the treatment of syntactic relationships, but different practices arose also over whether lexical items were to be entered unsplit or as separate stems and endings; the general analysis and syntactic analysis groups used split entries, the code matching group used unsplit ones.

In the code-matching method each dictionary entry was first assigned codes indicating grammatical functions and semantic classes. Analysis proceeded word by word through the text from left to right; the specific function applicable in the given text was selected by comparison of codes of contiguous words; mathematical processes were applied to strings of codes to select codes of the English output. The method was tested in August 1959. "The translation was excellent. No information was provided as to how it had been achieved. Other workers at Georgetown hazarded the guess that the procedures were almost entirely *ad hoc* . . . Miss Lukjanow was reticent in discussing her methods and did not produce a translation of either a random text or a prepared text of any greater length." (Macdonald 1963). The project reviewed the method and decided that, while some code-matching was necessary in MT, complete reliance on code-matching was unsophisticated and clumsy, and limitation to a single left-to-right pass was unnecessarily restrictive. Shortly afterwards, Lukjanow left Georgetown and joined the Corporation for Economic and Industrial Research (Arlington, Va.) where she continued her research for a while, reporting on its general principles at the Los Angeles conference in February 1960 (Lukjanow 1961).

The syntactic analysis method proposed by Garvin analysed sentences in terms of immediate constituents (Ch. 3.4), concentrating at each level of analysis on the item conveying most grammatical information, called the 'fulcrum'. The method was not ready for testing by the date set, and in fact was not tested at all, since Garvin left Georgetown in March 1960 to go to Thompson Ramo Wooldridge (Los Angeles), where he developed further what later became known as the 'fulcrum technique' of syntactic analysis (see 4.6 below).

The 'general analysis' method identified relationships between elements at three levels: morphological analysis (word-formation, identification of word classes (case, number, person, etc.), identification of idioms), syntagmatic analysis (agreement of adjectives and nouns, government of nouns by verbs, modification of adjectives, verbs, and adverbs), and syntactic analysis (identification of subjects and predicates, relationships of clauses). This method was the only one ready for any sort of test by early 1958, and then only on one prepared sentence, although admittedly of particular complexity. (The test was reported by Zarechnak (1959)). A second more rigorous test of the method was conducted in June 1959 on a prepared text of 100,000 words in the field of organic chemistry and on a random text of 1500 words. The results were examined by an independent chemist at Georgetown who concluded that "the texts conveyed the essential information although their style was clumsy and the reading of them was time-consuming". This was considered a success, and significantly, at this point the General Analysis Technique was renamed 'Georgetown Automatic Translation' (GAT); it was this method which was to be developed in later years.

There remained the 'sentence-by-sentence' method of A. F. R. Brown. This was designed for French–English translation. In a lecture given to the Association for Computing Machinery in June 1957, Brown (1958) reported that by January of that year he had devised rules for dealing with 220 sentences in chemistry. He described his method thus: "I opened a recent French chemical journal at random, went to the beginning of the article, and set out to formulate verbal rules that would translate the first sentence. It had about forty words, and it took ten hours to work out the rules. Turning to the second sentence, I added new items to the dictionary, invented new rules, and modified existing rules until the system would handle both sentences. The third sentence was attacked in the same way, and so on up to 220." (There could be no better description of the 'pure' cyclic approach; cf. 4.4 and 8.2). Brown was confident that in this way "most of the major difficulties have been met and solved" for French, and that "further progress

. . . should be very rapid." By June 1957 the program had been coded and tested on an ILLIAC computer. (However, dictionary lookup had not yet at this stage been mechanised.) In the programming for moving, substituting, and rearranging elements much use was made of sub-routines which in Brown's view were "so general as to be almost independent of what languages are concerned", a feature which he emphasised in later developments.

Two years later, in June 1959, the system was ready for testing (at the same time as GAT). On a prepared French text of 200,000 words and a random text of 10,000 words the results were considered to be nearly as acceptable as those for GAT. Later the same month, at the Paris Unesco conference, Brown gave a demonstration of his French system; this was the first public demonstration of a MT system with an unprepared text. By this time, the method was developing definitely into a general programming system designed to provide facilities for various linguistic and MT operations under full control of the linguist, who was able to alter and expand data and rules whenever desirable. In recognition of this development, Brown's system was renamed the Simulated Linguistic Computer (SLC).

The computer implementation of the GAT method, the SERNA system, was largely the work of Peter Toma (1959), initially alone. Toma had joined the Georgetown project in June 1958 to work on dictionary searching and syntactic analysis in Zarechnak's group. (Toma had worked previously at the California Institute of Technology and for the International Telemeter Corporation on the Mark I system under Gilbert King.) Toma and his colleagues obtained access to the Pentagon's IBM 705 computer during its 'servicing time', and between November 1958 and June 1959 worked continuously throughout every weekend (Toma 1984). According to Toma, the test of GAT in June 1959 was run on the Pentagon computer.

There is some controversy over the significance of Toma's contribution to the Georgetown system. Toma claims that SERNA, acronym of the Russian 'S Russkogo Na Angliskij' (*from Russian to English*), was entirely his own creation, but Zarechnak (1979: 31–32) contends that Toma's responsibility was limited to coordination of the programming efforts while Zarechnak had overall responsibility for the linguistic formulations. While this may be true, there is no denying that Toma's programming skills made possible the "first significant continuous outputs for Russian to English", as Dostert readily acknowledged (in the preface to Macdonald 1963).

On 25 January 1960 a demonstration of GAT (SERNA) was staged at the Pentagon before representatives of government agencies, re-running some of the earlier tests of the Russian–English translations of organic chemistry. Early in 1961 the programming system for GAT was converted for use on the IBM 709. The opportunity was taken to introduce certain improvements in the efficiency and accuracy of the operations. As a result, so many alterations of the SERNA programs were necessary that in effect there was a new system; it was now called the Direct Conversion programming system, and placed under the direction of John Moyne (1962).

Apart from Russian and French, research teams at Georgetown also examined other languages. Chinese was investigated by a team advised by John de Francis, producing in 1962 a Chinese–English MT dictionary using telegraphic code for Chinese characters, and starting work on a MT system for mathematics texts. There was some work on the comparative syntax of English and Turkish, and during 1961 some discussion about setting up a pilot project for English–Turkish translation (Macdonald 1963). Brown did a tentative study of Arabic–English MT on the SLC basis (Brown 1966). Much more substantial was the work of the Comparative Slavic Research Group set up in October 1961 under Milos Pacak. This group investigated Czech, Polish, Russian, and Serbo-Croatian with the objective of establishing a common intermediary language, for use in MT systems for these languages into and from English.

By late 1961 the SLC French–English system had been adapted for Russian–English, and it could also now be run on the IBM 709. SLC was now no longer restricted to one specific language pair but it had become a generalised programming system (Brown 1966). As a MT system for French–English translation, the SLC method remained largely the special and sole concern of Dr Brown (Zarechnak & Brown 1961); but as a programming system it was often used to support the GAT Russian–English system. At the Teddington conference in September 1961, the demonstration of GAT was run on SLC only, since conversion of the SERNA programs to the IBM 709 was not yet complete. As a result of this demonstration, EURATOM (at Ispra, Italy) decided to install the Georgetown system using SLC programming, both for producing translations for their personnel and as a basis for further research (Ch. 11.1 below).

Another demonstration of GAT was conducted in October 1962 at the Oak Ridge National Laboratory, under the auspices of the US Atomic Energy Commission. This time the texts were in the field of cybernetics, using both prepared and unprepared texts. An example translation is taken from Dostert (1963):

> By by one from the first practical applications of logical capabilities of machines was their utilisation for the translation of texts from an one tongue on other. Linguistic differences represent the serious hindrance on a way for the development of cultural, social, political, and scientific connections between nations. Automation of the process of a translation, the application of machines, with a help which possible to effect a translation without a knowledge of the corresponding foreign tongue, would be by an important step forward in the decision of this problem.

It was admitted that the system, developed primarily for the field of organic chemistry, had problems with the new vocabulary and style of cybernetics literature, but clearly there was confidence in the Georgetown team's ability to improve the programs and dictionaries, and the Oak Ridge authorities decided to install GAT for producing internal translations.

In the event, the GAT Russian–English systems were installated at Ispra in 1963 and at Oak Ridge in 1964 at or just after the termination of the Georgetown project in March 1963. So came to an end the largest MT project in the United States. Some MT research on a Russian–English system continued at Georgetown under the direction of R. Ross Macdonald after 1965 (Josselson 1971), but it was to be on a much smaller scale and without CIA sponsorship. The reasons for the unexpected withdrawal of support in 1963 are unclear. Zarechnak (1979) believes the official version citing unsatisfactory quality was not completely honest, while Toma (1984) alludes to internal conflicts between linguists and programmers leading to wholesale resignations. Whatever the cause, there could be very little further experimental development of the Georgetown systems after their installation at Ispra and Oak Ridge. Indeed, they remained virtually unchanged until their replacements by Systran (Ch. 12.1) at Ispra in 1970 and at Oak Ridge in 1980.

However, there were also more intrinsic reasons for the end of the development of the linguistic aspects of the Georgetown systems, which are to be found in consequences of the general 'empirical' approach of Dostert. He outlined the basic working premises of the project as being "text-focused in the sense that the lexical buildup and the structural inventory is essentially . . . text-derived", the analysis of actual data and the "progressive improvement of experimental runs by means of a feedback procedure". The developments of the GAT analysis programs were, therefore, cumulative: programs were tested on a particular corpus, amended and improved, tested on another corpus, amended again, and so forth. The result was a monolithic grammar of "monstrous size and complexity" with no clear separation of analysis and synthesis (Kay 1973). Despite its complexity, syntactic analysis was very rudimentary, devoted to nothing more than resolving ambiguities in the assignment of word-classes through examination of preceding and following sequences of grammatical categories.

Although the GAT system of analysis was described as consisting of three, later four, 'levels' (Zarechnak 1959; Zarechnak & Brown 1961; Zarechnak 1962), what was involved was essentially a number of 'passes' seeking to establish different types of interrelationship. After initial dictionary lookup (GAT used two dictionaries, one of unsplit common words such as prepositions, conjunctions, pronouns, but also some irregular nouns, and another, larger, dictionary of stems and endings) came 'morphemic analysis'. This established relationships between adjacent words (e.g. identification of word classes, cases, number, person, etc.), thereby resolving some homograph problems (Pacak 1961, 1966, 1967). The next stage was 'syntagmatic analysis', which identified three types of word combination (agreement, government, and apposition). The third 'level' of analysis was 'syntactic analysis', which sought to establish the subject and predicate parts of the sentence. Finally, a fourth 'level' was added to refine the transfer of Russian cases in English by identifying certain phrase structure relationships. Though the methods made good use of such traditional grammatical notions as agreement, concord, subject–predicate, etc., there was yet no clear conception of grammatical rule or syntactic structure. The rules were consequently *ad hoc*, formulated to deal with particular structures as they were encountered in texts being examined. Above all, the rules were designed solely for one-directional Russian–English translation. Analysis was intended to provide the grammatical classifications which were to select from the possible English alternatives and to decide the eventual word order. "Such information about the structure of Russian and English as the program used was built into the very fabric of the program so that each attempt to modify or enhance the capabilities of the system was more difficult, and more treacherous than the last." (Kay 1973). Indeed, at Ispra it was decided to develop a new system rather than modify the existing one (Ch. 11.1) and at Oak Ridge the only changes made to GAT concerned those necessary for transfer from an IBM 7090 to an IBM 370; the linguistic aspects were left untouched (Zarechnak 1976).

Nevertheless, operators of the two systems have regularly reported the satisfaction of users with the output even when receiving unedited versions (Jordan *et al.* 1977; Kertesz 1974; Perschke 1968). In 1973 a questionnaire was sent to users of both the Ispra and the Oak Ridge installations, and used in conjunction with interviews and records of users' reactions to the unedited translations (Henisz-Dostert 1979). Over 90% of the 58 respondents rated the translations as 'good' or 'acceptable'; 82% found that information had been translated sufficiently comprehensively; 59% found the translations 'readable' (although they took 32% longer to read than human translations). Only 19% thought that there was a possibility of misinformativeness; while 80% did not believe they had experienced it. Respondents judged that 87% of the sentences had been correctly translated (even if understood only with difficulty) and that 76% of the technical words were correct or understandable. In sum, 96% of the users said they would recommend MT to colleagues. It is quite apparent from these perhaps surprisingly favourable results that many users would rather have low quality MT than no translation at all.

4.4 RAND CORPORATION (1950–1960)

Research on MT at the RAND Corporation began early in 1950 with the very tentative experiments by Abraham Kaplan which Olaf Helmer reported on at the 1952 MIT conference (Ch. 2.4.3). As we have seen, Kaplan took up Weaver's suggestion that statistical studies of context might assist the resolution of multiple meaning. Despite its limitations and the tentativeness of the conclusions, this study encouraged the belief that problems of ambiguity in MT could be overcome and that statistical analyses were a valuable research method for MT.

However, a research team was not in fact set up at RAND until 1957, headed by David G. Hays with Professor Kenneth Harper of UCLA as consultant. Harper's interest in MT had begun in 1953 with a paper on the morphology and syntax of Russian mathematics texts. This was also a statistical study, from which Harper concluded that Russian word order was roughly the same as in English, therefore word-for-word translation was feasible for this kind of text.

Also influential in the setting up of the project were the early papers by

Oswald — also on the faculty of UCLA — firstly the paper with Fletcher (1951) on problems of syntactic analysis of German, which advocated the coding of grammatical functions for the identification of 'noun blocks' and 'verb blocks'; and secondly the paper presented at the 1952 MIT conference in which he put forward the concept of microglossaries for specific subject fields established from statistical analyses of the relevant literature.

These researchers shared a common conviction in the value of statistical analyses of grammatical data. Detailed empirical analysis was a dominant feature of research at RAND. From the beginning the team had a clearly formulated research methodology (Edmundson & Hays 1958; Harper & Hays 1960; Hays 1963): a large corpus of Russian physics texts was prepared, a text was punched up onto IBM cards, a glossary for every text word was prepared providing grammatical information and English equivalents, the computer (IBM 704) program matched text and glossary to produce a rough translation, the result was studied by post-editors who indicated errors of coding and translation, the post-edited text was analysed, the glossary and translation rules were refined in preparation for the next text, and so the process was to continue in cycles of translation and post-editing. Obviously the first rough translations were crude word-for-word versions and much post-editing was required; but it was hoped that the successive incorporation of refinements in the glossary and translation rules would result in a "gradual elimination of the post-editor." Until then, the post-editor was a linguistic analyst, supplying the correct English equivalent (preferring the first one offered if it was satisfactory, even if it were not the best!), adding correct English inflections (e.g. plural forms), inserting pronouns, verb auxiliaries, and articles, and indicating grammatical relationships. (Edmundson *et al.* (1961) provided detailed instructions.)

Within a few years the RAND team had an impressively large corpus of texts, some 250,000 running words (Harper & Hays 1960; Harper 1961), compiled partly in cooperation with the University of Michigan project (4.5 below). It was a firm conviction of the RAND group that deficiencies in MT analysis programs were attributable to lack of data: "existing grammars of languages are incomplete, ill-adapted for purposes of machine translation, and prolix with regard to a specific area of discourse. In addition, we have felt that the determination of sentence structure would prove useful in dealing with both grammatical and semantic problems of machine translation" (Harper & Hays 1960). The team concentrated therefore on establishing word classes and sentence structures empirically, with no preconceptions about the 'correctness' of the results. Working on post-edited texts they employed two main methods: dependency analysis and distributional analysis.

Dependency analysis produces a tree-like representation of sentence structure, in which there is one word which is independent (usually the finite verb) and every other word depends on one and only one other word in the same sentence (Ch. 3.4 above). In the RAND formulation, dependency is "partly syntactic, partly semantic. Syntactically, one occurrence depends on another if the inflection of the first depends on the nature of the second;

semantically, one occurrence depends on another if the meaning of the first complements or modifies the meaning of the second" (Harper & Hays 1960). It is acknowledged that the concept is "closely akin to the immediate constituent analysis of Harris, and to the approach suggested by Oswald." When implemented in a computer program, the method searched for dependency relations in a series of passes, e.g. in the analysis of *I saw a red rose*, the dependency of *rose* on *saw* was established only after it had first recognised the dependency of *red* on *rose* and of *a* on *rose*.

Distributional analysis continued the study of Kaplan on contextual resolution of ambiguity. Harper (1956) held that even contiguous words can help in syntactic clarification: "there are no serious problems of syntax which cannot be resolved by reference to the grammatical features of pre- or post-words". They can help also in semantic clarification, e.g. the English equivalent for the Russian conjunction *i* (*and, but, also, even*) could be found, he claimed, in 90% of cases by reference to the grammatical classes of contiguous words; likewise for the preposition *po* by reference to preceding noun classes. The objective of distributional analysis, therefore, was to subcategorise classes for greater specificity of syntactic codes. Analysis started from dependency pairs of very broad classes, e.g. subject–verb, adjective–noun pairs; and examination of the data from post-editing lead to the identification of specific sub-classes. For example, subjects can be a) animate nouns or first-person pronouns, in the nominative case, or b) animate nouns, in the instrumental case; and verbs can be a) active verbs, or b) passive verbs or passive participles, or c) first-person verbs. One result would be a list of verbs which may have animate actor dependent nouns. Distributional analysis was employed by Hays (1960) for the identification of 'semi-idioms' or phraseological constructions such as *depend on, consist of, give up, play a role*; and as the basis for the identification of transformations: the recognition of a "pair of dependency types, linking different grammatical types, but equivalent in meaning".

For Harper distributional analysis was the essence of the empirical approach: "Distributional classes represent facts of language, but the optimum procedure for analysis of this very large number of facts must probably come from experience. We must simply begin . . ."; and it had to be accepted that membership of classes will change with new data. The task was seen as a long-term effort; limiting their data to physics texts meant that the grammar produced by the RAND team might not be applicable to other subjects (i.e. Harper recognised the importance of sublanguage grammars, as well as subject-specific glossaries, Ch. 3.2).

Research at RAND was thus always basically devoted to fundamental linguistic data processing rather than operational MT systems; and its results, data, and dictionaries were made freely available to other researchers in a spirit of scientific cooperation. By 1960 "it had become clear that the broader field of computational linguistics deserved general attention, and that machine translation should either be pursued as a developmental task, using existing techniques for a practical purpose, or set aside to await progress of a fundamental nature" (Hays 1967). Research continued on dependency grammar and on grammatical theory; a large text corpus of Russian was created, nearly four times the size of the previous one and with fuller syntactic information; and numerous improvements in computer handling of language data were developed. A later project at RAND relevant to MT was the development of the MIND system (Ch. 17.8).

4.5 UNIVERSITY OF MICHIGAN (1955–1962)

Research at the Willow Run Laboratories of the University of Michigan in Ann Arbor began in 1955 under the directorship of Andreas Koutsoudas and continued until 1962 (Bar-Hillel 1960, Josselson 1971). The Michigan group had close contacts with the RAND team, sharing a similar empirical approach to MT methodology and cooperating in the compilation of a large text corpus of Russian physics literature.

Like many other MT groups in the mid-1950s Michigan suffered from journalistic extravagances. In 1956 Koutsoudas felt obliged to respond to one such report in an Associated Press dispatch: "We wish to disclaim to our professional colleagues any responsibility for the publicity release on our mechanical translation project which was printed in today's newspapers. The implication that we are very far along toward practical translation was due to an overenthusiastic misinterpretation by a journalist." (*MT*3(2) Nov. 1956). In fact, the Michigan group concentrated primarily on statistical analyses of its Russian corpus and did not implement even an experimental MT program. Nevertheless the team was so sure that "within a generation machine translation will be a *fait accompli*, as will machine reading" that it could devote some of its time to the standardisation of printing fonts for future OCR machines (Koutsoudas & Machol 1956).

As at RAND, the work of decriptive linguistics was treated with much scepticism. It was argued that not only were existing descriptions of individual languages incomplete "particularly where syntax is concerned" and deliberately avoided semantic considerations (for the sake of formal rigour), but also that the different aims of MT research required the development of rules or procedures to connect *pairs* of languages (Koutsoudas 1960). The aim of statistical analyses was to establish appropriate contextual clues for identifying word classes, discovering syntactic relationships, resolving homonymy, and identifying idiomatic expressions. Its treatment of homonyms was typical of the empirical approach; it consisted in "translating small groups of words, listing in the dictionary multiple meanings under each word in the group, and finding algorithms which make it possible to choose the proper set of meanings for the group" (Koutsoudas & Machol 1956). The complexity of the approach, even for a small set of words, is clearly demonstrated in Koutsoudas & Korfhage 1956) where English equivalents are given for every context (i.e. every word with which it may occur in a phrase) even if the same translation has to be repeated many times and, in some cases, zero translations have to be noted, e.g. in a vocabulary subset of just 8 items *teori* is given 3 translations, *theory* twice and zero once.

A further example of the Michigan approach is to be found in Koutsoudas & Humecky (1957). Part of the results concerned an analysis of Russian forms ending in *-o*, *-e* or *-ee*. It was found that these could be adverbial modifiers if (i) preceded by period or comma and succeeded by a comma not followed by *cto* or *cem* , or (ii) followed by a non-infinitive verb form when not preceded by *kak*, or (iii) preceded by *esli* or auxiliary verbs and succeeded by an infinitive; and so on for another five examples of conditions. Attached to each statement was an indication of its frequency of occurrence in the corpus.

In the face of such masses of detail for even such small segments of Russian grammar it is not surprising that the Michigan group did not implement a MT system — getting no further than some tentative hand simulations — and so it turned increasingly to speculations on the design of a computer program which would learn to modify itself. Inspired by current research on information theory and on automata theory, the idea was that if a MT program were to translate all except one of a set of sentences correctly it should be possible to devise a self-modifying component which would automatically amend the MT program to translate all the sentences correctly, and without introducing excessive complexity (Koutsoudas 1961). Apparently, even an experimental prototype of such a learning program was not attempted, only the mathematical theory was elaborated, based on a categorial grammar approach (Smoke & Dubinsky 1961).

4.6 RAMO-WOOLDRIDGE AND BUNKER-RAMO (1958–1967)

Research at the Ramo-Wooldridge Corporation (later the Bunker-Ramo Corporation and part of the Thompson-Ramo-Wooldridge group) in Canoga Park, California, started in 1955, receiving a grant for an initial study from the US Air Force in March 1957, and beginning full-scale research in March 1958 on a Russian–English system. Until 1960 the research group was directed by Don R. Swanson (Bar-Hillel 1960); in March 1960 it was joined by Paul Garvin from Georgetown University (Macdonald 1963), who as its director steered its activities towards development of his 'fulcrum' method of analysis. Before this, the Ramo-Wooldridge group had been most strongly influenced by the RAND approach (Professor Harper acted as a consultant in its early stages), sharing a strongly empirical attitude and a cyclic approach to the development of systems. In addition it shared the same interest initially in the corpus of Russian physics texts built up by RAND in cooperation with the Michigan group, although later it turned to experiments on translating newspaper articles from *Pravda*.

Like the RAND group, it saw its research work as "not simply the production of a machine translation program, but mainly to do linguistic research, primarily with emphasis on semantics, by use of computing machinery" (Ramo-Wooldridge 1958). It was, nevertheless much less committed than RAND to fundamental linguistic research *per se* and more determined to set up a working (albeit experimental) MT system. "It is not our belief that one attempts to solve all problems before going to the computer . . . we start by using the expert knowledge of both Russian and English that members of our research team have in order to gain initial understanding of the problem and its probable solution. We then mechanise the solution and test it out on our computer." (Mersel 1961). The emphasis was on those problems which occurred frequently, not those of greatest intellectual difficulty: "the mere running of large amounts of text will by itself not solve any problem", however, "the running of large amounts of text serves to test previous solutions, allows one to get a better feel for the most frequent problem areas . . . and gives sufficient examples of words in actual usage to allow an attack on their multiple meanings." The research technique was "a cycle of observation, idea, mechanisation, test, correction, and new observation" using both humans and machines with the ultimate aim of mechanising the whole cycle.

A brief outline of its basic system and an example translation from *Pravda* (7 September 1960) is to be found in a 1961 report (Ramo-Wooldridge 1961). With characteristic pragmatism, translations were produced by successive refinements of an initial rough word-by-word rendition: "With each step, our automatic process gains new insights into the meaning of the Russian text. Each new insight is used to improve the English translation. Thus, starting with the Russian text, we progress from a jumble of English words to a succession of coherent English sentences". The article was first keypunched directly in Cyrillic script, then automatically transliterated. In the following dictionary lookup stage Russian words were replaced in sequence by English equivalents or by alternatives (if the Russian was a homograph), producing a crude word by word version. Any words not found by dictionary lookup were then tested against a list of endings. In the following stages, the English forms were inflected to conform with Russian endings (e.g. verbs put into past tense), and identifiable idioms were translated as units. The next stage was described as "the heart of our machine translation process" allowing "us to go beyond a crude word for word translation to capture the essential meaning of Russian sentences." Syntactic routines detected 'pivot' words (such as finite verbs and heads of noun phrases) and formed 'packages' on the basis of the grammatical information provided by the dictionary. Then there followed stages in which some alternative translations of 'multiple meaning' words were eliminated, certain combinations were recognised as 'idiomatic', e.g. *depend* and *on*, articles were inserted and prepositions were added on the basis of information from Russian case markers. Lastly, some rearrangement of 'packages' was attempted to give closer convergence to English word order, e.g. the postposition of a modifying participial phrase (*These considered by us serious problems*), and the inversion of subject and object (*By Prof. Suvarov was considered the problem of radiation*). The result was the following 'translation' (extract):

> IN THIS MESSAGE, IN PARTICULAR IT MENTIONED, THAT BY FBI AND ORGANIZATIONS OF THE CIVIL POLICE PROCEEDED WITH SEARCHES OF TWO EMPLOYEES/SERVING

> OF THE TOP-SECRET NATIONAL AGENCY OF THE SECURITY/SAFETY, WHICH/WHO DISAPPEARED IN THE END OF JUNE. WAS REPORTED, THAT THESE EMPLOYEES/COLLABORATORS ARE BERNON MITCHELL AND WILLIAM MARTIN, WHICH/WHO LONG/LENGTHY TIME/PERIOD WORKED IN THE NATIONAL AGENCY OF THE SECURITY/SAFETY, THE USA. VANISHED EMPLOYEES/COLLABORATORS OF NSA ARE/ARE-FOUND NOW IN MOSCOW AND APPLIED WITH/FROM REQUEST TO APPEAR ON PRESS-CONFERENCE OF SOVIET AND FOREIGN CORRESPONDENTS. MITCHELL AND MARTIN SOLVED/DECIDED TO BREAK-WITH/TEAR-FROM THE USA AND REQUESTED POLITICAL ASYLUM FOR/AT/BY/FROM THE SOVIET GOVERNMENT IN/ON/WITH-RESPECT-TO POLITICAL MOTIVES.

The text still contained numerous alternative versions not yet resolved, as well as, of course, many stylistic infelicities. Nevertheless, it could claim to be no worse than many other MT efforts at the time, perhaps no less comprehensible to those who accepted its limitations, and the system appears to have been relatively fast (an average speed of 1/150 seconds per translated Russian word was claimed).

Reference to 'packages' in the above description indicates further points of similarity with the RAND approach, and, as will become apparent later, it also reveals the increasing influence of Garvin's ideas on syntactic analysis.

The debt to Harper was explicitly acknowledged in a 1958 report (Ramo-Wooldridge 1958) when discussing the technique of organising sentences into strings of 'nominal word blocks', i.e. a noun and its dependent modifiers forming a linear 'package'. The influence of RAND is reflected further in such statements as: "Thus in essence we approach syntactic problems unhypnotised by their reputation for complexity and account for most of them with an elementary (but still largely effective) model. The price we pay for such irreverence is that we are left with a clutter of exceptions to our otherwise orderly set of rules." And indeed, whereas some rules were quite simple, e.g. "insert "OF" before genitive noun coded C" (i.e. first word of nominal block), and "insert "TO" before dative noun coded C", others had to be remarkably complex. The following was a rule for pluralisation: "add (S) following any 'potentially genitive' feminine singular nouns carrying code O" (i.e. word not first in block) "provided the preceding word is neither a preposition nor a 'potentially genitive' feminine singular adjective".

The complexity is attributable essentially to the linear conception of syntactic relations (Ch. 3.4), even though by this time the group was beginning to recognise non-linear dependencies. The problems of dealing with syntactic analysis without an adequate model are nicely illustrated in this quotation: "In pondering the prolixity of Russian inflectional forms, and at the same time the number of ambiguities involving the genitive case, it is at times tempting to wonder whether the entire Russian language might not be grossly simplifiable merely through borrowing, adopting, leasing, stealing, or otherwise appropriating the English preposition 'OF'!" (Ramo-Wooldridge 1958). Such exasperation may well have been felt by others but at least this team was honest.

Further illustration of the approach at Ramo-Wooldridge is to be found in the treatment of 'multiple meanings' and dictionary lookup procedures. As far as homographs were concerned, the group concentrated for practical reasons on the most common ones in the corpus, principally prepositions, and for this study it built upon investigations by Harper, formulating such rules as: "if DO follows within eight words of OT in any sentence, translate OT as FROM and the Russian DO as English TO", "if ZA is followed by a symbol, translate as PER, otherwise FOR+DURING", and more complex rules such as: "NET — if OF was inserted before a potential genitive at the beginning of a word block preceding or following NET, suppress the English equivalent for NET and substitute THERE IS NO for OF". In the routines for dictionary lookup no single method was adopted: some items were entered as units (stem plus ending), others separately as stems and endings; in order to find the latter a routine for splitting stems from endings (morphological analysis) was needed. The reason for having both types of entry was primarily historical — "not known how well or how easily the splitting procedure could be made to work", and expansion of the glossary entailed too much work. However, subsequent experience showed that there was a practical advantage in that words could be found either directly or by morphological analysis. (For similar reasons later MT projects have adopted the same procedure, e.g. TAUM, Ch. 13.1).

Like many others, the Ramo-Wooldridge team was optimistic about the future of MT: "During the period of two years we will have seen a 32-fold increase in lookup rate with only a doubling of computer cost. The cost of dictionary lookup will no longer present an economic argument against the practicality of machine translation." (Ramo-Woodridge 1958).

The influence of Garvin was already discernible by February 1960 (Mersel 1961); Garvin had been a consultant to the Ramo-Wooldridge project while still at Georgetown. The syntactic routine was now described explicitly as a series of passes and as a series of searches for "a predicative or gerund to use as the pivot of the sentence" in which "great use is made of the government characteristics of the predicative." (The basic system was much the same but the theoretical foundation was more secure.)

With Garvin's assumption of leadership in March 1960, the group turned more specifically to the development of his 'fulcrum' approach to analysis. Its formulation received progressive refinements over the years (Garvin 1961, 1963, 1967b, 1968, 1972, 1980). Garvin characterised his approach as 'problem-solving' rather than 'theory-oriented', by which he meant the "solution of translation problems by computational means through utilisation of linguistic and systems know-how, rather than first trying to develop a theoretical 'understanding' of the translation process and then applying this understanding through some form of computational implementation."

(Garvin 1980). In this way he distanced himself both from the empirical 'brute-force' approach and from the theoretical 'perfectionist' approach (Ch. 8.2 below). A feature of what he called his 'engineering' solution was the inclusion of grammatical information within parsing programs, rather than the practice of other MT groups which separated linguistic data and processing algorithms (Garvin 1967; see also Ch. 9.9). It was his belief that this approach produced greater computational efficiency in syntactic analysis. The 'fulcrum' parser is essentially a linguistic pattern recognition algorithm which directs searches at different portions of sentences in order to identify grammatical patterns. The sequencing of searches is crucial; at each stage (or 'pass') the algorithm uses only as much grammatical information as appropriate to the particular pattern being sought. In other words, the complex system of rules making up the 'grammar' of a language is distributed over a complex algorithm.

One consequence was that the algorithms were language specific, i.e. in this case procedures were specifically designed for the analysis of Russian. Another feature of the practicality of the approach was that it was 'translation-oriented', i.e. the method sought to produce not all possible parsings of a sentence (as in 'theory-oriented' systems, such as at Harvard and MIT, Ch. 4.9 and 4.7) but only the most probable. As a consequence, probabilistic values were assigned to syntactic structures, e.g. a sequence which could in theory be either subject–predicate–object or object–predicate–subject was most likely to be the former and this interpretation was assumed to be correct.

The two basic principles of the 'fulcrum' approach are the concept of the fulcrum and the pass method. The fulcrum of a structure is the element carrying the maximum amount of information about the structure and its relationships; it is the 'pivot' or key element which governs the other dependent components of the structure, e.g. head nouns of noun phrases determine the forms of articles and adjectives (case, number, gender). Structures are built up in a series of passes: each pass is designed to identify a particular kind of fulcrum and the elements which depend on it. Initial passes identify nominal groups (noun phrases), prepositional phrases and predicates (verb groups); later passes establish dependency relations between groups. For example, in:

> These various compounds of copper have been treated in the technical literature on many occasions

the algorithm identifies the fulcrum *compound* and its modifiers *these various* and *of copper*, and then later recognises the whole structure as dependent on the verbal phrase *has been treated*. At each stage, attempts are made to resolve semantic ambiguities by the examination of elements related syntactically to the ambiguous element. Thus, the dependency of *of copper* confirms that *compound* has its chemical sense and not its 'association' sense.

As we have already indicated, the fulcrum model is essentially an advanced development of the dependency model which had already been adopted by the group; Garvin's contribution was to formulate it more precisely and to implement it more thoroughly. Its implementation in a Russian–English system at Bunker-Ramo Corporation (as Ramo-Wooldridge had now become) was developed with the sponsorship of the US Air Force (Rome Air Development Center) and the National Science Foundation. The system served as the testbed for MT research and the foundation for an advanced version 'Fulcrum II' (also sponsored by the Rome Air Development Center).

The new version (Garvin 1967b) was to be characterised by more efficient algorithms, an updated sequence of passes and searches for fulcra, the inclusion of iterative search sequences, the capacity for producing English output text, and in particular the introduction of heuristic techniques. Heuristic methods were seen as natural extensions of the 'problem-solving' approach to language analysis (Garvin 1962, 1968). The heuristic component was intended to test whether all mandatory analytical processes had been correctly completed. Thus, if a verb in a predicate can only be transitive and the recognition program has not identified an appropriate object then a mistake of analysis has occurred. The origin of the mistake could have been an incorrect decision about case ambiguity (e.g. a noun form which could have been nominative or genitive); the heuristic component was to search back for this decision point, revise the analysis and complete the structure.

The method could also use the statistical information on the probabilities of particular structures given certain configurations of grammatical forms. In the first version of the fulcrum analyser the most probable interpretation was adopted. In Fulcrum II the lower probabilities could be tested if further information on higher-level relationships indicated the necessity. Thus the initial identification of a Russian form as a genitive singular noun might be revised in a broader context as a nominative plural noun. As Garvin (1968) points out, the heuristic component of the revised fulcrum approach was deliberately modelled on contemporary AI research on problem-solving systems. In this respect, Garvin foreshadowed more recent applications of AI techniques in MT research.

Garvin was unable to implement the improved version of the fulcrum approach because the MT project at Bunker-Ramo "was terminated in 1967 for lack of funds." He remains convinced that his approach was basically correct, partly because he sees recent implementations of the fulcrum method in some AI research, but more specifically because "only a problem solving approach such as the one I have been advocating can be expected to yield worthwhile results in the long term." (Garvin 1980).

4.7 MASSACHUSETTS INSTITUTE OF TECHNOLOGY (1953–1965)

The Massachusetts Institute of Technology made the first appointment of a research worker in the MT field. As we have seen (Ch. 2.4), this was the appointment in May 1951 of Yehoshua Bar-Hillel, a mathematician at the

Hebrew University of Jerusalem. For two years Bar-Hillel investigated the possibilities of MT, instigated meetings, published reviews, and made some important theoretical contributions. However, he did not himself do any practical research. In July 1953 he returned to Israel. Victor H. Yngve took over and set up the research project in the Research Laboratory of Electronics at MIT. It was funded from 1954 until 1965 primarily by the National Science Foundation, although support was also given by the US Army Signal Corps, the US Air Force Office of Scientific Research and the US Navy Office of Naval Research.

From the beginning, MT research at MIT had a strongly theoretical bias. No attempt was made to construct interim systems which though serving some practical needs were producing output of low quality. The goal of research at MIT was throughout "to work toward the achievement of language translation completely by machine and of a quality that rivals translations made by hand" (Yngve 1967). The researchers at MIT were "not looking for short-cut methods that might yield partially adequate translations at an early date" but for "definitive solutions that will constitute permanent advances in the field." (Yngve 1961). At MIT research was focused on advances in linguistic theory, particularly the theory of transformational grammar, and on the development of programming tools for linguistic research. In both areas, researchers connected with the MIT project made important contributions of significance going well beyond the specific domain of MT research. (A complete bibliography of the MIT group is given in Yngve 1967.)

The need for good programming tools became apparent very early at MIT, as it did elsewhere (cf. the development of SLC at Georgetown, Ch. 4.3). At this time there were no high-level languages such as FORTRAN and ALGOL, which in any case were designed primarily for mathematical work and were not suitable for non-numerical applications. Such were the complexities of early computers that linguists engaged in MT relied on expert programmers to implement their procedures in assembler code, they did not attempt to program themselves. As a result neither linguist nor programmer were fully effective. At MIT it was concluded that the solution was a programming system which allowed the linguist to write his procedures in a notation specially devised to fill his needs. The answer was COMIT, the first programming language devised for string-handling and pattern-matching. It was the product of collaborative work with the Computation Center at MIT. Research began in 1957 and a version was ready the same year, thus antedating by two years or more the first reasonably full implementation of the programming language LISP, the list-processing and symbol-manipulation language also devised for linguistic research and later adopted particularly in Artificial Intelligence (cf.Ch. 15 and 18 below).

Yngve claimed (1967) that COMIT was learned very easily by linguists ("about six one-hour periods are sufficient to train a novice"), and enabled the team to formulate ideas clearly and concisely ("The availability of the COMIT notation greatly increased the productivity of the group even before we could run a single program in COMIT."). Sammet (1969: 435) corroborates this opinion, comparing COMIT favourably to LISP: "One of the outstanding things about COMIT is the discrepancy between its apparent and surface difficult notation and the actual ease of writing and using the language. This contrasts sharply . . . to LISP, whose notation is inherently simpler than COMIT but which seems to be much harder to learn and use." Sammet (1969: 416–436) gives a good general description of COMIT, its development, technical characteristics and theoretical foundations. Descriptions of COMIT with specific reference to its MT applications have been given by Yngve (1958, 1960a, 1967: 454–465).

Yngve began his linguistic MT research in the expectation, shared by many at the time, that statistical techniques could be applied to descriptions of syntax, and, more generally, as we have seen (Ch. 2.5), that good MT output could be achieved by progressive improvements refinements starting from the "surprisingly good" word-for-word translations. He believed also that the 'information theory' of Shannon (Shannon & Weaver 1949) could be applied to problems of MT (*MT* 1(1/2), 1954).

In 1955 four linguists joined the MIT Research Laboratory to work under Yngve (*MT* 2(1) July 1955). One of them was Noam Chomsky, who had studied under Zellig Harris at Pennsylvania and had been a member of the Society of Fellows at Harvard, and who was later to be appointed Professor of Linguistics at MIT. During the time he was connected with the MT project, Chomsky wrote a number of influential papers on mathematical linguistics and also his 'revolutionary' book on transformational generative grammar (Chomsky 1957). In subsequent years, the syntactic theory of Chomsky was to underpin the theoretical foundations of MT research at MIT.

Yngve was one of the first to recognise the crucial importance of syntactic analysis for the production of adequate MT (Yngve 1955, 1955a, 1957). Whereas other groups saw syntax as primarily an adjunct to lexicographic transfer, as a means of resolving SL ambiguities and rearranging TL output, Yngve placed syntactic transfer at the centre of his MT model. It was argued that syntactic analysis was basic not only to the resolution of word order problems but also to any procedures involving relationships of words in patterns; this would include idiomatic structures, semantic restrictions on co-occurrence (e.g. of nouns and verbs), pronouns and their antecedents, and even the recognition of the 'field of discourse'. Translation was seen as a two-step process: a decoding of the input text into a representation of the 'message' (a 'transition language') and its encoding into an output text in another language. The conception was inspired at least in part by 'information theory'. To go beyond word-for-word translation required a method of specifying the structures to be transferred. Initially Yngve saw this specification in terms of a Markov finite-state model (Yngve 1955), but when the more complete formulation of the 'transfer' approach appeared the model was clearly based on the syntactic theory of Chomsky (Yngve 1957). The 'recognition routine' applied rules of SL grammar to identify word classes and phrase structures of input sentences; the 'construction routine' produced the output text applying rules of TL grammar; between them was the 'structure transfer routine' which converted input structure into corresponding output structure. One point stressed by Yngve was the distinction between 'stored knowledge' (the grammar) and routines (of analysis and synthesis) which applied grammatical rules: 'abstract' knowledge about the structures of languages was to be separated from details of programming designed for a particular MT system (cf. Ch. 9.9 below).

The MIT method demanded detailed investigations of the syntax of source and target languages before routines of analysis, synthesis, and structural transfer could be devised. Most research was devoted to German and English (the project was funded to develop a German–English MT system), but members of the MIT team also studied French, Arabic, Finnish, and Chinese. Much of this work was purely theoretical and not immediately applicable to MT as such. A prime example is the substantial research of Edward Klima on negation in English (1964), which made an important contribution to the theory of transformational generative grammar. Other prominent linguists connected for a time with the MIT project included Robert B. Lees (English nominal compounds), James D. McCawley (Finnish syntax), and Gilbert H.Harman (mathematical linguistics). The work of others, though based on linguistic theoretical foundations, was intended to be more practical in so far as they were designing routines for MT systems; however, the routines were rarely fully tested in actual implementations.

The method of syntactic analysis proposed by Matthews & Rogovin (1958) was designed to identify the phrase structure of input sentences by discovering "those rules of grammar which must have been applied in order to produce that particular sentence". In practice, it was a bottom-up parser recognising immediate constituents and building up to a complete phrase structure representation (Ch. 3.4 above). A distinctive feature was the succession of alternating left-to-right and right-to-left passes through sentences, designed particularly to cope with problems of German syntax, e.g. the location of verbal prefixes and participles at the end of sentences (*Er kommt heute zurück; Er hat es nicht gesehen*) and of finite verbs at the end of subordinate clauses (*Er sagt dass er heute nicht zurückkommt*). After 'initialisation' (recognition of word boundaries), dictionary lookup started at the end of the sentence: first the final word was sought in a small dictionary of separable prefixes and then the other words of the sentence were sought in the main dictionary in a right-to-left scan. Compounds were treated on the lines indicated by Reifler (1955, cf. 4.1 above.). The next scan, left-to-right, located the finite verb and placed it at the end of the sentence (conjoined verbs and prefixes could now be sought in the dictionary). The following right-to-left scan identified dependent structures (subordinate and relative clauses, participial phrases), e.g. by punctuation and conjunctions, and placed them at the beginning of the sentence, marking their original position in the main clause (or, in the case of nested structures, in the dependent clause). The next scans identified the boundaries of noun phrases and prepositional phrases, and then the type of sentence (active or passive) and the subject noun phrase (on the basis of case endings). Finally, the structures of dependent clauses were analysed in the same way.

The program was written in COMIT for the MIT's IBM 704 computer. The authors did not claim that it could analyse all German sentences; but they thought the basic conception was sound, and improvements easily incorporated. Whether there was any more research on this method is not clear. In the event, by 1961 Matthews (1962) had formulated a more advanced parser based explicitly on the 'analysis by synthesis' approach, i.e. that phrase structures could be established by discovering the rules by which they had been generated (in the sense of Chomskyan generative rules). The basic idea was that all the possible phrase structures should be derived which terminate in the same number of symbols (word classes) as in the input string (the sentence to be analysed), and that then the derived phrase structures should be compared symbol-by-symbol with the input string. Those that matched were to be considered plausible analyses of the sentence. The method was admitted to be inefficient, but it was claimed that it could be improved by incorporating various short-cuts, e.g. by not deriving structures shorter than the input string, and by doing a 'preliminary analysis' of 'linguistically significant' features in order to define the class of derivations to be attempted. Nevertheless, the practical value of the approach remained uncertain.

The fullest exposition of the MIT approach was probably the detailed specification of an Arabic–English system by Satterthwait (1965). The complex problems of morphological analysis of Arabic were carefully examined. In syntactic analysis, Satterthwait returned to the 'immediate constituent' model, particular attention being paid to the identification of discontinuous structures (a major difficulty in Arabic). For the production of English sentences, Satterthwait adopted Yngve's mechanism for generating English sentences based on (i) information on the structural relations in the Arabic sentence, (ii) information from the bilingual dictionary about structural constraints on items of English vocabulary, and (iii) rules for the generation of English phrase structures.

Yngve's sentence-production routine for English operated on unordered lists of phrase structure rules, working from top to bottom, and motivated by specific requirements of vocabulary items (Yngve 1967). A by-product of this program was the formulation of what is perhaps Yngve's best-known contribution to linguistics, the 'depth hypothesis' (Yngve 1960). This is the discovery of the 'principle' that while there seems to be no limit to the number of embedded clauses in English if they are right-hand constituents (*This is the cat that killed the rat that ate the malt that* . . . etc.), there is a limit to the number of left-branching embeddings — a limitation determined by the restricted span of the human memory. The hypothesis explained various phenomena of English syntax: the difference in form and function of active and passive sentences, the function of the anticipatory *it*, the positions of interrogative pronouns, adverbs, direct and indirect objects, and so forth. It is an example of the reciprocal influence of MT research and linguistics that Yngve hoped for in the theoretical orientation of the MIT project.

Inevitably perhaps, the intensive exploration of the syntactic approach eventually discovered its limitations. By the mid-1960s it was clear to Yngve, as it was to most MT researchers (Ch. 8.8 below) that MT research had come up against the "semantic barrier" (Yngve 1964); syntactic analysis still left many ambiguities, which in Yngve's view could only be resolved if the machine can 'understand' what it is translating. As first steps in this direction, Yngve saw the work at MIT of Elinor K. Charney (1962) on the semantico-logical interpretation of sentence structures and of Jared L. Darlington on the translation of ordinary language into the terminology of symbolic logic. It is true that this work pointed ahead to the substantial research elsewhere in later years on the interrelations of logic and linguistic semantics, although as yet the findings have had little application in MT research.

There is no denying the importance of the contributions of the MIT project to the theoretical foundations of MT and of related spheres of linguistics and computer programming, but the prospect of any operational MT system receded more and more as the years passed. In 1964 research at MIT came to an end (along with other US projects) and in 1965 Yngve moved to Chicago. The NSF continued to fund his MT research for a while, but Yngve's interests turned increasingly and ever more strongly towards problems of theoretical linguistics. In the afterword to an article originally published in 1964, Yngve (1979) characterises his current research as the development of "a linguistic theory . . . that focuses on people rather than on language", requiring "a complete restructuring of linguistics from the ground up". The goal of MT is not forgotten, however, since "the approach promises to provide a solid foundation for research in mechanical translation and computational linguistics." Evidently, Yngve has remained true to his guiding principle of MIT research, a convinction that MT must be built on theoretically sound linguistic foundations.

4.8 NATIONAL BUREAU OF STANDARDS (1959–1963)

The Los Angeles NBS office had done some very tentative work in the early 1950s (Ch. 2.4.1), but there had been no follow up. A research project was set up at the Washington headquarters of the National Bureau of Standards in 1959. This was the project on Russian–English translation directed by Ida Rhodes (Rhodes & Alt 1962).

There had been interest in problems of syntactic analysis at NBS since 1957: Richard B. Thomas and P. I. Herzbrun had experimented on the SEAC computer with statistical analysis of syntactic patterns of English (Thomas 1957; NBS 1957). The initial impetus was an interest in the improved mechanised searching of patents. This statistical research led to the probabilistic aspects of the predictive syntactic analyser, which is the principal achievement of the NBS research on MT.

These statistical studies were seen as preliminary investigations which had determined "the types of difficulties likely to be encountered" in a MT system. Ten categories of difficulties had been identified. The NBS team believed they could cope "with only the first five, which depend on syntactic analysis"; the others involved "semantic considerations" which were to be tackled later.

The basic conception of the NBS system of MT was the familiar one: look up SL words in dictionary, get SL grammatical information and TL equivalents, determine SL structural relationships, and produce TL output rearranged in light of this information. The originality and innovatory achievement of Ida Rhodes was the method of SL syntactic analysis. In essence the approach was very simple: taking each word in turn, on the basis of information about its potential grammatical categories (subject, verb, adjective, etc.) predictions are made about the categories of succeeding words and tests are made to see if earlier predictions can be fulfilled. Predictions could be grammatical (e.g. that the noun following an adjective should agree in number, gender, and case), or lexical (e.g. that particular verbs govern nouns in particular cases, genitive, dative, etc.), or physical (e.g. that capital letters indicate a name or abbreviation or new sentence). Some predictions had to be fulfilled immediately, others were optional. The aim was to establish a complete sentence analysis within just a single left to right pass. During analysis the system built up two 'pools': one of predictions, the 'foresight pool', and one of unexpected occurrences to be resolved later, the 'hindsight pool'. Every predictable occurrence was checked against the 'foresight pool' and any fulfilled predictions were erased. Any words occurring which had not been predicted (notably conjunctions, prepositions, adverbs, particles, punctuation marks) were put in a 'hindsight pool' for resolution by later items. At the end of the sentence no unfulfilled predictions should remain in the 'foresight pool' and no problems should remain in the 'hindsight pool'.

The system was first described in detail in a report widely distributed in 1959 (Rhodes 1959, later published as Rhodes 1961); later developments in the 'hindsight' technique were given by Rhodes & Alt (1961) and developments in the treatment of clauses and phrases were given by Alt & Rhodes (1961). From the first demonstration of 'predictive analysis' the NBS approach aroused considerable interest. Bar-Hillel (1960) was impressed by its practicality and efficiency, which he attributed to Rhodes' success in combining her long programming experience and her intuitions as a native Russian speaker; and he was surprised, in view of her evidently minimal knowledge of linguistics, by "how much of the practical aims of MT can be attained with so little use of structural linguistics". His enthusiastic endorsement of the NBS approach was shared by other MT researchers, in particular by the Harvard team which devoted considerable resources to the development of the 'predictive syntactic analyser' after 1960 (Ch. 4.9).

By 1960, it was claimed (Rhodes 1961a) that the NBS system was capable of tackling the following problems: "(i) The stem of a source word is not listed in our glossary . . . (ii) The target sentence requires the insertion of key English words, which are not needed for grammatical completeness of the source sentences. For instance, the complete Russian sentence *on bednyi* (literally 'He poor') must be translated as: 'He (is) (a) poor (man)'. (iii) The source sentence contains well-known idiomatic expressions. (iv) The occurrences of source sentence do not appear in the conventional order", e.g. problems of inversion. "(v) The source sentence contains more than one clause". The remaining unsolved problems were those of homonymy, polysemy, syntactic ambiguity in SL texts, misprints, incompleteness and grammatical errors in SL texts, and uncommon and local usages.

The NBS project was always severely practical and limited in its aims. Ida Rhodes (1966) was convinced that "a faithful translation cannot be achieved even when carried on by the most knowledgeable and competent human being." Computers could cope well with "a formal, systematic mental process", but "Language . . . is actually a notoriously lawless, arbitrary, capricious, wayward child of the human mind." Only parsing was mechanisable; the problems of semantics seemed insuperable: to achieve good quality translations the system would have to encompass the entire encyclopaedic knowledge of the human translator. In her view, although MT research should strive for the utmost possible, the practical limitations should be accepted. Research at NBS continued until about 1963, but little advance was made on the basic design of the 'predictive syntactic analyser' and the team did not develop a working MT system. Ida Rhodes (1967) saw "no royal road to MT. Only the rocky road of gruelling toil, unremitting attention to minutiae"; and at the end, only crude practical and essentially poor quality products.

4.9 HARVARD UNIVERSITY (1954–1964)

Research on MT at Harvard University dates from 1950, when at the instigation of Professor Howard Aiken, one of the recipients of Weaver's memorandum, Anthony G. Oettinger began his doctoral dissertation on a computer-based dictionary. Soon after its presentation in 1954 (the first thesis on MT), and particularly from 1956, the important Harvard MT group began to be formed under Oettinger's leadership. Funding by the National Science Foundation started in 1958 and the first of the massive Harvard research reports, all entitled *Mathematical linguistics and automatic translation*, appeared in January 1959. Research was to continue at Harvard until 1972, although after 1965, when Oettinger was no longer director, the emphasis moved to general computational linguistics and research specifically on MT virtually ceased.

Until 1960 research at Harvard concentrated on the development of a large-scale Russian–English dictionary and on its utilisation for word-for-word translations into English. From 1959 the activities of the group turned primarily to problems of syntactic analysis. For this purpose, the Harvard team adopted the 'predictive syntactic analyser' approach initiated at the National Bureau of Standards, and became the major developers of this method, later known as 'multiple-path analysis'. This change from lexical to syntactic interests marks a significant break in the activities of the Harvard group; the syntactic research will be treated after outlining the important Harvard contribution to dictionary construction.

The Harvard researchers were strong believers in empirical methods and in the value of using the computer as tool for the massive data handling required in MT work. The Harvard dictionary was seen to provide "(a) an immediately useful device for lightening the burden on professional translators, speeding up their work, and improving its accuracy and timeliness; (b) a system of automatic word-by-word translation . . . ; (c) an experimental tool to facilitate the extensive basic research still necessary to develop methods for faithful smooth translation of technical Russian into English." (Oettinger *et al.* 1959). The first aim was scarcely achieved, but it was not surprising since, as later researchers realised, the requirements of an automatic dictionary for direct consultation by translators are quite distinct from those of a MT dictionary (Ch. 17.6). As for the second aim, word-for-word translations were indeed produced by the Harvard group, but they can hardly be considered particularly useful, since apart from keeping strictly to Russian word order, no attempts were made to select from the numerous alternative versions offered for many of the Russian words, and no effort was made to supply prepositions corresponding to Russian case endings or to insert articles. There remained the third purpose, an experimental tool, and there is no doubting the valuable contribution of the Harvard team in thoroughly exploring the problems of dictionary compilation.

Descriptions of the Harvard Automatic Dictionary are common (e.g. Oettinger *et al.* 1959, Giuliano & Oettinger 1960) but the most extended and detailed description is to be found in the nearly 400 pages of Oettinger's book *Automatic language translation* (Oettinger 1960). The first third of the book discussed the nature of computers and their programming (with examples mainly from UNIVAC I, the machine at Harvard) and the problems of applying computers to non-numerical tasks; the need for such a detailed introduction is indicative of the general ignorance of computers and their capabilities at this time among linguists and indeed the public at large. The next section was devoted to the 'problem of translation', first distinguishing it from transcription and transliteration, then discussing the possibility of translation in general and automatic translation in particular. Oettinger advocated a gradualist methodology, starting with good word-by-word approximations, adding some manipulation of word order as required, and dealing with idiomatic expressions. (By 1960, as he readily agreed, the Harvard system had gone no further than the first stage.) The next substantial sections investigated in detail the morphology of Russian (inflection, conjugation, and derivation) and the classification of Russian vocabulary, as a preliminary to discussion of the compilation of a dictionary in which stems and endings were entered separately, in order to reduce storage needs (on punched cards or magnetic tapes). To identify endings it was found necessary to devise a new system of classification of Russian inflections (8 classes of adjectives, 38 of nouns, and 46 of verbs). Compilation was partly manual and partly automatic. For its corpus of lexical items the Harvard group favoured selection from a general dictionary and from specialised technical dictionaries of mathematics and electronics, followed by up-dating whenever new words were encountered in texts. By 1960 the Harvard dictionary file contained about 22,000 stem entries, representing more than 10,000 distinct Russian words or about 100,000 inflected forms (Giuliano & Oettinger 1960). The final third of Oettinger's book illustrated the operation of the dictionary, the lookup procedures and the production of word-by-word translations. Text words were first reduced to their stems, by the suffix-stripping program used in dictionary compilation. As in most systems of the time, lookup involved prior sorting of the words of a text alphabetically, temporary storage on magnetic tape, and then item by item matching against the dictionary tape, and producing an augmented output tape from which the words could then be put back into text order. This final tape could then be printed out in full, for further analyses of dictionary entries, or it could form the basis of a word-for-word translation. The translation of a four page text, roughly 1000 words, required an hour-long computer run (Giuliano & Oettinger 1960); or "about 17 words per minute on a UNIVAC I, and about 25 words per minute on a UNIVAC II" according to Bar-Hillel (1960); but it was hoped that with more powerful machines, e.g. the IBM 709 or the UNIVAC 1105, and with the vast storage capacity of the photoscopic disk (see Ch. 4.2 above), the speed could be increased by 20 to 40 times (Bar-Hillel 1960). By 1961 about 40,000 runing words had been translated (Giuliano 1961). These 'translations' included all the English variants for a given Russian form, without distinction, and so unravelling the sense took considerable effort. For example, one text begins:

> NEW/MODERN/NOVEL METHOD/WAY MEASUREMENT/ METERING/SOUNDING/DIMENSION SPEED/VELOCITY/ RATE/RATIO LIGHT/LUMINOSITY SHINE LUMINOUS PRESENTED/INTRODUCED/PRODUCED/IMAGINED AKADEMIK-OM G.S.LANDSBERG

(where slashes indicate alternatives, and in which AKADEMIK was left untranslated). This was interpreted (by the post-editor) as:

> A NEW METHOD OF MEASUREMENT OF SPEED OF LIGHT PRESENTED BY ACADEMICIAN G.S.LANDSBERG.

Oettinger admitted the poor acceptability of these products: they were hardly any use to those who, while having a good knowledge of Russian, did not have the technical background; expert technical translators "seem hampered rather than assisted"; and only technical editors with either no or only rudimentary knowledge of Russian could find much use for them.

Some obvious developments were envisaged at this time in order to improve word-for-word translations (Giuliano & Oettinger 1960), such as providing English interpretations of Russian endings, and the "automatic inflection" of English noun and verb forms (instead of giving just the infinitive form of a verb, for example). More significant, however, were the plans to tackle syntactic problems. One suggestion was the implementation of a Trial Translator, which tested various transformation rules (the results to be evaluated by independent linguists and Slavists). Another was a proposed Formula Finder, which could deduce translation rules on the basis of annotations by analysts of texts and the final post-edited versions; the resulting formula could then be tested by the Trial Translator. The notion was developed in detail by Giuliano (1961): the idea was obviously attractive, but it both overestimated the algorithm-handling power of the computers of the time (and indeed, of many years to come), and grossly underestimated the human fallibilities of post-editors, linguists, and analysts.

However, these plans were not pursued at Harvard. For a time they were continued by Giuliano who had moved in 1959 to the Arthur D. Little Corporation and initiated collaborative research on Russian–English MT with the Harvard group (*CRDSD* 5 (Nov. 1959)). As mentioned above, in 1960 the decision was made by the Harvard group to investigate the method of syntactic analysis developed at the National Bureau of Standards.

This was the 'predictive syntactic analyser' (Rhodes 1959). It was believed that the approach "reveal(ed) that syntactic structures have an hitherto unsuspected degree of simplicity, regularity, and universality, and that, up to a certain point, they yield themselves to correspondingly simple and elegant, yet powerful, methods of analysis." (Oettinger & Sherry 1961). It is indeed true that the method was simple in its approach. Its advantages in the view of the Harvard researchers (Oettinger & Sherry 1961) were the use of a computationally simple push-down store, the fact that input was scanned once only and in one direction only, and that the amount of internal storage was relatively limited.

The basic premise of predictive syntactic analysis was that on the basis of an identified grammatical category (article, adjective, noun, etc.) the following category or sequences of categories could be anticipated with an empirically determinable measure of probability. The system had the following characteristics (Oettinger & Sherry 1961, Sherry 1962): under the general control of a push-down store (i.e. last in first out) a sentence was parsed one word at a time left to right, the action taken for each word being determined by a set of predictions associated with the word class or classes to which the word had been assigned in dictionary lookup. At the beginning of the analysis certain sentence types were predicted in terms of word class sequences. Examination of each word was in two stages: first to test whether any of its word classes 'fulfilled' one of the predictions, starting from the most probable one, then either to modify existing predictions or to add further predictions. For example (Sherry 1962): "a noun assigned the preferred argument of *subject* would cause (1) the *subject* prediction to be wiped from the pool, (2) the *predicate head* prediction to be modified, so that only a predicate that agrees with the subject in person, number and gender can be accepted, and (3) two new predictions, a *compound subject* and a *noun complement*, to be entered at the top of the new pool. The *compound subject* is predicted because the noun was selected as the subject; the *noun complement*, a prediction of a genitive noun phrase, is predicted by every noun . . ."

Predictions were of different types: some predictions had to be fulfilled immediately (e.g. by the next word), others could be satisfied more than once (e.g. adjectives agreeing in number and case with a noun), and other predictions were obligatory, they had to be fulfilled if the analysis was to be complete otherwise the assigned structure would be ungrammatical. Any word class not selected by the first matching prediction in the 'pool' (i.e. the most probable one) was stored in a 'hindsight' store which could be consulted subsequently if the prediction selected was found to be incorrect. At the end of the sentence, analysis was complete if no obligatory predictions remained unfulfilled and if any component had not been included in the total parsing. The system included, therefore, a certain amount of backtracking, which was found to be necessary in particular for dealing with words which are tied to later occurrences, e.g. adverbs preceding verbs, and for identifying nested constructions, e.g. relative clauses.

However, certain problems emerged very quickly. Firstly there was the danger of exponential growth of predictions. Already in 1961 Sherry recognised that "on average, more than two new predictions are added for each analysed word", and that therefore the system must impose limitations, it must immediately wipe those which it is known can no longer be fulfilled, and identify those which temporarily cannot be fulfilled.

It was also soon apparent that a single path system was not adequate: only the most probable path through the series of predictions was taken during parsing, but the enforced selection of one path meant that incorrect choices were made and the results were often unsatisfactory. Obviously, analysis had to take account of other paths and so the Harvard group developed the method known, appropriately, as multiple-path predictive syntactic analysis. Developed initially for English analysis (Kuno & Oettinger 1963a, Kuno & Oettinger 1963b, Kuno 1965, Kuno 1966), it was later adopted for Russian analysis on the IBM 7090 (Plath 1967). In the multiple-path technique all possible predictions were pursued. Whenever a word was a homograph, or had more than one grammatical category, or could initiate a number of constructions, each prediction was added to the pool. At the end of analysis, only those paths in which all predictions had been satisfied would be accepted as parsings of the sentence. To improve efficiency, so that analyses would not be pursued which could not possibly succeed, various methods of 'path elimination' were introduced. One approach was the 'shaper test': for example, a particular prediction might specify more words than were left in the sentence and so it could be rejected; equally if, for example, a prediction required a comma to be present in the remainder of the sentence then a quick test could establish whether there was one or not. Another test involved counting the number of nested structures predicted; a limit of seven was enforced on empirical grounds (following Yngve's 'depth hypothesis' cf. Ch. 4.7 above). More particularly, efforts were made to reduce the repetitive analysis of the same structure in the same way every time a new predictive path was attempted. For example, the phrase *the old man* would be reanalysed as a noun phrase every time a new attempt was made to establish the alternative parsings of the sentence *The police followed the old man in a car*. This feature was acknowledged by the Harvard group (Kuno 1965) as a serious disadvantage when compared with immediate constituent parsers (Ch. 3.4), but one which, it was hoped, could be reduced substantially by procedures to identify identical paths (Plath 1967). The eventual outcome of these developments was the plan for an Augmented Predictive Analyser (Kuno 1966), equivalent in power to but less demanding in storage than other implementations of context-free grammars. Later these ideas were to be developed and improved by Woods in his Augmented Transition Network parser (Woods 1970; Ch. 9.13). These various improvements of the predictive analyser undoubtedly increased its efficiency, and processing times for analysis decreased dramatically between the 1963 version (Kuno & Oettinger 1963b) and the 1965 version, which Harvard made available as a Russian analyser to other researchers through the SHARE scheme (*TA Informations* 1965). Nevertheless, one major unsatisfactory feature remained, the production of multiple parsings (Kuno & Oettinger 1963b, Kuno 1965). The designers hoped, of course, that multiple parsings would occur if and only if the sentence was genuinely ambiguous, but in practice, many more parsings were frequently produced than could possibly correspond to meaningful differences. For example, a table in Kuno (1965) reveals that as many as 136 analyses were generated for the sentence:

> Gravely concerned with spreading racial violence, President Kennedy used his press conference to issue counsel to both sides in the struggle.

Even the apparently innocuous sentence

> People who apply for marriage licenses wearing shorts or pedal pushers will be denied licenses.

produced 40 analyses (including presumably the humorous vision of 'marriage licenses' dressed in 'shorts'). It is surely obvious that many of the parsings of these sentences could not possibly correspond to any acceptable interpretations. Furthermore, Kuno had to admit that there were other sentences in their corpus of 40 to 50 words in length, which "we could not even try to analyse . . . for fear of excessive processing time". Lastly, and most damaging of all, it was found not infrequently that the analyser failed to produce the parsing corresponding to what would be accepted as the 'normal' interpretation of the sentence. The results for the Russian parser (Plath 1967) were somewhat better than these English examples: some 90% of 73 sentences were provided with "semantically acceptable analyses", i.e. 10% either received no analyses at all or lacked the 'correct' analyses; the average number of analyses was 3.3 per sentence and a table suggests that the production of more than 20 analyses was uncommon even for quite long sentences. Many of the difficulties are, of course, common to all parsers lacking semantic controls, e.g. the problems of prepositional phrases (Ch. 3.6).

Just as before 1960 the Harvard project concentrated almost exclusively on problems of dictionary compilation, after 1960 most research was devoted to methods of analysis and very little to work on structural transfer and English synthesis. Plath (1967) admitted in discussing his own work on Russian–English MT that there was at Harvard "the absence of working systems for synthesis and structural transfer" so that "an accurate assessment of the potential adequacy of the current output as input to these terminal phases of the translation process is clearly impossible". From the evidence of his article, the versions produced offered little real advance on the earlier word-for-word translations, no attempt being made to select between alternative renderings either of lexical items or of syntactic constructions. The only genuine improvements being in the translation of idiomatic syntactic forms and in the indication of the word most likely to be 'correct'. Examples of the rules used for syntactic transfer were given at an early stage of Harvard activity in syntactic problems by Foust & Walker (1962). The syntactic transfer component was to produce an English sentence by inserting words, rearranging sequences or modifying elements. For example, a literal translation of a Russian 'if' construction as *if to neglect preliminary reduction* would be modified by inserting 'one' and 'the' and by changing the infinitive to a finite form: *if one neglects the preliminary reduction*. As an example of rearrangement, the output *in developed (by) us device* would become *the device developed by us*. The transfer rules were explicitly devised for Russian to English only, and founded on recognisably *ad hoc* sources: "syntactically analysed texts, conventional grammar books . . . and the intuition of the authors". It is clear from Foust & Walker (1962) that this work was considered simply as an initial approximation, covering only the major and most frequent constructions, and it was hoped that additional rules for further texts could be added to the system without difficulty. Although Oettinger (1960:120) wrote of generalisation to other languages and of developing a transfer notation of sufficient abstractness to constitute an 'intermediate language', it is clear from Plath (1967) that these developments could not be realised in practice within the Harvard approach.

Although most work at Harvard was concerned with Russian–English translation, a certain amount of interest was paid to other languages. In 1961, Kuno (1962) reported on ideas for Japanese–English MT. The main problems were seen as those of word identification and dictionary lookup, since Japanese script does not indicate word boundaries, and of syntactic analysis, since major functional indicators occur at the end of phrases and clauses. For the former, Kuno proposed 'longest-match' searches and a system of temporary stores; for the latter, he proposed a predictive analyser operating from the end of the Japanese sentence, i.e. right to left, in order that the postpositional indicators (particles) could be used to predict preceding syntactic structures.

The predictive syntactic approach had been adopted initially with considerable enthusiasm for its practical computational virtues and not for any intrinsic theoretical properties. It was seen as complementary to Chomsky's theory of syntactic synthesis (Ch. 3.5), as an advance on Bar-Hillel's and Lambek's theories of categorial grammar (Ch. 3.4), in agreement with the observations of Yngve (Ch. 4.7), and, because it was not being limited to analysis of Russian, as applicable generally to all languages. Formally, the system was an implementation of a finite state grammar (Ch. 3.4). Later, as development progressed, the mathematical properties of predictive analysers became apparent (Plath 1967 gives references), and the formal equivalence of such grammars to context-free grammars, specifically to (non-deterministic) pushdown store transducers, gave theoretical foundations to procedures developed empirically.

Interest in mathematical aspects of language processing increased and in the research pursued during the 1960s the Harvard group moved gradually away from any immediate intention to develop a working MT system. The unexpectedly slow development of a working system (as indicated above) certainly contributed to this change of emphasis. Typical are comments in which the MT goal is seen as only one possible application of the research, e.g. Kuno (1965) envisaged: "the designing of a system for information retrieval, question answering or mechanical translation developed around the analyser with man-machine interaction incorporated at proper places". Already by 1965, work on Russian analysis had ceased "temporarily" (*TA Information* 1965), and research concentrated increasingly on computational problems of English grammatical analysis, design of man-machine interactive systems and on theoretical questions of formal and mathematical linguistics. By 1966 Oettinger was no longer director of the project team; from 1964 he had been an influential member of the ALPAC committee whose recommendations in 1966 ended large scale funding of MT in the United States.

4.10 UNIVERSITY OF CALIFORNIA, BERKELEY (1958–1964)

The research project in the Computer Center of the University of California, Berkeley, began officially in October 1958 with a grant from the National Science Foundation, primarily for the development of a Russian–English MT system (Lamb 1961). After a short period under Louis G. Henyey (*CRDSD* 3 (1958)), the director of the project was Sydney M. Lamb. The group adopted initially a fairly 'empirical' approach, but soon turned to a fundamentally 'theoretical' orientation (Bar-Hillel 1960). Elements of empiricism may possibly be seen in Lamb's attitude to the question of accuracy. Because 100% correctness was not achievable and in order to avoid having to make guesses, translations would have to present alternative versions. In addition, accuracy demanded translations as close as possible to the original: "Departure from the wording of the input text should be allowed only to the extent necessary to insure readability and intelligibility. It is therefore unnecessary, and maybe even undesirable, that the English translation conform in all respects to the rules of English style" (Lamb

1961). In general, therefore, procedures should avoid syntactic analysis of features which have no bearing on the form of the output translation. Such considerations may have influenced the 'word-orientation' of much of the Berkeley research, but otherwise empiricism gave way completely to basic research.

From the beginning, Lamb stressed the need for full linguistic information before writing translation programs. He ridiculed trial-and-error MT methods as "trying to cook tiger stew without having caught the tiger" (Lamb 1961, cf. Ch. 8.2 below). The Berkeley group concentrated much effort on the development of research tools and maximally efficient routines, e.g. a segmentation routine for splitting Russian words into component parts, a comprehensive coding system for Russian grammar, the development of a large Russian–English dictionary capable of covering a vocabulary of over 300,000 words, a lookup and segmentation routine working at a rate of 7500 words a minute, a system of graphemic coding permitting direct input in any script (Cyrillic, Greek, Latin), and a system for obtaining relevant linguistic information about Russian scientific texts. An example of the latter was the analysis program for investigating the rules underlying Russian word formation (Lamb 1962), but whether it was implemented in practice is doubtful.

The dictionary system for an IBM 704 was described in detail by Lamb & Jacobsen (1961). Its major features were the incorporation of segmentation routines as part of dictionary lookup (Lamb rejected the Harvard approach of segmenting before lookup as it resulted in too many searches for impossible stems), and the coding of morphemes (stems, prefixes, suffixes, derivational afixes) in a tree structure. For computational efficiency the dictionary structure was stored in two parts: 'letter tables' and truncate lists'. The first letter of a word referred directly to its entry in a 'first-letter' table, the contents of which were addresses in a 'second-letter' table for words beginning with that first letter; the second letter of the word determined which address of the table was to be consulted for access to the 'third-letter' table, and so forth. At any point, the search could be terminated if appropriate by the 'truncate lists' indicating segmentation cuts. As described, the lookup procedure was estimated to run at 8 milliseconds per word (tested on a 30,000 word text). By 1964, it was claimed that improvements had reduced times by a hundredfold (Lamb 1964).

The basic objective of Lamb's approach was an "efficient MT system" which could be achieved, in his view, by applying the principles of good linguistic analysis, i.e. on "separating various things from one another on the basis of recurrent partial similarities". The principle applied most obviously to segmentation of Russian noun and verb paradigms. But it applied also to the design of MT systems, in the separation of algorithmic procedures (computer programs) from the linguistic data (cf. Ch. 9.9 below). For Lamb, it implied also separation of translation processes into stages in accordance with a stratificational view of linguistic systems.

Much of Lamb's work on the Berkeley MT project was devoted to the elaboration of his linguistic theory of 'stratificational grammar' (Lamb 1966,

Lockwood 1972), which in certain respects may be considered a rival to Chomsky's transformational generative grammar. As an MT model the most detailed descriptions are to be found in papers by Lamb dating from 1962 (Lamb 1965) and 1964 (Lamb 1973).

Lamb's model of language posits a series of 'strata' (or levels) within which and between which linguistic units are related: phonemic (or graphemic), morphemic, lexemic, and sememic. (The number and constituency of strata varies from version to version of the theory.) Elements of a stratum are combined according to the 'tactic' rules of the stratum, e.g. on the phonemic stratum of English, tactic rules permit the combination of /s/ and /k/, as in *skill* and *risk*, but not of /s/ and /d/, and on the morphemic stratum, tactic rules determine the applicability of derivational prefixes and suffixes. Tactic rules on the lexemic stratum are comparable to phrase structure rules and those on the sememic stratum are concerned with such semantic relationships as agent and action, modifier and modified. Realisational rules relate elements of different strata, e.g. that the morpheme /good/ is realised by the phoneme sequence /g u d/, and that the lexeme /understand/ is realised by the morphemes /under/ and /stand/. Realisations are not one-to-one: a lexeme such as /good/ is realised as /bet/ when followed by the comparative lexeme /er/, and /stand/ can be realised as a morpheme /stood/ if the lexeme /PAST/ is present. Above the lexemic stratum is the sememic, which deals with semantic components of lexemes (e.g. lexeme /ram/ as a realisation of the conjunction of sememes /sheep/ and /male/), with synonymy (e.g. lexemes /start/, /begin/, /commence/ as possible realisations of a single sememe /initiate/), with homonymy (e.g. lexeme /light/ as realisation of either /pale/ or /un heavy/) and with idioms (e.g. the lexeme combination /pass/ and /away/ as one realisation of /die/).

As a MT model, the stratificational approach envisages translation as a system of decoding and encoding, which proceeds from the graphemic stratum of the source language through its morphemic and lexemic strata to the sememic stratum. Here the links are made to the sememic stratum of the target language, and the process continues then from the sememic stratum through the lexemic and morphemic strata to the final graphemic output of the target language text. The basic linguistic units taken through the processes are the lexemes. Lamb characterised his own approach as word *by* word translation, examining each word within the broadest environment, not being limited by sentence boundaries or immediate contexts. The central objective was lexemic, or if possible sememic (semantic), transfer into target language texts, not sentence-for-sentence transfer. The emphasis of the Berkeley group's research was, therefore, on lexical and semantic aspects of translation and not on the development of syntactic analysis. (In crude terms, the approach was basically 'word-centred', but more sophisticated than 'lexicographic' approaches, Ch. 4.1–2 above).

Lamb acknowledged that there were certain practical problems in implementing the stratificational approach in MT systems. One involved the resolution of lexical ambiguities. When a particular morpheme can be the realisation of more than one lexeme, only consultation of the conditions attached to the realisation of each candidate lexeme can determine which is the correct analysis. In other words, the decoding of ambiguous morphemes (and lexemes) demands first the identification of possible realisates and then the testing of each by the tactics to determine which of them would encode in the form actually present. In effect it is a kind of 'analysis by synthesis' (cf. Ch. 4.7 above), except that it operates in a more restricted manner. Such a tactic decoding procedure was implemented in the Berkeley MT analysis program (Lamb 1964).

Apart from research on dictionary lookup, the contribution of the Berkeley group was, therefore, primarily of a theoretical nature. It was also mainly on Russian–English MT, but there was a cooperative project with the group in Mexico (Ch. 7.3) on a Russian–Spanish dictionary and, particularly towards the end of Lamb's leadership of the project (Lamb moved in 1964 to the Linguistic Automation Project at Yale University), there was a substantial amount of research on Chinese–English MT. A good deal of work was done on Chinese lexicography (Booth 1963, Lamb 1964); and research continued on Chinese grammar under Chang Yi Dougherty until the beginning of the POLA project (Ch. 11.2).

4.11 UNIVERSITY OF TEXAS, LINGUISTICS RESEARCH CENTER (1958–68)

Research on MT began at the University of Texas after a seminar in October 1958 conducted by Professor Winfred P. Lehmann and S. N. Werbow on problems of German and English syntax. Invited to the seminar were a group from Georgetown University which included Leon Dostert, A. F. R. Brown, and Peter Toma (Werbow 1961; Toma 1984). After the seminar, informal studies on MT were continued by members of the Department of Germanic Languages. In May 1959 a contract was agreed with the US Army (Signal Research and Development Laboratory) for research on a German–English MT system. Subsequently, in 1961, a grant was received from the National Science Foundation for the development of a computer-based system for linguistic analysis. At this time the research group was established as the Linguistics Research Center (LRC) under the direction of Winfred Lehmann, with Werner Winter and Stanley Werbow heading research on linguistic analysis and Eugene Pendergraft the development of programming (Werbow 1961, Tosh 1965). In later years, most funding came from the Rome Air Development Center of the US Air Force.

From the beginning, the Texas group was concerned with more than research on German and English MT. As Werbow remarked (1961) interest in MT at Texas had grown from theoretical linguistic studies, "research in German syntax, historical work with Early New High German, with analysis of modern written German, and also with the study of contemporary spoken German" and "the syntax of English". It was natural, therefore, that research at LRC was closely involved in research on formal linguistic theories. Particular interest was paid to the developments of transformational grammar, both in theory and in MT applications (e.g. Yngve and others at MIT, Ch. 4.7 above), and to developments on the Discourse Analysis project at the University of Pennsylvania under Zellig S. Harris (Ch. 3.5). The LRC team took the long-term perspective on MT research; before attempting to develop translation programs they undertook systematic detailed comparative studies of German and English syntax.

The achievements of the project up to 1968 are summarised by Lehmann (1965) and by Tosh (1968, 1969, 1970) and in greater detail by Tosh (1965). Translation was held to take place at three levels of increasing complexity: lexical, syntactic, and semantic; to which corresponded three MT models: word-for-word translation, syntactic translation (incorporating lexical transfer and syntactic analysis and transfer), and the ultimate aim: transformational-semantic (incorporating semantic analysis and transfer). The LRC model was designed for 'semantic' translation. What had been achieved by 1965 was characterised as 'syntactic transfer', and was obviously modelled on Yngve's approach at MIT (Ch. 4.7). In conformity to the true 'transfer' model (Ch. 3.9), it had three clearly defined stages: SL analysis, transfer, and TL synthesis. The research strategy adopted was to establish phrase-structure analyses of a set of German sentences and separate independent phrase-structure analyses of their English equivalent sentences, and then to devise transfer rules to convert the structures into each other, both from German (SL) to English (TL) and from English (SL) to German (TL). Since the aim was a bidirectional MT system the syntactic transfer rules had to be reversible. For lexical transfer, it was proposed (Tosh 1965) that numerical codes would indicate equivalences of German and English lexical senses, e.g. 1009 for German *edel* and English *noble*, 1008 for *gross* and *noble*, 1005 for *gross* and *large*, etc. The intention was to establish classes of bilingual sense equivalences, which would correspond in some respect to the classes of syntactic equivalnces. There was some hope that these classes could be the basis for multilingual equivalences. Somewhat later, Tosh (1969) suggested the use of *Roget's Thesaurus* to establish interlingual codes (presumably on the lines of the research at Cambridge, Ch. 5.2 below), but these ideas were not followed up.

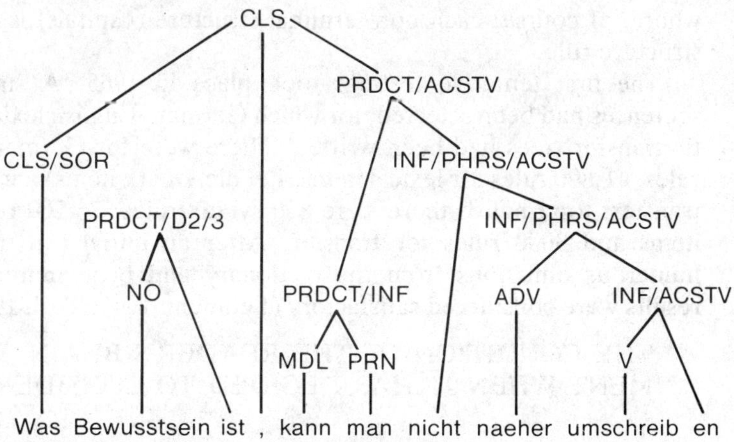

Fig. 9 — LRC analysis (German).

As an illustration, Tosh (1965, 1968) described in detail the rules of analysis, transfer, and synthesis for the German sentence *Was Bewusstsein ist, kann man nicht näher umschrieben* and its English equivalent *What consciousness is none cannot further circumscribe*. The analysis for the German sentence is shown (simplified) in Fig. 9 above; the analysis for the English sentence in Fig. 10:

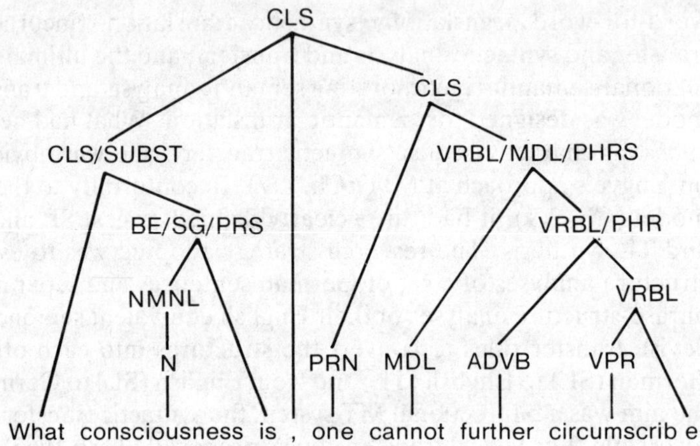

Fig. 10 — LRC analysis (English).

An example of a transfer rule was one converting the syntactic structure *kann (man) nicht (umschreiben)* to *(one) cannot (circumscribe)* and vice versa. It was formulated as the bidirectional rule:

kann+PRN+nicht+INF/PHRS/ACSTV <———> PRN+
cannot+VRBL/PHRS

where, of course, each non-terminal structure (capitals) is itself a phrase structure rule.

The first tentative testings took place in 1965. A small corpus of sentences had been selected, for which German–English lexical and syntactic transfer rules had been written. There were for German: 2600 syntax rules, 41,800 rules for lexical items (i.e. dictionary items) and 6200 rules for transfer; for English there were 800 syntax rules, 76,200 rules for lexical items and 3000 rules for transfer. After an initial run which revealed numerous omissions from the dictionary and programming errors, the results were considered satisfactory (Lehmann 1965, Tosh 1968):

THE CONDITION OF THE READER'S BRAIN AT THIS MOMENT WHEN IT HAS DECIDED TO CONSIDER WITH THE

AUTHOR SUCH A COMPLICATED SUBJECT IS THAT OF WAKEFUL ATTENTIVENESS.

The provisional nature of the results was clearly recognised (Tosh 1968). Only those rules necessary for the analysis and synthesis of the sentences of the corpus had been programmed; and, furthermore, only one possible syntactic output had been considered for each sentence (that which the human translator had provided). Despite the limitations of the linguistic data, there were "already sufficient implicit relationships to permit unplanned for . . . paraphrases." For the future, there was the problem of pronominal reference, and above all the development of a "more sophisticated model . . . in which there is a grammar of structural semantics".

These plans were not to be realised. After 1965 development of the German and English system continued at a somewhat lower level. On the other hand there were some small scale pilot projects to test the generality of the model on a number of other languages. Tosh (1969) mentions the compilation of lexicographic data for French, Spanish, Hebrew, Japanese, and Chinese. There was also beginning some rather more extensive research on Russian. Around 1965, the Russian Master Dictionary, which had been developed with US Air Force support at the University of Washington (Ch. 4.1), was incorporated into the LRC research program (Josselson 1971). By 1967 the LRC database contained some 140,000 dictionary items for Russian, on which the algorithms developed for the German and English system had also been tested, although perhaps only to a limited extent (Tosh 1970).

It was around this time, however, that LRC research plans were interrupted. MT research at Texas came to a temporary hiatus from about 1968 until 1970 when the German–English project was revived on a rather more ambitious level (Ch. 10.3).

4.12 WAYNE STATE UNIVERSITY (1958–1972)

The Russian–English MT project at Wayne State University, Detroit, was set up in July 1958 under the direction of Harry H. Josselson of the Department of Slavic Languages and Arvid W. Jacobson of the Department of Mathematics. Its sponsors were the Office of Naval Research. The project took care not to duplicate the research of other MT groups, which was only wise in view of the number engaged on Russian–English translation at the time. It sought, therefore, both an individual methodology and areas of investigation not covered in depth by others (Josselson 1961).

It was decided to limit the subject field to mathematics, mainly in the area of differential equations, both to concentrate the vocabulary problems and to reduce structural diversity. Initially three Russian texts with extant English translations were selected in order to work with parallel texts in compiling dictionaries and programs. Eventually, the project's dictionary was based on fifteen mathematics articles and the Russian–English glossary of the American Mathematical Society (Wayne State Univ. 1968; Josselson 1972).

The emphasis was on "careful linguistic analysis of the material prior to any effort to program", with the aim of "developing practical translation procedures yielding fluent and accurate text". As for overall methodology, the team adopted the 'cyclic' approach: prepare dictionary and programs, test on a text, update dictionary, revise program, run a new text, etc. (Josselson 1961).

For their specific area of MT study, the Wayne State team chose to concentrate on problems of ambiguity, both at the lexical and the morphological level, and on problems of syntactic structure analysis. The study of ambiguity reported by Janiotis & Josselson (1962) indicates a fairly standard approach: six types of ambiguity were identified, three could be resolved by structural analysis (homographs of different word classes, inflectional ambiguity, compound verb phrases), the others by contextual clues (idioms, homographs in same word class, polysemes); only with genuine polysemes could no obvious solution be seen.

More original was the Wayne State approach to grammatical analysis. The grammatical codings assigned to Russian lexical items was based not on traditional word classes (as in many MT systems) but on a reclassification in terms of syntactic functions and distribution. Nine classes were identified: nominal, predicative, modifier, infinitive, gerund, adverb-particle, preposition, conjunction, declined relative. The classes cut across traditional divisions; thus, 'modifiers' included adjectives, participals, numerals, demonstrative pronouns, and possessive pronouns, while 'predicatives' included short-form adjectives, verbs, and comparative adverbs (Josselson 1961).

Syntactic analysis was specifically "language oriented"; no general model was developed "although we used the fulcrum concept of Paul Garvin in the design of our routines" (Garvin had been consultant to the project while still at Georgetown and remained so after his move to Ramo-Wooldridge). The first set of routines grouped immediate constituents into phrases consisting of a core word (Garvin's 'fulcrum') and its dependents. These 'blocking' routines formed noun phrases, prepositional phrases, verb phrases including adverbs, etc. The next stage, 'profiling', classified each sentence constituent according to potential functions, e.g. subject, predicate, adjunct. The third procedure, 'parsing', sought to identify the specific syntactic role of each 'block' in relation to the finite verb (the 'predicative') as fulcrum. The result, in many cases, was multiple analyses of sentences. In addition, after 14 years of development, Josselson (1972) had to admit grave weaknesses. "The principal weakness of the parsing routine is that it cannot parse sentences with more than one predicative" because routines did not "mark the boundaries of clauses and hence were unable to ascertain which predicative was in the main clause and which were in subordinate clauses, or whether the sentence contained more than one main clause." Whether such fundamental failings are attributable to the fulcrum approach as such must remain very much an open question, but they are unfortunately severe indictments of the limitations of the Wayne State methodology.

The project team saw the purpose of its research increasingly as contributing to Russian linguistics rather than to MT as such. A change in the project's title from 'machine translation' to 'computer-aided translation' was intended to reflect a shifted aim, from a "fully automatic high quality translation" system (cf. Ch. 8) to "an experimental system of computer oriented strategies for analysing Russian sentences . . . We now envision a system of performing translation by means of man-machine symbiosis." (Josselson 1972). It was probably this expansion of horizons which ensured the continuation of the project until 1972, while other US projects of the same vintage did not survive the ALPAC report (Ch. 9.1).

4.13 OTHER UNITED STATES GROUPS (1955–1965)

The early MT interest in California (Ch. 2.4) continued for some years with a number of generally short lived projects. Three Californian aviation and aerospace companies set up Russian–English projects. Norair, a division of Northrop Corporation, had a project under Ron Manly, which involved the "construction of an 'intelligence language"', i.e. an interlingua (*CRDSD* 7, Nov. 1960). Autonetics, a division of North American Aviation, aimed for a system on their own RECOMP II computer which might produce "rough, understandable, but not publishable" translations. A "microglossary of approx. 100 scientific terms" was compiled; trials on seven texts resulted in 69% of words correctly translated, 1.5% incorrect, 14% of the untranslated words made sense, but another 14% were "gibberish" (*CRDSD* 9, Nov. 1961; 10, May 1962). At Palo Alto, the Lockheed Missiles & Space Company began a project in July 1960 led by B. D. Rudin on an 'empirical' research project towards a reciprocal Russian–English MT system (*CRDSD* 11, Nov. 1962). Research continued until 1964 or later on categorial grammars, statistical analyses, and structural linguistics (*CRDSD* 13, Nov. 1964).

Victor Oswald, one of the MT pioneers (Ch. 2.4 and 2.5) continued his involvement in a project reported from the Planning Research Corporation in Los Angeles, on "the potential technical and linguistic system requirements for machine translation" including the "analysis of the probable requirements for accuracy and volume of both the commercial and governmental users of translation machines." This group included also Harold P. Edmundson and William Mitchell (*CRDSD* 5, Nov. 1959).

The objective of the project set up in 1961 at the Summer Institute of Linguistics, Santa Ana, under Joseph E. Grimes was expressed as follows: "using SIL Concordance Program for the IBM 650 computer as a research tool, an exploration is being made of the possibilities of doing mechanical translation by comparing lexical strings in parallel texts, i.e. an original text and a translated version of it". The initial work was done on English and Comanche texts; later some cooperative studies were undertaken on Mexican languages with the group at the University of Mexico (Ch. 7.3). MT activities were suspended in 1962 (*CRDSD* 11, Nov. 1962).

Peter Toma did MT research in Los Angeles both before and after going to the Georgetown project (Ch. 4.3). In 1957 he did some research on

Russian texts at the California Institute of Technology using a Datatron computer (*CRDSD* 1, Nov. 1957; Bar-Hillel 1960); and he was also involved with the research at the International Telemeter Company for the USAF system (Ch. 4.2). After leaving the Georgetown project in 1962, he set up his own company, Computer Concepts Inc., in Los Angeles (*CRDSD* 10, May 1962). The AUTOTRAN Russian–English system was claimed to be "fast efficient and accurate" A dictionary of 100,000 stem entries was compiled for the fields of atomic energy and medicine. The system, programmed for the IBM 7090, was said to be operational in July 1963 producing translations of "excellent quality" and a "very high degree of accuracy." (*CRDSD* 13, Nov. 1964). Evidently the system was an early prototype of Systran (Ch. 12.1).

Another spin-off from Georgetown was the Russian–English system developed by Ariadne Lukjanow based on her code-matching technique (Ch. 4.3). A company named Machine Translation Inc. was set up in 1961 in Washington, DC to finance a "production system". It was intended also to market a Russian–German version. It was announced that the "complete production system is in the final stages of checkout and will be completed in the spring of 1962" (*CRDSD* 10, May 1962), but not long afterwards, in November 1962, it was reported by the editor of *CRDSD* that "work on production system . . . has been discontinued" (*CRDSD* 11, Nov. 1962).

In connection with its MT project, IBM sponsored MT research at a number of centres during the mid-1960s (Ch. 4.2). Fang Yu Wang began in 1960 at Yale University a "study of grammatical signals in Chinese–English machine translation" (*CRDSD* 11, Nov. 1962). Asher Opler at the Computer Usage Company in New York was sponsored by IBM between 1962 and 1964 to develop a French–English system, based on the ideas of Sakai (Ch. 7.1 below), to be implemented on the IBM-USAF machine (*CRDSD* 11, Nov. 1962; *CRDSD* 13, Nov. 1964). And at Tufts University, Medford, Mass., Mason N. Crook began an evaluation study of the Russian and Chinese IBM systems (*CRDSD* 13, Nov. 1964).

The most important of the 'minor' Chinese–English MT projects was the one which began at Ohio State University in July 1961. This was a research project set up with a National Science Foundation grant under the leadership of William S-Y Wang (*CRDSD* 9, Nov. 1961). The group was concerned principally with linguistic investigations on the syntax of Mandarin Chinese. Its theoretical framework was that of transformational grammar (*CRDSD* 10, May 1962). A focus of the research was a comparative study of the verb constructions of Chinese and English. From 1962 the research concentrated on Chinese phonology. One of the researchers of the team was Charles Fillmore, whose case grammar was to influence many MT projects (Ch. 9.16). In the mid-1960s Wang joined the Berkeley group and began research on the Chinese–English POLA project (Ch. 11.2).

In the early 1960s it was common for numerous projects to be described as being relevant to MT in some way. Many projects involving optical character readers and speech recognition were treated as MT projects, e.g. the OCR project at Baird Atomic (cf. Ch. 8.10) and the speech analysis projects at the Bell Telephone Company: "a limited vocabulary automatic word recogniser might be adapted to a 'word for word' translation between two languages" (*MT* 1(2), August 1954).

Rather more directly relevant, but nevertheless not now classifiable as MT projects, were a number of investigations of basic linguistic methods. The most well known at the time was the project under Zellig Harris at the University of Pennsylvania (Ch. 3.5), a group which had never had MT as such as its objective but whose method of 'string analysis' influenced a number of MT projects and remains an important technique to this day (cf. Sager 1981). Other projects during the period included one at the Georgia Institute of Technology, under B. J. Dasher, which was described as devoted to "linguistic problems of MT", specifically German and Spanish (*CRDSD* 10, May 1962, *CRDSD* 13, Nov. 1964), and one at Indiana University under Fred W. Householder and John Lyons studying the "automation of general semantics" and "artificial regular languages . . . suitable for . . . MT . . ." (*CRDSD* 7, Nov. 1960).

5

Groups and projects in the United Kingdom and Western Europe (1954-66)

5.1 BIRKBECK COLLEGE, LONDON (1955–1959)

For some time after its initial formulation, the only test of Booth's and Richens' proposed mechanical dictionary for MT (Ch. 2.2 above) had been on puched card machinery. The basic problem, as Booth pointed out on numerous occasions, was the grossly inadequate storage capacity of machines designed for numerical calculation. Not until 1953 was Booth able to give some figures for running a word-for-word MT using Richens' stem and affix method (Booth 1953). The test was run on the APEXC computer designed by Booth and built at Birkbeck College in the University of London. The program was slow: the fastest time achieved was 30 minutes for a 1000 word passage using the APEXC and tabulator output; when using teletype output the time needed was 2 hrs 15 mins! In addition, of course, Booth had to admit the output was "inelegant" although he contended it could be "easily understood by a person expert in the subject of the paper." Booth was one of the British pioneers in computer design and construction, and his subsequent work on MT at Birkbeck was part of the research of the Electronic Computer Laboratory, which was primarily concerned with developing computational techniques and improving computer hardware (Booth 1980).

Booth had returned from the 1952 MIT conference convinced, like Dostert (Ch. 4.3), of the urgency of constructing protoype MT systems. In September 1955 at a conference on 'Information Theory', Booth (1956a) contended that it was of "great importance to achieve some results in the mechanical translation of language in the near future, otherwise the whole subject is likely to fall into disrepute." Booth had, therefore, decided on a small-scale experiment with a "language which is sufficiently restricted to make possible its running on an existing machine" and chose as a "worth-while project . . . the conversion of Standard English into Braille" in the belief that "problems which occur in translation to contracted Braille occur also in the translation of real language" This was the motive behind the work of John P.Cleave on Braille transcription (cf. Booth *et al.* 1958).

By this time Booth had developed his method of fast dictionary lookup, the 'binary division' technique, which he usually called the 'logarithmic method' (Booth 1955a). During 1955 the Birkbeck laboratory obtained the sponsorship of the Nuffield Foundation for "a modest programme . . . to render scientific French into acceptable English" (Booth 1956). Booth had selected French, firstly, in order to "avoid competition with American projects" and secondly, because French was seen as "an easy starting point". It was evidently in connection with this project that a "microglossary and microgrammar in meteorological French" had been constructed in a joint project with a group working under Professor J. R. Firth, professor of linguistics at what is now the School of Oriental and African Studies of the University of London.

The Birkbeck approach was characterised by Booth (1965) thus: "our program started off from zero on the assumption that we could do word-for-word translation (which of course we can't) and then worked its way up through an increasing list of complications . . .", i.e. the empirical cyclic method (Ch. 4.4 and 8.2). As at many other places at the time, there was considerable ignorance, if not naivety, over the linguistic problems of translation. Typical are the remarks of Cleave & Zacharov (1955) on the generation of target language equivalents: "This involves two things. First, adding the correct word-endings. This is a simple procedure according to the rules of the "target" language since the sentence structure and grammatical function of each foreign language word have already been determined. Secondly, arranging the "target" language word equivalents in the conventional word order of that language. This is an entirely mechanical operation . . ." Judgment should be tempered, however, in recognition of the formidable computational difficulties involved; the APEXC itself had only recently become reasonably reliable in operation (Booth *et al.,* 1958) and programming techniques had advanced hardly beyond direct machine coding (cf. the chapter on MT programming in K. Booth, 1958).

The French–English MT project was the work of Leonard Brandwood. Within six months (Booth 1958), he had developed a program for French analysis. This was conceived primarily as the identification of stems and endings, described by Brandwood (1956) in considerable detail. Syntax was considered unproblematic since French "word order is more or less identical with that of English". A program for rearrangement was written but could not be implemented because of the APEXC's limited storage capacity (Cleave 1957). For the same reason, the system could be tested only on a very small 'microglossary' of, it would appear, no more than about 1000 words. The results were encouraging. An example translation of a mathematics text, "undistinguishable from that produced by many human operators", was given by Booth (1958):

We demonstrate in this chapter the fundamental theorem of M.

> Poincaré, after having studied the integrals of a system of differential equations, considered as functions of initial values

Booth was so encouraged that shortly afterwards he felt able to write: "We are of the opinion that most of the problems which attend the translation of French into English by machine have now been solved" (Booth 1956). All that seemed to be necessary was a larger computer. The team were now "examining the application of the computing machine to language in general" and "work is now proceeding on the analysis of the German language . . ." using the "invaluable analysis of Oswald and Fletcher" (cf. Ch. 2.4).

The report of this research (Booth *et al.* 1958) reveals the care taken by the team to gather information about German grammar which they believed could be formalised in a way suitable for MT analysis. Some of this work by Brandwood (1958) on the German relative clauses and prepositional phrases foreshadowed future problems for MT. In order to account fully for the sequencing of noun phrases within relative clauses Brandwood concluded that some semantic information must be included in dictionary entries. For example in:

> Allerdings wird die Wirkung dieser Felder auf Elektronen, welche sie zu verschiedenen Zeiten durchlaufen, verschieden sein.
> (To be sure, the effect of these fields on electrons which traverse them at different times will be different.)

either *sie* (referring to *Felder*) or *welche* (referring to *Elektronen*) could be subject of *durchlaufen*. The only way of knowing which analysis should be made is with information that 'electrons' can 'traverse' 'fields' but not vice versa. "A dictionary for the machine must be compiled which classifies words and indicates not only which ones can be constructed together but also in what way." Similarly with prepositional phrases. As Brandwood put it: "In translating . . .

> Wir haben darauf hingewiesen, dass die Laplacesche Gleichung für die elektronenoptischen Felder gegenüber den lichtoptischen Medien eine Einschränkung bedeuten.

the English word order varies according to whether neither, one, or both prepositional phrases are interpreted as dependent on the preceding noun *equation*." Brandwood believed that certain standard sequencing rules might be possible, but recognising the *ad hoc*-ness of such solutions suggested it would be "more satisfactory to have a system of word classification on the lines suggested (for) the relative pronoun", i.e. indicating semantic features.

It is apparent that the Birkbeck team were not able to program the German–English system, primarily because of insufficient storage capacity in the computers available. In effect, active work on MT at Birkbeck had died away by 1959, but already by this time there was a strong interest in applications of the computer to other linguistic processes (Booth *et al.* 1958), and in later years, increasing attention was paid to programs for stylistic analysis, for the analysis of text statistics and for the production of concordances (cf. Levison 1962).

Research on computational linguistics at Birkbeck ended in 1962 when Booth left England for the University of Saskatchewan. There, some research on MT was taken up by his wife, Kathleen Booth, on English–French translation (Ch. 12.5), and this was continued in some form when the Booths moved to Lakehead University, Thunder Bay, Canada.

5.2 CAMBRIDGE LANGUAGE RESEARCH UNIT (1956–1967)

Research on MT at Cambridge began, as we have seen (Ch. 2.6), with the informal meetings of the Cambridge Language Research Group in 1954. Considerable interest was aroused by the originality of the approaches put forward at the August 1955 meeting in King's College, Cambridge. In 1956 a grant was received from the National Science Foundation to pursue MT research, and the Cambridge Language Research Unit (CLRU) was formed, a research organisation independent of the University of Cambridge, with Margaret Masterman (Mrs Braithwaite) as director. In later years research grants were also received from the US Air Force Office of Scientific Research, the Office of Scientific and Technical Information (London), the Canadian National Research Council, and the Office of Naval Research (Washington, DC). Although MT was the primary interest in the earlier years, other fields of research were and have been pursued vigorously at the same time: information retrieval, automatic classification, computer simulation, on-line computer interaction, and recently 'breath-group' analysis. (The bibliography in Masterman (1970) reflects the great variety in CLRU research interests.) By 1967, active research on MT at CLRU had declined; many of its members had moved elsewhere, mainly within the Artificial Intelligence field and often with a continued interest in MT (e.g. Martin Kay and Yorick Wilks, Ch. 17.8 and 15.1 below). However, the study of MT problems has continued at CLRU to this day, albeit at a much lower intensity than during the 1950s and 1960s.

The Cambridge (CLRU) group has been characterised throughout by a diversity and prolixity of theories and methods. There were four main themes in its MT research: the thesaurus approach, the concept of an interlingua, 'pidgin' translation, and lattice theory. The focus was primarily on semantic problems of MT, and syntactic questions were treated secondarily. Although procedures were intended to be suitable for computers, most of the proposals were tested only by manual or punched card simulations because access to a computer proved to be difficult for many years.

The principal objective of CLRU was the investigation of methods which would, in the long term, produce good-quality fully automatic idiomatic translations. The fundamental problem was recognised to be that of polysemy or 'multiple meaning'. The ultimate solution was believed to be translation via an interlingua, but it was recognised that considerable semantic research had to be undertaken before even the outlines of a genuine interlingua could be discerned. The CLRU adopted two basic lines of research: the development of a crude prototype interlingual system producing 'pidgin' (essentially word-for-word) translations, and the development of a complex, sophisticated tool for improving and refining the lexical expression of unsatisfactory MT output, dealing particularly with problems of polysemy. In both lines of research, a central role was played by the notion of a thesaurus (a structured conceptual (semantic) classification of vocabulary), as the tool for output refinement and as the basis for an interlingua.

Thesauri, of which *Roget's Thesaurus* is the most familiar example, classify vocabulary into groups of words (and phrases) having similar meanings and arrange them under a number of 'heads'. These headings may be interpreted as the contexts in which the listed words may occur; and in principle, such contexts are extra-linguistic, i.e. not language specific but interlingual. Any particular word may (and often does) appear under more than one 'head', i.e. in more than one context, according to its different senses. Thus, *work* would appear under both Intellectual labour and Manual labour. The particular context would determine which 'head' was relevant: in *He's been working on that problem for two months* the occurrence of *problem* would indicate Intellectual labour. In abstract (mathematical) terms, the structure of thesaural interrelationships could be defined as a lattice, in which every word could be located according to its presence or absence under each of the thesaural 'heads'. The potentialities of applying lattice theory to linguistic patterns were examined in great depth by the CLRU team, not only for semantic (thesaural) operations but also for syntactic operations (e.g. Parker-Rhodes 1956, 1956a, 1961).

In one line of CLRU research, the thesaurus approach was investigated as a method of improving the unsatisfactory translations produced by existing MT systems. These word-for-word translations were to be treated as interim 'pidgin' English versions, i.e. following Richens' view of his and Booth's early efforts (Ch. 2.2 above) and Reifler's comments on the Washington University MT output (Ch. 4.1 above). Such 'pidgin' versions were to be made idiomatic by the additional operation of a thesaural 'retranslation'. The thesaurus would provide access to the rich variety of synonyms and idiomatic usages which could not be incorporated in bilingual dictionaries. In the thesaural approach then, the choice of appropriate TL version for a particular 'pidgin' word was envisaged as first a search for the correct 'head' (context) and then selection from the list of synonyms (Masterman 1957). For example, the word *plant* would be found to have a number of different contexts, e.g. plant as place, 184: as insert, 300: as vegetable, 367: as agriculture, 371: as trick, 545: as tools, 683; etc., each number standing for a list of synonyms which might appear in the context of *plant*. Initially, it would not be known which of these lists of synonyms of *plant* should be chosen. However, if *plant* was preceded in the text by *flowering* then consultation of this word in the thesaurus would give another set of synonym lists, e.g. flower as essence, 5: as produce, 161: as vegetable, 367: as prosper, 734: as beauty, 645; etc. Only one of these lists is common to both *flower* and *plant*, namely the list under the 'head' Vegetable; and this is clearly the correct context. In many cases there would be more than one, and selection would then involve searches for words common to all the synonym lists. This procedure was applied to the translation of Italian *alcune essenze forestali e fruttiferi*, viz. FOREST AND FRUIT-BEARING ESSENCE-S. The thesaurus heads for *forest, fruit, bearing,* and *essence* were consulted: *fruit* and *forest* both appear under Vegetable, *fruit* and *bearing* both under Production, *bearing* and *essence* both under Meaning, etc. A complex process of comparison of lists established links between Production and Meaning via Intrinsicality and Prototype, and produced *example, specimen, pattern, prototype* as alternatives of ESSENCE (Masterman 1956).

The parallel line of CLRU research continued Richens' ideas on interlingual translation (Richens & Booth 1955, Richens 1956a, 1956b, 1956c) It started from the basic distinction between lexical items (stems) and grammatical 'operators' (e.g. endings or function words). Lexical items were to be transferred via a crude interlingual dictionary of 'naked ideas' (Nude), semantic elements structured as a thesaurus. The operators were also to be analysed into interlingual functional categories, e.g. 'used to indicate past time', 'used to indicate inanimate objects'. (Some of this research was the work of Halliday, e.g. Halliday 1956, and may perhaps be seen as containing seeds of his functional approach to grammatical description in 'systemic grammar', e.g. Halliday 1973, 1985.)

The result of the operator analysis was a 'syntactical thesaurus' structure, i.e. groupings of operators under 'heads' such as In/animacy. The fact that such heads might also be used for lists of lexical items, and the fact that the analytical method proceeded by dichotomous cuts, strengthened the conviction that language systems were basically lattices. However, the 'thesaural' approach to syntax was found less satisfactory than the alternative of a simple classification of grammatical functions as noun-like or verb-like or qualifying functions, together with a simple 'bracketting' procedure for indicating structural relations (a 'syntactic lattice').

The procedure for 'bracketting' was described by Parker-Rhodes (1961, 1962, 1966). Classification of word classes, phrases and clauses was based on dependency relations, and individual words were coded according to their potential occurrences as governors, dependents, either or neither in each type of group (coordinate structure, adverbial group, participial clause, nominal group, etc.). Analysis consisted in the examination of sequences in order to identify potential governors and potential groupings ('brackettings'). An example analysis was:

> ((a (rather lazy) cat) (chases (falling (leaves and butterflies;)))) (of course these (can (easily get away.)))

Bracketting was the major method of defining boundary conditions for thesaural operations.

Semantic analysis, however, was throughout the focus of CLRU research. Much work was done on improving thesaural structures. A major problem was the very notion of synonymy. Sparck Jones (1962, 1965) investigated in depth the question of devising automatic methods of semantic classification. This research was closely linked with the extensive studies at CLRU of semantic aspects of information retrieval, where again the thesaurus concept was central (Needham & Joyce 1958), and which suggested fruitful analogies with MT systems (Masterman *et al.* 1959).

Probably the most important contribution of the CLRU team was to explore more thoroughly than ever before the theoretical and practical difficulties of constructing an interlingua based on a finite set of primitive semantic components. Much research effort was expended on the building of Nude (interlingual) dictionaries, primarily for translating Italian and Latin. The main difficulty was the establishment of the interlingual semantic components themselves. Evidently, thesaural 'heads' alone were insufficient. More refined analysis was necessary in order to distinguish between rows of synonyms. One possibility explored was the inclusion of primitive classifiers (derived ultimately from iconic and 'logical' categories). The classifiers proposed (Masterman 1961) were suggested in part by Ivor Richards' *Language Through Pictures* series for teaching languages (e.g. Richards & Gibson 1952–58). They included HE, SHE, I, YOU, DO, BE, BANG (suddenness), ONE, PAIR, KIND, HOW, CAUSE, CHANGE, MORE, LESS, FOR, SPREAD, MAN, THING, FOLK, BEAST, PLANT, etc. Such classifiers, in suitable combinations, could subdivide thesaural lists; e.g. the 'head' 839 LAMENTATION:

KIND	lamentation, mourning, grief, sobbing, tears
ONE BE	sob, sigh, complaint, whine
BANG KIND	flood of tears, crying, howling
ONE BANG BE	outburst of grief, cry, scream
THING	weeds, crepe, passing-bell, dirge, wake, funeral
SHE THING	widow's weeds
MAN DO	mourner, weeper
DO	lament, mourn, fret, groan
MORE DO	burst into tears
LESS DO	sigh, shed a tear

and so forth (Masterman 1961).

Augmentation of thesaural lists in this way could serve a further purpose by adding message-structuring information ('syntactic' information in a broad sense). For example (Masterman 1962), the semantic gist of the sentence:

> This man can eat, all right; but he can't, for the life of him, fight

might be expressed by the sequence of 'minimal semantic units', plus indications of basic operators (colons for noun-like functions, slashes for verb-like functions) and bracketting:

(THIS: MAN:) ((HE: (CAN/ DO/ (MUCH: EAT:))) (BUT: NOT:) (HE: (CAN/ DO/ (MUCH: FIGHT:))

The closeness in meaning of this sentence to:

This man is greedy, but pusillanimous

would be shown by the similarity of the 'semantic message' analysis of the latter (omitting syntax):

THIS: MAN: HE: MUCH: WANT/ EAT/ BUT: HE: SMALL: WANT/ FIGHT/

The complexity of the thesaurus and the analysis procedures for producing such 'semantic shells' was recognised to be well beyond the capabilities of any then (and perhaps even now) conceivable computer. In addition, of course, a MT system would need complex bilingual dictionaries (from SL to interlingua, and from interlingua to TL). The semantic universe is so enormous that in "compiling a realistic dictionary for MT, the scale of a bilingual large Oxford English Dictionary (18 volumes) would be far too small; a 200-volume dictionary would be more like what would be required" (Masterman 1962). Evidently, while the long-term aim might be the development of a thesaurus-based interlingua, there had to be more limited practical research objectives.

The further investigation of 'pidgin' translations was one obvious option. The idea was to test "the whole Mechanical Pidgin idea to destruction, in order to see what can be done with it and what cannot" (Masterman & Kay 1960). The characteristics of 'pidgin' were held to be: the predominant use of phrases, rather than words, as dictionary units; the employment of specialised dictionaries; the use of constructed symbols, e.g. 'pidgin variables' such as (W)THAT and 'pidgin' grammatical markers such as -ISH and -WARD for adjectives; the avoidance of certain problems of translation (such as articles, case endings and prepositions); the provision of ideally just single equivalents (no alternatives indicated); and strict adherence to the word sequence of the original. The thesis propounded was that 'pidgin' translation represented absolute minimal MT, and that consequently no more elaborate system could be justified unless it produced translations "noticeably better than Mechanical Pidgin" (Masterman & Kay 1960).

Experiments were made with Latin–English, producing the following for Julius Caesar's familiar *Gallia est omnis divisa in partes tres . . .*:

Gaul is all divided in part(s) three, of which one inhabit−they the+Belgians, the+other the+Aquitains, third one of+themselves language the+Celts our the+Gauls call−they+are/−they−would. These all language, custom, law−s from+one+another differ−they. The+Gauls

> from the+Aquitains the+Naronne the+river, from the+Belgians the-+Marne and the+Seine divide−s . . .

As a second experiment, the 'pidgin-improving' devices developed were applied to a (unedited) Russian–English translation of a *Pravda* article produced by the IBM system (Ch. 4.2); Gilbert King was at this time a consultant of the CLRU project and a believer in the validity of the CLRU approach (King 1958). First, an extract from the IBM version:

> In this meaning very urgent located in magazine article about first *entsiklike* (message) chapter Roman-Catholic church *papy Ioanna* XXIII with/from that it inverted at the end June present year to *episkopan*, sacred*kan* and believing, consisting in Catholic church.

The CLRU 'pidginised' version was:

> *From+this+point+of+view* very timely−is which+is+located in journal − − article − − about first encyclical−? (message−?) head−'s Roman-Catholic church−? pope−'s John XXIII with/from which that+one address−ed *at+the+end* June−ish present year−'s to bishop−s−ward priest−s−ward and to+believers, *belonging+to* Catholic church−?

The justification for investigating 'pidgin' MT was twofold. Firstly, most MT output was (and was likely always to be) non-idiomatic and in need of some semantic refinement, i.e. via a CLRU-type interlingual thesaurus. Secondly, investigation of 'pidgin' versions compelled close examination of the 'bits of information' contained in the texts, the semantic phrasing or patterning of the message; it forced MT research to concentrate on its primary goal: the transfer of the meaning of messages (Masterman 1967).

Further insight on semantic phrasing was obtained from work by Shillan (1967) on the articulatory segmentation of texts, the natural phrasing of messages into information blocks containing on average two stress-points. For example:

> Canada is divided/ into ten provinces/ and two territories./ Each province is sovereign/ in its own sphere/ and administers its own/ natural resources./

The segmentation of texts in this way suggested that phrase-by-phrase translation might be a more 'natural' approach than traditional sentence-by-sentence translation. However, in addition, further light on basic message structures was suggested by the notion of 'semantic squares' (Masterman 1965), a theory describing a patterning of semantic contrasts, reiterations, and recapitulations which would appear to underlie argument and paragraph structures, and which transcends specific language structures. The basic unit of a 'semantic square' was a coupling of phrases with two stress points. The relationship between stress patterns ('breathgroups'), reiteration, and semantic information structure has remained a focal point of Masterman's research to the present day (e.g. Masterman 1982).

In the mid-1960s the CLRU group investigated the possibilities of interactive English–French MT for the Canadian National Research Council (Masterman 1967a). The proposal was a machine-aided system in which the translator is on-line to a thesaural dictionary from which lexical items are retrieved by 'requests' formulated in 'natural phrasing' units and with which the translator interacts by question and answer routines. For example, to translate HE FLEW TO THE FRONTIER the operator would begin by entering the phrasing-frame:

operator: HE xx-ED TO THE xx
machine: DO YOU MEAN
  A HE MOVED TO SOME POINT?
  B HE CROSSED SOME OBSTACLE?
  C HE COMMUNICATED WITH SOME BEING?
operator: A
machine: DO YOU MEAN
  A HE DEPARTED TO SOME DESTINATION?
  B HE TRAVELLED TO SOME DISTANT REGION?
  C HE FLED TO SOME REFUGE? etc.
operator: B
machine: HOW DID HE TRAVEL?
  A BY PLANE?
  B BY SEA?
  C BY ROAD? etc.
operator: A

The operator then typed in the two stressed words: FLEW and FRONTIER and the machine would print out:

IL PRIT L'AVION POUR LA FRONTIÈRE

Included among the techniques was a method derived from the notion of 'semantic square'. The translation of HE WENT TO THE POLICE established first the option HE COMMUNICATED WITH SOME ANIMATE BEING, and then HE REVEALED-ALL TO THE ENEMY (rather than 'told a story' or 'consulted with some authority'). A matching of POLICE and ENEMY produced the French *les flics* (whereas the matching of POLICE and AUTHORITY would have produced *la police*).

The project was important as one of the first to investigate interactive MT (and in comparison with later systems it was certainly crude) but it was believed to have added significance in that on-line MT could reveal the actual methods used by human translators. Insight into actual translation processes ought to lead to improved automatic systems and aids of genuine value to practising translators (cf.19.5, and Masterman 1979).

The CLRU research team saw its approach (primarily the emphasis on interlingual thesaurus research) not as a rival to other MT systems, but as complementary. It concentrated on those extremely difficult and complex areas of semantics which other projects tended to shy away from. For this it was criticised as being too idealistic. (A particularly sharp attack on the CLRU approach by Bar-Hillel (Ch. 8.3 below) was answered by members of the group in a compendium of CLRU research: *Essays on and in machine translation* (CLRU 1959).) The fact that no MT system as such emerged from CLRU research is an irrelevance. In recent years, research in Artificial Intelligence has turned increasingly to the areas of investigation which were first examined in depth by the Cambridge project. Some of CLRU research was found to be along unfruitful lines; perhaps the ideal of a genuine interlingua was showed conclusively to be a chimera. On the other hand, features of the CLRU conception of semantic message structure have lived on in various guises in both AI and MT research (cf. Ch. 15 below).

5.3 UNIVERSITY OF MILAN (1959–1966)

The approach of the MT research group in the Centro di Cibernetica e di Attività Linguistiche, Milan, headed by Silvio Ceccato, had the long-term objective of establishing a MT method based on the supposed thought processes of human translation. Translation was conceived as the passage from SL to TL via mental constructs underlying the text in question. The goal of linguistic analysis was to study the relations between thought processes and expression, and to establish the basic structures of thought content. "A man who is translating is thinking; his understanding of the original text is thinking, and his translated text designates his thoughts." (Ceccato 1966). In brief, it was an 'interlingual' approach to MT, but one which, Ceccato was always at pains to stress, did not start from linguistic principles but from philosophical foundations. Indeed, Ceccato prefaced all his substantial articles by detailed expositions of his philosophical premises (Ceccato 1961, Ceccato & Zonta 1962, Ceccato 1966, Ceccato 1967).

Ceccato was a member of the Italian Operational School of philosophy (Scuola Operativa Italiana, established in 1939), which had been engaged for a number of years in developing models of mental activities, one mechanical model Adamo II being exhibited at an Automatism Exhibition in 1956 in Milan (Albani *et al.* 1961). In 1955 he and Enrico Maretti, an engineer responsible for Adamo II, were invited to present their nascent ideas on MT at the 'Information Theory' conference in London (Ceccato & Maretti 1956). Ceccato continued to develop his ideas until, in February 1959, a grant was received from the US Air Force Research and Development Command (Rome Air Development Center), through its European Office of Aerospace Research, to engage in MT research primarily towards Russian–English translation (US House of Repesentatives 1960). At a later date the project was also reporting to EURATOM (Ceccato & Zonta 1962). The group conducted almost exclusively theoretical studies, with occasional small-scale simulations, examining Italian, German, and Latin as well as English and Russian, and remained active until about 1966 (Josselson 1970).

The primary argument of the Italian Operational School school of philosophy was that the contents of thought should be regarded as activities and not, as in traditional philosophy, as objects (whether observational objects or characteristics of observed objects). Instead of analysing thought in relation to already extant 'things' or 'concepts', they proposed to study thought and its contents in terms of the operations required to construct these contents mentally. In this way, they claimed to eliminate the mind–body and concrete–abstract dichotomies. Four fundamental operations were identified: differentiation, figuration, categorisation, and correlation. Differentiation was defined as the activity by which changes of state are perceived and which "allows us to speak, for example, of warm and cold, of light and darkness, of hard and soft, of attention and inattention, of silence and noise, of good and bad moods, etc." (Albani *et al.* 1961). Figuration was defined as the activity of constructing forms and spatial localisation; in conjunction with differentiation, it gives rise to perception and representation. Categorisation was defined as the activity of mental classification, which "gives us the mental, or logical, categories, including, for example, substance, accident, subject, object, and, or, with, also, by, state, point, line, surface . . ."(Albani *et al.* 1961); it was regarded as an operation based on memory of temporally distinct differentiations. Correlation was the activity of thought itself, relating or ordering "material received from . . . other activities". It was defined as a triadic relation of a correlator (a mental category) and two correlata (either other mental categories or the results of other types of activities). Representations of the thought content of sentences or phrases were given as networks of correlational triads.

It was Ceccato's contention that traditional linguistics was inadequate for MT; it could not deal with discontinuous structures (e.g. that in: *In a deck chair, worn and depressed, there sat a young woman* we know *worn and depressed* must refer to *woman* and not to *deck chair*), or with homography and polysemy (e.g. "the four different situations" designated by *with* in *to sing with grace, to sing with Callas, to sing with a microphone, to sing with the dawn*). This was because grammar "was born not so much as a key for interpreting discourse, and thus to pass from the words to the designated thought; but rather to systematise language . . . In any case, grammar presupposes that whoever uses it already knows how to think . . ." (Ceccato 1967). What was needed, therefore, was "to build up a new grammar, with research going far beyond the normal classifications of words and the normal rules which suffice for the guidance of humans" (Ceccato 1966). In particular, it was considered important that 'intermediary' representations of thought content were not to be determined by structures of particular languages or of quasi-linguistic (including logical) forms (Ceccato 1961), because "Languages are not fabricated from one another, but are all built up on thought and must contain the indications to express it" (Albani *et al.* 1961). Ceccato was consequently opposed to the idea of an interlingua based on 'universal' or 'common' linguistic features.

Ceccato's method had the following stages. First, "correlational 'tabellone'" are set up: "For each word, the correlational possibilities of the thing which it designates are examined." e.g. "'water' designates a correlatum, either first or second, of a correlation whose correlator is 'and', 'or', 'with', etc.; but it cannot be the second correlatum of a correlation whose correlator is 'between', because a plural is required for this position; we can say 'water and', 'and water', 'water or', 'or water', 'water with', 'with water', 'water between' but not 'between water'". The set of correlators themselves were considered to be "relatively few in number even in the richest and most highly developed trains of thought: we may say between 100 and 200 in all". They included the conjunctions and prepositions, punctuation marks, and relations such as subject–predicate, substance–accident (i.e. noun-adjective), apposition, development–modality (i.e. verb–adverb), and comparison (Albani *et al.* 1961). The intention was that the correlators should be universals, but as a "concession to practical considerations" the table of correlators was "designed instrumentally, as a linguistic-correlational chart", one for each of the languages Russian, English, Italian, German, and Latin.

After every word had been classified by its correlational possibilities (quite a task in view of the fact recognised by Ceccato (1966) that "for certain words, nearly all the possibilities are open. The word 'water', for instance, will occupy more than 160 positions."), the next stage was to establish the conditions which apply, or had to be satisfied, for each possible correlation. Some of these limitations were general (e.g. that if one correlatum had been identified, the other must be found); others were specific (e.g. adjective–noun and subject–verb agreements). The final stage of grammar construction was the classification of the correlations themselves according to their potentialities as correlata within other correlations.

To deal with polysemy, Ceccato proposed "a much subtler analysis than the one carried out so far in relation to the tabellone; we now need an analysis of what the words designate" (Ceccato 1966). For this he suggested classifications of, for instance, *apple* as "an observatum, physical, with a form, and . . . a specimen of the class of edible things", and the construction of 'notional spheres' in which 'developments' (i.e. verbs), 'things' (nouns) and their 'aspects' would be linked by 'basic relations'. It was claimed that the set of these relations was limited, "not more than a few hundred" and Ceccato (1966) listed 56 such as 'member: part', 'species: genus', 'part: whole', 'thing produced: thing which produces it', 'thing produced: place of production', 'thing contained: container', 'thing supported: support', etc. Thus *sleep* was linked to *bed* (activity: usual place), and to *night* (activity: usual time), and *bed* was linked to *bedroom* (object: usual place), and to *furniture* (species: genus), and so forth.

The understanding of a sentence (or text) involved, therefore, the construction of a correlational net on the basis of information about the correlational possibilities of each word, the possible linkages among correlations, and limitations on relations within the 'notional sphere'. Translation involved the transformation of a correlational net into an equivalent net appropriate to the correlational possibilities of words and correlators of the target language. Such transformations would include, for example, the insertion of articles and the completion of elliptical constructions (e.g. for Russian–English translation, cf. Perschke in: von Glasersfeld *et al.* 1962).

Although perhaps a number of simulations were performed — Zonta states: "input vocabulary for our current programme includes about 50,000 inflected Russian forms, corresponding to about 2500 headwords and punctuation marks (Ceccato & Zonta 1962) — only three "microexamples" of translations are reported, of the Italian sentence *Un giglio ci sta bene* into English (*A lily goes well*) (Ceccato 1966), and of the English sentences *Were I tired, I should weep* and *Engineer Small has a little train* into Italian (Ceccato 1961: 175ff.; Ceccato 1967).

These examples confirm the conclusion evident from this outline that correlational analysis was no more than a version of immediate constituent analysis (Ch. 3.4), based on traditional grammatical categories and relations (nouns, prepositions, subject–predicate, verb–adverb), and constrained by limits on the collocation of semantic features (also of a traditional nature: 'physical', 'edible', etc.) For example, the analysis of *Engineer Small has a little train* gives the correlational net shown in Fig. 11 (Ceccato 1967).

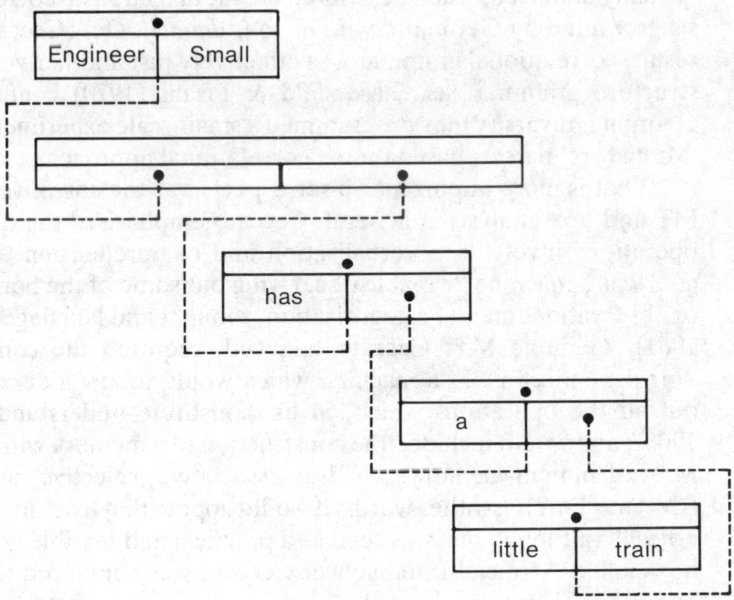

Fig. 11 — Correlation net

This may be seen as equivalent to the immediate constituency analysis:

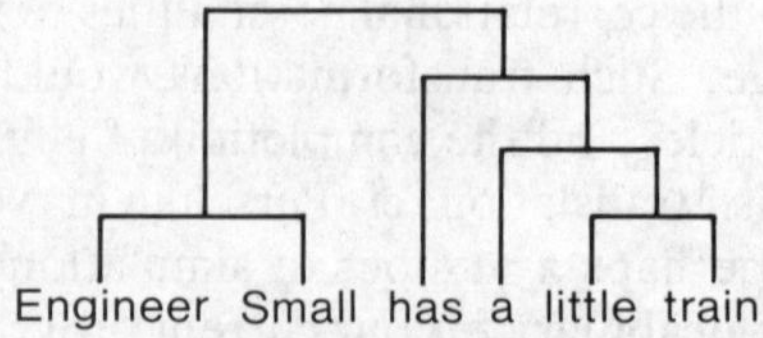

Only the idea of 'notional spheres' represented a new departure, although even in these the types of relations were familiar, and their application in analysis was not described. In theory, analysis was to take into account intersentential relations, but in practice analysis was restricted to sentences as units. Finally, the transformations of correlational nets (roughly, phrase structures) in translation were not much different than other syntactic transfer routines of the time.

From the viewpoint of practical achievement in linguistic analysis, Ceccato's method was no advance on traditional approaches. He dismissed contemporary linguistics, but in effect his 'philosophical' approach reinvented traditional grammatical categories and classifications. His introspection had discovered not the universal processes of thought but the basic categories of the language in which he thought (Mounin 1962); as indeed he virtually admitted, when describing the modificationsto correlational analysis prompted by German *damit, davon, danach*, etc. (Ceccato 1966). As a result, correlational grammar was effectively just another version of phrase structure grammar, as Glasersfeld & Pisani (1970) confirmed when at Georgia University they programmed a small-scale experimental parser, the 'Multistore' parser, based on the correlational approach.

What is more important, in retrospect, was the cognitive orientation to MT and text analysis in general. Ceccato emphasised the dynamic mental operations involved in verbalisation and comprehension. Ultimately the goal was a machine "capable of carrying out some of the human operations of observation, mental categorisation, thought and language" (Albani *et al.* 1961). Genuine MT, Ceccato believed, required the construction of a 'linguistic machine', "a machine which would follow a discourse, carrying out all the operations which, in us, constitute understanding" (Ceccato 1966); and would include "the construction of a memory with the characteristics of human memory, which is associative, selective, and propulsive" (Ceccato 1967). In other words, it would appear that his primary interest was not MT (although this was seen as a practical and feasible goal) but what is now called Artificial Intelligence; Ceccato was convinced that despite the enormous difficulties, it was "desirable to continue our study of thought and language in man; both for the general theoretical value of these studies and for their contribution, considerable in the past, and certain to increase in the future, to the project of the mechanization of intelligent activity" (Ceccato 1966).

Limited and tentative though they were, we may regard aspects of Ceccato's cognitive (and interlingual) approach as genuine foreshadowings of some future AI methods (Ch. 15 below); his 'notional spheres' have obvious analogies with semantic networks; correlational nets are similar (in conception if not in form) to the conceptual dependency networks of Schank; and the correlational analysis of sentences and texts may be seen (again in conception if not fully in practice) as an early form of semantics-based parsing.

5.4 NATIONAL PHYSICAL LABORATORY, TEDDINGTON (1959–1966)

The Autonomics Division of the National Physical Laboratory (NPL) at Teddington, near London, began work on a 'pilot' Russian–English MT system in 1959 (McDaniel *et al.* 1967, 1967a, 1967b; Szanser 1966, 1967). The research formed part of a wider programme of investigations into automation and robotics. From the start, the aims were both practical and limited: a demonstration of the practicality and feasibility of Russian–English MT of scientific and technical texts for the expert reader. The research ended in 1966, when the computer used throughout the project was scrapped. This was the experimental machine ACE designed and constructed at NPL as a development of Turing's pioneer work at the NPL just after World War II.

The basic dictionary was obtained initially from a copy of the Harvard University Russian–English dictionary. This was revised and adapted, and ultimately contained about 15,000 words represented by 18,000 entries. As in the Harvard dictionary (Ch. 4.9 above), stems and endings were entered separately except in the case of irregular forms which were left unsplit. Some differences in the representation of Russian morphological forms were introduced (McDaniel & Whelan 1962), with consequential extra work which meant the dictionary was not fully operational until 1963 (McDaniel *et al.* 1967a). As in most systems at the time, dictionary lookup was serial, matches being made against stems on the longest match principle and idioms being identified and translated as wholes. If a word did not appear in the dictionary, some attempt was made to 'anglicise' the Russian by two routines, one which transliterated stems (on the argument that many new scientific words in Russian have 'international' stems), and another which identified common international and Russian prefixes and supplied English equivalents , e.g. *radio-, elektro-, mnogo- (many), poly- (semi-)*.

It was intended to introduce progressive refinements of the basically word-for-word translation by syntactic operations. A number of procedures were investigated, but few were implemented before the end of the project (Szanser 1966; McDaniel *et al.* 1967a). The first refinement was the recognition of 'nominal blocks' (noun phrases with adjectival and noun modifiers) in order to resolve homographs via the establishment of word classes, and to identify places for the insertion of English prepositions. A second refinement was a similar procedure for predicate blocks (finite verbs and modifiers), including recognition of reflexive verbs in order to ensure output in appropriate English passive forms. Further syntactic routines were simulated satisfactorily but not implemented. These included the identification of clauses by location of conjunctions, relative pronouns, etc., the identification of coordinate structures, and the recognition of subject–verb and verb–object government. Other syntactic procedures investigated included the resolution of ambiguities, such as case ending ambiguities (including insertion of English prepositions), adverb and short adjective ambiguities (e.g. whether Russian *tochno* is to be translated *is accurate* (short adjective) or *accurately* (adverb)), and third person pronoun ambiguities (e.g. Russian *ego* as *his, its, him* or *it*); and finally some study was made of the treatment of ellipsis (e.g. the common omission of the copula in Russian).

In view of the low level of syntactic analysis actually incorporated, the system produced translations which were little better than word for word versions. An example from Szanser (1966):

> THESE MUTUAL INTERFERENCES HAVE OWN REASONS AND/ALSO DEPEND ON POWER/OUTPUT, QUANTITY(S) AND/ALSO RANGE(S) OF TRANSMITTERS FROM RECEIVING EQUIPMENT, LOCATION/ARRANGEMENT OF THEIR AERIALS, DIFFERENCE(S) OF FREQUENCIES OF TRANSMITTERS OR THEIR HARMONICS FROM FREQUENCIES OF RECEIVERS AND/ALSO, AT LAST/FINALLY, FROM INTENSITY OF RADIATION TRANSFERRING AND/ALSO AMPLIFICATION/MAGNIFICATION/GAIN OF RECEIVING DIRECTED AERIALS IN NOT WISHED DIRECTIONS/TRENDS.

The example illustrates also the lack of any semantic analysis (beyond the limitation of vocabulary to specialised fields), although again some plans were being made at NPL before termination of the project (Szanser 1966).

Intended always as an experiment in MT feasibility, it was fitting that the project concluded just as the operational system had reached a stage when its practical usefulness could be evaluated (Szanser 1967). In May 1966, practising scientists in British universities, government research institutes, and industry were invited to submit Russian articles for translation. In general, the results were received favourably; a grading of users' comments in terms of perceived 'usefulness' produced a mean rating interpretable as "slightly less than 'good' " (Szanser 1967). However, the inadequacies of the lexicon and the inclusion of too many alternatives were points of criticism (McDaniel *et al.* 1967b).

Although the theoretical contributions of the NPL team were negligible and the operational system represented little advance on basic word-for-word systems, the NPL project did produce translations which could be evaluated by scientists in a practical environment. It remains to the present day the only operational MT system developed so far in Great Britain.

5.5 RESEARCH IN FRANCE (1959–66)

In December 1959 the Centre National de la Recherche Scientifique (CNRS) established a MT research body, the Centre d'Etudes de la Traduction Automatique (CETA), at two centres in Paris and Grenoble, under the general direction of Peres (*CRDSD* 8, May 1961; *TA* 1(1), April 1960). Both centres were to work towards a system for translation from

Russian into French. Within one year the centres employed 25 research workers (*TA* 2(4), 1961). According to the US House of Representatives report (1960) contact with US research was maintained by a "member of the US Air Force" who served "as the US representative on the mutual weapons development team, for exchange of technical data on automatic language translation research within France".

At Paris, the team under A. L. Sestier was engaged on the study of the syntax of German and Russian; a successful trial syntactic analysis of Russian on an IBM 650 was reported in September 1961. Most of its activity was devoted to problems of dictionary compilation and searching (e.g. Meile 1962), and by 1962 the Russian dictionary contained 12,000 stems and multiple paradigmatic classes had been established (Dupuis 1966). However, not long afterwards, the Paris section ceased involvement in MT research and from 1963 onwards all CETA activity was centred at the University of Grenoble.

The Grenoble group is now one of the longest established MT groups, directed by Bernard Vauquois since its creation in 1960 (Vauquois 1966a). An early decision of this group was that MT could be successful only if analysis was pursued to a much 'deeper' level than most contemporary systems. It was acknowledged that at the current stage of MT research semantic analysis was not a practical proposition and that consequently most attention had to be paid to 'deep syntactic' analysis, and to methods of syntactic transformation. The aim was to produce representations which would serve as the source for TL synthesis; in other words, CETA was working towards an interlingual representation (at least as far as syntax was concerned), a conception which was later to be termed a 'pivot language'. A particular long-term emphasis of the CETA group at Grenoble was the great attention paid to the establishment of powerful algorithmic programs based on rigorous modelling of linguistic formalisations. The aim became to "établir le système de traduction automatique au moyen d'une succession de modèles logico-linguistiques" (Vauquois 1966a). This emphasis lead to substantial investigations of algebraic and formal linguistics (e.g. Vauquois' 1962 paper (Vauquois 1966) concerned primarily with problems of morphology), and to the development of the notion of 'sub-grammars' to increase the algorithmic efficiency of analysis programs (Vauquois *et al.* 1965).

The Grenoble group began research on three MT systems for Russian–French, German–French, and Japanese–French. The latter was brought to an early end by the departure of Yamada in July 1962 (cf. Ch. 7.1 below), but it was resurrected at intervals during later years. The Russian–French system received highest priority; by 1966 the linguistic foundations for morphological and syntactic analysis were said to have been completed (Vauquois 1966). The German–French system was also said to be progressing, though with much less urgency than the Russian–French project. For their Russian dictionary, the Grenoble group was able to build on the corpus of some 700,000 words compiled at RAND (Ch. 4.4).

Although it is evident that some of the principal chacteristics of this MT group had already been formulated by 1966 (notably the syntactic interlingua and rigorous formalism), research was still at an early stage and had not (except at a theoretical level) had much impact on the general direction of MT research at this period. As we shall see (Ch. 10.1 and 13.3), the Grenoble group was to be most influential after research in the US had been interrupted by the ALPAC report (Ch. 8.9 below).

At the same time as the Paris and Grenoble groups were set up, a MT group began in 1962 at Nancy composed of Bernard Pottier, Guy Bourquin, and Legras, also sponsored by the CNRS. There was some talk at the time that this group should also form part of the CETA project, to be known as the 'Section de Nancy'. However, it remained independent. A successful experiment on English–French translation was reported in late 1960 (*TA* 2(4), Dec. 1961); however, this must have been a very tentative exploration as it is evident that MT research at Nancy has always been of a long-term theoretical nature: statistical analyses of English scientific vocabulary (including semantic studies), some studies of French syntax (particularly by Pottier), and similar work on Spanish (*TA* 5(1), 1964). Although always including MT within its perview, the Nancy group has had wide interests in many areas of computational linguistics. It remains active to the present day (cf. Ch. 14.2 below).

There was also a short-lived group (1961–62) set up by the Association pour l'étude et le développement de la traduction automatique et de la linguistique appliquée (ATALA), and led by Michel Corbé of Unesco and Robert Tabory of IBM-France. The aim was an English–French system, basically of the 'syntactic transfer' type and influenced by Yngve's work at MIT (Ch. 4.7). The methodology was based on the 'empirical' approach at RAND and Ramo-Wooldridge (Ch. 4.4 and 4.6), and there were hopes of using a photoscopic memory device of the IBM type (Ch. 4.2). The preliminary work on English syntax was reported by Corbé & Tabory (1962). The proposed parser would identify sentence fragments and determine their interrelationships in a series of four passes. There is no evidence that the system was implemented.

5.6 RESEARCH IN BELGIUM (1961–64)

At the University of Brussels a project was set up during 1961 under the leadership of Lydia Hirschberg (*TA* 2(4), Dec. 1961). Funded by EURATOM its aim was the investigation of methods and procedures for Russian–French MT. The approach adopted had similarities with Harris' string analysis and with dependency grammar (Josselson 1970). A good deal of theoretical work was accomplished, but it seems that only morphological procedures were actually implemented (Blois *et al.* 1968). From 1962 the group worked closely with EURATOM's computer centre CETIS on the adaptation of the Georgetown system for Russian–French MT, leaving the GAT Russian analysis program unmodified and developing French synthesis procedures (*CRDSD* 10, May 1962). But by 1966 MT research had ceased in Brussels; EURATOM's involvement had been transferred fully to CETIS at Ispra (Ch. 11.1). However, by this time, the Brussels group was already mainly involved in the development of the computer-based multilingual dictionary DICAUTOM for the European Coal and Steel Community (later, as EURODICAUTOM (Ch. 17.7), expanded for the European Communities).

5.7 RESEARCH IN WEST GERMANY (1963–68)

In West Germany MT activity before the mid-1960s was surprisingly limited. There was some research at Freiburg under Herbert Pilch on syntactic analysis and synthesis of English, intended for a MT system of the 'syntactic transfer' type, possibly with Finnish as a target language (Zint 1967). At the University of Cologne, Paul O. Samuelsdorff worked for a time on Hebrew–English MT, basically a 'direct' system (Zint 1967); subsequently Samuelsdorff experimented with an English–German system on similar principles (Bruderer 1978:129-131).

A more substantial experimental system in West Germany was the investigation at IBM Deutschland (based in Stuttgart), from 1963 until about 1968, of a system for English–German MT of texts in the fields of data processing and electronics (Schirmer 1969, Batori 1969). The system belonged clearly to the 'direct translation' type: analysis and synthesis were closely intertwined ("eng miteinander verflochten"); and the basis of its syntactic method was similar to Garvin's fulcrum approach (Ch. 4.6). Initial dictionary lookup (a bilingual English–German dictionary of 11,000 entries) was followed by programs for homograph resolution, identification of coordinate structures and constituent structure relationships, modification of certain English syntactic structures into ones corresponding to German usage (e.g. present participles into subordinate clauses), generation of German noun, adjective, and verb endings, and transformation of structures into German word orders. The research at IBM in Stuttgart did not, however, progress beyond a tentative experimental stage.

5.8 OTHER WEST EUROPEAN GROUPS

As in the United States there were a number of short-lived or abortive groups. In Scandinavia a group was founded at Stockholm in November 1960, led by Stig Comet, with the intention of establishing a MT society. In Finland a group was set up at Kasvatusopillinen Korkeakoulu, Jyväskylä, led by Lennart Schäring and Teuvo Kuikka, to begin preliminary studies for Finnish–Swedish MT (*CRDSD* 11, Nov. 1962). Finally, a group set up under Nicola Wolkenstein at the University of Pisa in 1964 planned to develop an Italian–English MT system (*CRDSD* 13, Nov. 1964). Nothing was heard subsequently of any of these projects.

6

Groups and projects in the Soviet Union and Eastern Europe (1955–1967)

Research in the USSR on MT began soon after the demonstration of the Georgetown-IBM experiment in early 1954 (Ch. 2.6). Three major research groups started at this time; two in Moscow and one in Leningrad. One Moscow group was set up at the Institute for Precision Mechanics and Computer Technology; another was established in the Steklov Mathematical Institute. The third Moscow group was formed at the Electromodelling Laboratory of the All-Union Institute of Scientific and Technical Information. The Leningrad group was set up as the Experimental Laboratory for Machine Translation in the University of Leningrad. Shortly afterwards, a number of other groups with MT research interests were formed: one at the First Moscow State Pedagogical Institute of Foreign Languages, and another at the Institute of Linguistics in Moscow. Other groups began at Gorky, Kharkov, Kiev, Petrozavodsk, Tiflis, and Erevan. The growth in MT research workers was very rapid, from a handful experimenting in 1954 on English–Russian and French–Russian to many hundreds by 1959. A conference on MT held in Moscow in May 1958 was attended by 340 representatives from 79 institutions (Harper 1961). Many had no doubt only a passing interest in the field, but nevertheless the amount of activity was impressive. From the beginning, Russian researchers were particularly anxious the follow the progress of MT in other countries, and many of their publications summarise and comment upon current developments; particular mention should be made of the invaluable manual and bibliography by Mel'chuk & Ravich (1967).

6.1 INSTITUTE OF PRECISION MECHANICS AND COMPUTER TECHNOLOGY (ITMVT)

Research on a English–Russian system began in January 1955 at the Institute of Precision Mechanics and Computer Technology (Institut tochnoi mekhaniki i vychislitel'noi tekhniki AN SSSR); by the end of 1955 the first experimental tests were done on the BESM computer of the USSR Academy of Sciences.

The experiment was described in detail by Mukhin (1956) and Panov (1960). The aim was similar to that of the Georgetown-IBM experiment: to demonstrate the technical feasibility of MT. 'A dictionary of 952 English and 1073 Russian words was compiled to translate a mathematical text on differential equations. The simplistic *ad hoc*-ness of the approach can be illustrated by the procedure for translating *much* and *many* (Panov 1960: 27–28; Panov 1960a), a sequence of yes/no questions linked by transition codes.

1(2,3)	Check imediately preceding word for *how*
2(0)	*skol'ko* (numeral, invariable)
3(4,5)	Check immediately preceding word for *as*
4(0)	*stol'ko zhe* (numeral, variable)
5(7,9)	Check given word for *much*
6(0)	Not to be translated (adverb)
7(1,11)	Check immediately preceding word for *very*
8(0)	*mnogii* (adjective, hard stem, with sibilant)
9(8,12)	Check preceding word for preposition, and following word for noun
10(0)	*mnogo* (adverb)
11(12,10)	Check following word for noun
12(0)	*mnogo* (numeral, variable)

(where the two numbers in brackets indicate the next rule if the answer is 'yes' or 'no' respectively). To translate *much* in *The subject would have been much better standardised*, the sequence is: 1 - answer 'no', go to 3; 3 - 'no'; 5 - 'yes'; 7 - 'no'; 11 - 'no'; 10 - translation is *mnogo*. In *This is most useful and for many reasons* the sequence is: 1,3,5,9,8 giving *mnogii*. The computational (and linguistic) cumbrousness of such procedures is on a par with those of the Georgetown-IBM experiment (Ch. 4.3; cf. Panov (1960) and Sheridan (1955)).

Experiments were also made with texts from *The Times* newspaper and from Dickens' novel *David Copperfield*, without any expansion of the dictionary. The Dickens translation was admitted to be "extremely imperfect" but it was believed to show that although designed for mathematics sufficient general vocabulary had been incorporated to give reasonable results (Panov 1960).

Just as Dostert had at Georgetown (Ch. 4.3), Panov (1956) drew certain principles for future MT work from the experiment. He advocated: the maximum separation of the dictionary from the translation program; the separation of analysis programs and synthesis programs; the storage of lexical items under stem forms; the inclusion of grammatical information in dictionaries; and the determination of multiple meanings from contextual information. Similar principles were, of course, reached by the American researchers at an early stage, as we have seen.

The linguistic aspects of the program were the work of I. K. Bel'skaya, who continued the further development of the English–Russian system at ITMVT. This system (Bel'skaya 1957, 1960) was one of the best known of the early Soviet MT research efforts. Its dictionary contained 2300 words from texts on applied mathematics. The restriction to one relatively narrow scientific field was justified both to ensure a reasonable reduction of polysemy problems and to keep within the limitations of the available computer facilities. English words were entered in canonical forms, thus necessitating the convertion of words such as *wanted* to *want*, *stopped* to *stop, lying* to *lie*, etc. The system had three phases, each consisting of a number of cycles (or 'passes'). 'Vocabulary analysis' included dictionary search, identification of the word classes of unmatched lexical items and resolution of homographs by recognition of morphological forms or by examination of the immediate context (on the same lines as described above by Panov). The second phase was 'Grammatical analysis': first an examination of verb forms (to determine tense, mood, etc., and whether inversion of Russian word order would be required), then identification of phrase boundaries (from punctuation marks and verb groups), recognition of noun groups and then of constituent adjectives and their relationships to nouns (for ensuring correct agreement in Russian), lastly recognition of English structures which would need word order changes for Russian. The final phase was the 'Grammatical synthesis' of Russian, i.e. the inflection of Russian verbs, adjectives, and nouns, in that sequence. (This last phase was considered to be sufficiently general that it could be applied to analysis output from languages other than English.)

The program worked well for those sentences on which the algorithms had been based, and Bel'skaya (1960) also reported satisfactory manually simulated tests on 100 "unknown" texts, including literary texts by Galsworthy and Edgar Allen Poe. (Illustrative extracts were included in her article.) She claimed that results on the latter, together with the earlier tests on Dickens (above), demonstrated that "the applicability of MT depends on whether it is possible to identify the implicit set of rules governing this or that particular sphere of language application, be it as narrow a sphere as say, Wordsworth's poetry, and further, whether these rules can be formulated into a formal set." Bel'skaya was one of very few MT researchers believing still at this date in the possibility of MT of poetic works.

It would appear that the 1958 version of the system was not implemented on a computer (Harper 1961). It would seem very likely that the system was beset by the same problems encountered in other empirical systems, principally the inadequacies of *ad hoc* routines not derived from extensive examination of text (Harper 1961). The inadequacies of the word-for-word approach of the system were well described by Rozentsveig in 1968 (quoted by Roberts & Zarechnak 1974): the programs "did not compare the correspondences between the systems of the target and source languages in translating. It is therefore significant that the synthesis of a Russian sentence was obtained depending on the English input information for each word and the position of each word within the English sentence. Synthesis routines were used after the word order in English had been transformed in accordance with the requirements for word order in Russian . . ." Similar criticisms were made of the word-for-word 'direct' approach in US systems (cf. Ch. 8 below).

The Institute's work on translation from Russian has been described by T. N. Nikolaeva (1958). The intention was to develop a program for analysing Russian which could be used for any target language. The Russian dictionary contained therefore only grammatical information and no TL equivalents. Morphological analysis preceded dictionary lookup in order to determine the 'dictionary form' (e.g. for nouns, the nominative singular). Problems caused by mathematical formulae were dealt with by assigning word classes (adjective, noun) as appropriate. A good deal of attention was paid to problems of Russian -sya verbs (which may be reflexives or passives), and to the homography of the case endings. Syntactic analysis aimed to identify the roles of components within the sentence (e.g. 'subject', 'direct object', 'instrument' etc.); each word was examined in turn, in a left to right scan, with backward and forward consultation of adjacent words as necessary. It is evident that this project involved extensive study of Russian morphology and syntax. The analysis program was written for the KIEV computer of the USSR Academy of Sciences, and was tested in April 1960 (Mukhin 1963).

The Institute's MT research effort included work on German–Russian MT. A German–Russian glossary for which "some 1500 pages of mathematics were studied" was compiled by S. S. Belokrinitskaya, who also investigated the semantics of German prepositions (Harper 1961). The translation algorithms were constructed on the same principles as those for the English–Russian system, with an enhanced dictionary lookup program in order to deal with the complexities of German compounding, and with additional components in the syntactic analysis to identify subordinate clauses (Kulagina *et al.* 1961).

There was also research at ITMVT on translation from Chinese and Japanese. Some early illustrations were included by Panov (1960) and by Bel'skaya (1957) to demonstrate the general applicability of the method used in the English–Russian system. In later years, research followed the lines indicated by the Russian–English system of Nikolaeva (Kulagina *et al.* 1961). Given the non-inflectional character of Chinese, syntactic analysis was the main focus, designed primarily to identify functions which would need to be represented in Russian by inflected forms (e.g. case endings of nouns). In the case of Japanese the problem of identifying word, phrase, and sentence boundaries was given special attention.

It is clear that Rozentsveig (1958) was correct to characterise the efforts of this group as "the rapid achievement of immediate, practical results",in conjuntion with "careful, detailed investigation of linguistic material, especially lexical." In many respects, ITMVT's philosophy was much like that at Georgetown (Ch. 4.3).

6.2 STEKLOV MATHEMATICAL INSTITUTE (MIAN)

Research at the Steklov Mathematical Institute of the Academy of Sciences (Matematicheskii institut imeni V. A. Steklova AN SSSR, i.e. MIAN) started at the end of 1954 under the general direction of the mathematician and computer specialist A. A. Lyapunov. After an initial 'empirical' experiment on French–Russian MT, research at the Institute was characterised by a strong theoretical orientation.

The French–Russian MT project developed by Olga S. Kulagina (in collaboration with Igor A. Mel'chuk of the Institute of Linguistics) produced its first translations on the STRELA computer in 1956. Testing continued until 1959 (examples of translations can be found in Roberts & Zarechnak (1974) and in Papp (1966: 109)). The translation algorithm was compiled empirically; first on the basis of existing human translations of French mathematical texts, then by supplementing the initial rules by consultation of further texts and of textbook grammars of French. As a result, some of the traditional word classes were modified. The dictionary, which contained 1200 French stems representing 2300 words, was compiled from examination of 20,500 running words of texts by the mathematicians Picard, Borel, and Appel (Papp 1966, Harper 1961). The stem form was identical with the singular for most nouns and with the masculine singular for most adjectives. Some verbs were listed under several stems (e.g. *faire* under *fais, fai, fass, fe*); irregular verbs had multiple entries, often full forms (e.g. *est, sont, soit, soient*). Excluded were verb forms which would not be expected in mathematical texts, such as first person singular and second person singular forms. Idiomatic constructions were included as units, e.g. *mettre en doute* ('call into question'). Also included as 'idioms' were compound conjunctions and adverbs such as *le long de* ('along'), *parce que* ('because'), and *à peu près* ('approximately'). Dictionary entries included grammatical information, not only genders, plural type, etc., but also prepositions which may precede or follow, thus providing clues for the selection of Russian cases. In general only one Russian equivalent was provided, on the grounds that the mathematical context reduced problems of homography. The routines for syntactic analysis consisted of complex series of yes/no questions (as in the English–Russian system of Panov and Bel'skaya). There seems to have been no attempt to describe the syntactic functions of the French homographs independently of the requirements of Russian syntactic and lexical formations (Harper 1963).

One by-product of this research was the advancement of programming theory, i.e. the identification of elementary algorithmic operations and work towards the development of programming languages (Rozentsveig 1958); the inadequacies of the existing languages for non-numerical applications were as obvious to the Russians as they were to the Americans. Another was the development of Kulagina's set theory model of language, in which grammatical categories and relationships can be defined on formal mathematical foundations. The definitions produced enable analysis of sentence elements into dependency-like structures and semantic components. For example, "the words *thick book* in the sentence *the thick book lies on the table* can be reduced to the element *book* or can be replaced by the element *thing* or the element *it*" (Rozentsveig 1958). Kulagina's model opened the strong vein of mathematical linguistics in the Soviet Union. In Oettinger's (1958) view Kulagina's switch away from practical MT to theoretical issues was a consequence of encountering problems when the techniques of the French–Russian system were applied on a larger scale. Whether this was the reason or not, henceforth the research strategy at MIAN could be characterised (Rozentsvieg 1958) as "the effective practical realisation of machine translation only as the result of profound theoretical research in the area of mathematics and linguistics." In this regard, Kulagina's work on mathematical linguistics was considered typical.

Improved versions of the algorithms were incorporated in the English–Russian MT system at the same Institute, developed under the direction of T. N. Moloshnaya. After the experience of the empirical approach to French–Russian MT, a more formal methodology was adopted (Rozentsveig 1958). For syntactic analysis a dependency model was adopted for the identification of noun and verb phrase (syntagm) structures. To cope with problems of morphology Moloshnaya found it necessary to establish a new system of word classes for the two languages. From a distributional analysis based on methods derived from Fries (1952) and Jespersen (1937), Moloshnaya identified 19 word classes for English and 17 for Russian. Homographs were resolved by a routine based on the examination of the possible word classes of contiguous words. The homograph routine preceded the dependency analysis of phrase structures. The experiment was on a relatively small scale, the dictionary containing just 1026 items from a text on differential equations (Papp 1966). Some steps were taken towards a multilingual system by dividing the dictionary so that the Russian part could be used with other languages and by making English analysis and Russian morphological synthesis independent programs (Rozentsveig 1958, Kulagina *et al.* 1961).

6.3 INSTITUTE OF LINGUISTICS, MOSCOW

The Institute of Linguistics in Moscow (Institut Yazykoznaniya AN SSSR) set up a group under the direction of A. A. Reformatskii. Its involvement was primarily at a theoretical level, working often in collaboration with other research groups. As we have seen, Igor A. Mel'chuk collaborated with Kulagina on the MIAN French–Russian system. Following this, he investigated requirements for a Hungarian–Russian MT system. Hungarian was chosen as presenting within itself many of the special difficulties met with in a number of languages, e.g. as an agglutinating language it posed problems common to Turkic languages spoken in the Soviet Union, its compound nouns and separable verb particles had similarities to features in English and German, and its word order was completely different from that of Russian. If a satisfactory approach could be found for Hungarian, then this might provide clues for solving similar problems in other languages (Papp 1966). Mel'chuk devised rules for morphological analysis, dictionary searching, homograph resolution, recognition of sentence structure, and Russian sentence synthesis. Although a selective glossary was compiled, the study was concentrated on the investigation of algorithmic problems. As a consequence of this research on Hungarian, Mel'chuk came to formulate his notion of an interlingua. The problems of Hungarian word order compelled the abandonment of a word-for-word approach (which might be feasible for French–Russian) and favoured investigation of common syntagmatic structures (e.g. of possession, adjectival modification). Similar investigations of many language pairs would build up a series of syntactic configurations, some common to all languages but most common to only some. From this set of interlingual structures would be selected those needed for particular SL and TL texts. A similar analysis of lexical differences and equivalences would produce sets of interlingual semantic units (e.g. indicating comparison, negation, 'larger than normal' size). In this view, the interlingua is the sum of all correspondences of the languages involved. The subsequent development of Mel'chuk's ideas resulted in his well-known 'meaning-text' model of language and in the elaboration of a highly influential MT model (Ch. 10.2 below).

6.4 LENINGRAD UNIVERSITY (ELMP)

Research at the Experimental Laboratory of Machine Translation at Leningrad University (Eksperimental'naya Laboratoriya Mashinnogo Perevoda Leningradskogo Universiteta imeni A. A. Zhdanova, i.e. ELMP), which started in 1958, was led by Nikolai D. Andreev; by 1961 over 100 researchers were involved in the group (Andreev 1961). The main thrust of this MT project was the development of the theoretical basis for interlingual MT. Andreev outlined his ideas on the interlingua on many occasions (e.g. Andreev 1958, 1967). His conception of an interlingua was that of an artificial language complete in itself with its own morphology and syntax (Papp 1966), and also capable of serving on its own as an 'informational language'. Decisions about the inclusion of particular features were to be based on the averaging of phenomena of various languages with a weighting given to the 'major' languages manifesting those features. For example, if more of the 'major' languages placed adjectives before nouns and subjects before predicates the interlingual syntax should do so also. A considerable research effort was dedicated to the abstract modelling of the linguistic and logico-semantic foundations of the interlingua. In addition, an impressively large number of languages were investigated. Andreev (1961) mentions research on Russian, Chinese, Czech, German, Rumanian, Vietnamese, Serbo-Croatian, English, French, Spanish, Norwegian, Arabic, Hindustani, Japanese, Indonesian, Burmese, Turkish, and Swahili. It was claimed that experimental algorithms for analysis from these languages into the interlingua were being developed, but how many advanced beyond preliminary sketches is not known. Synthesis programs for conversion from the interlingua were compiled for Russian only.

Not all research at Leningrad was concerned with interlingual investigations. Some experimental work on a practical Russian–English system was undertaken. The researchers L. I. Zasorina and T. S. Tseitin adopted the valency approach to syntactic analysis (Mukhin 1963), in which each word was examined for its potential combinations with other word-types (Ch. 3.4 above). Apparently, the project encountered particular problems in dealing with ambiguities of Russian case endings (Papp 1966) — as did many US projects, as we have seen. It appears that only limited tests were made involving no "more than 20 translated sentences" (Kulagina 1976).

6.5 FIRST MOSCOW STATE PEDAGOGICAL INSTITUTE OF FOREIGN LANGUAGES (I MGIIYa)

At the Pedagogical Institute of Foreign Languages in Moscow (Pervii Moskovskii Gosudarstvennyi Pedagogicheskii Institut Inostrannykh Yazykov), research on MT began in 1957 under the direction of I. I. Revzin; in later years the director was V. Y. Rozentsveig. Research here was concentrated on general theoretical studies of semantics (e.g. the work of A. K. Zholkovskii and L. N. Iordanskaya). Particularly important was the research on semantic analysis, in which semantic representations of sentences were derived from dictionary entries of words formulated as combinations of elementary 'semantic factors' and relations, e.g. 'time', 'action', 'possession' (Zholkovskii *et al.* 1961). The establishment of semantic factors necessitated careful analysis of semantic fields of near synonyms, e.g. differences between *property, owner, belong,* and between the various possible Russian equivalents of *appear* (viz. *poyavlyat'sya, vystupat', kazat-'sya, vyyavlyat'sya, predstavlyat'*, etc.) according to their contexts. As at the Cambridge Language Research Unit (Ch. 5.2 above), the emphasis was on problems of synonymy and paraphrase rather than homonymy, on subtle semantic differences rather than crude lexical transfer. Much of this work was related closely to the theoretical research of Mel'chuk on MT linguistics and was to culminate in the research on an interlingual English–Russian system (Ch. 10.2 below). The corpus for this semantic research was primarily foreign policy texts in English, French, Spanish, and Russian, with MT systems as long-term objectives. (See various articles by Zholkovskii and other members of the Institute in Rozentsveig (1974).)

6.6 ALL-UNION INSTITUTE OF SCIENTIFIC AND TECHNICAL INFORMATION (VINITI).

Basic linguistic studies of English and Russian syntax and morphology were conducted at the Electromodelling Laboratory of VINITI. Research by Z. M. Volotskaya on Russian verb formation, by E. V. Paducheva and T. N. Shelimova on Russian prepositions and cases, and by A. L. Shumilina and M. M. Langleben on Russian mathematical language was mentioned by Harper (1961) and Rozentsveig (1958). Much of this work was done with problems of information retrieval in mind, in recognition of some of the close relations between the two fields (cf. the similar views of the Cambridge Language Research Unit, Ch. 5.2 above). It would also seem that a substantial proportion of the research was undertaken in connection with Mel'chuk's work on interlingual MT; some was basically of a statistical nature.

6.7 OTHER SOVIET GROUPS

Outside the main centres in Moscow and Leningrad there were many Soviet institutions involved in MT research of some kind. As we have seen, the conference in May 1958 was attended by representatives from 79 USSR institutes; some of this interest resulted in the achievements reported from a number of institutions.

For example, there was research on MT from and into Russian at the Gorki State University (Rozentsveig 1958). It was evidently on a small scale, since according to Papp (1966) the experimental English–Russian system involved a dictionary, compiled from radio engineerig texts, containing no more than 500 items. More ambitious and theoretical was the important research under A. V. Gladkii on a semantic intermediary language in connection with an experimental German–Russian system at the Mathematical Institute, Siberian Division of USSR Academy of Sciences, Novosibirsk (Mukhin 1963; *CRDSD* 10, May 1962). This group later collaborated with Mel'chuk and others in the development of the 'meaning-text' approach (Ch. 10.2).

The MT research in institutes of the constituent republics of the Soviet Union had to tackle the additional problems of languages such as Uzbek, Georgian, Armenian, and Lithuanian which had been studied much less rigorously and systematically than English and Russian. Much effort had therefore to be devoted to preliminary linguistic research. Evidently, there was much MT activity. There was, for example, a project at the Vilnius State University in Lithuania (Vilniaus Valstybinis V. Kapsuko Vardo Universitetas) for a Russian–Lithuanian MT system, taking algebra textbooks as a corpus (*CRDSD* 9, Nov 1961). Mukhin (1963) mentions work on the morphological analysis of Tatar and Uzbek at the Computing Centre, State University, Tashkent, and research on Georgian at the Institute of Electronics, Automation and Telemechanics of the Georgian Academy of Sciences, in Tiflis (Institut Elektroniki, Avtomatiki i Telemekhaniki). This research was evidently on a fairly substantial scale. The group under Archil Eliashvili (and later C. B. Choidze) developed a Russian–Georgian MT system which employed a variant of Mel'chuk's dependency analysis for Russian (*CRDSD* 8, May 1961), and then turned to translation from Georgian. By 1963 (Mukhin 1963; *CRDSD* 13, Nov. 1964) research had extended to systems for translating into Russian, English, and German (the latter in conjunction with an East German researcher, cf. 6.13 below). The Georgian group continued research until the mid-1970s (Bruderer 1978).

Some of these institutions constructed operational MT systems, as Kulagina (1976) has reported. A system for Russian–Ukrainian MT was implemented by about 1966 at the Institute of Cybernetics in Kiev. "It was tested in three variants: dictionary translation" (i.e. strictly word-for-word), "dictionary plus morphology, and dictionary plus morphology plus elements of syntax". In the early 1960s, a system for Armenian–Russian MT was completed at the Computer Centre of the Academy of Sciences of the Armenian SSR, Yerevan. Although algorithms and grammatical information were separated, and also analysis and synthesis programs, it was still basically a 'direct' bilingual system with procedures oriented to the specific language pair (Ch. 3.9 above). A similar system for Russian–Armenian MT was constructed at the same centre during the mid-1960s.

6.8 SUMMARY OF THE USSR SCENE (1955–66)

As in the United States, MT research in the Soviet Union went through an initial stage of enthusiasm for the potentialities of the computer, fuelled often by exaggerated conceptions of the power of the new tool. Contemporary illusions about 'thinking machines', often markedly similar to those in the United States and Western Europe, have been well documented in Oettinger's review of early MT efforts in the Soviet Union (Oettinger 1958). As in the US this first phase was characterised by all-out assaults on MT systems, attempting to construct rules on an empirical basis, in the belief or hope that improvements could be made later. By about 1960, it had been realised that more substantial theoretical research was needed in order to progress beyond essentially 'word-for-word' systems (Harper 1961).

By the mid-1960s research on MT in the Soviet Union had produced a number of fairly crude operational word-for-word systems. Prospects for their improvement did not, however, seem good; and the considerable activity on MT-related linguistic theory did not promise immediately feasible systems as yet. In broad outline, the situation was much as in the United States, and funding for MT research declined somewhat after the mid-1960s. It is possible that the ALPAC report had some influence on sponsoring agencies in the Soviet Union, as Roberts & Zarechnak (1974) suggest (cf. 8.11 below). However, there was not the same dramatic hiatus in the Soviet Union and MT research continued to progress steadily as we shall see.

6.9 RESEARCH IN EASTERN EUROPE (1957–66)

In East Europe, MT activity began not long after the first USSR experiments. Soviet research was a great influence, although there was also considerable individual innovation. As in the Soviet Union and in many

Western European projects, progress was often severely hindered by the lack of computer facilities.

6.10 CHARLES UNIVERSITY, PRAGUE, CZECHOSLOVAKIA

A group of linguists at Charles University began the investigation of English–Czech MT in 1957. A special department was established in 1959, later split into the linguistic group of the Centre of Numerical Mathematics and the Section of Algebraic Linguistics and Machine Translation in the Department of Linguistics and Phonetics. Both groups worked closely with the Research Institute of Mathematical Machines (RIMM), where the programming work was undertaken. In January 1960, the first limited experiment was performed on the Czech computer SAPO. Subsequently, a second experiment was prepared for the EPOS I computer (Konečna *et al.* 1966). The subject field selected was electronics, for which an English–Czech MT dictionary was compiled from a text corpus of 100,000 words (Sgall & Hajičova 1966).

The usual stages of analysis and synthesis were adopted: dictionary lookup, morphological analysis, syntactic analysis, Czech synthesis. Morphological analysis matched words against a table of regular English endings; irregular forms were stored as wholes in the dictionary; and only idioms actually in the texts were included. For syntactic analysis, the project used the method of Moloshnaya (Ch. 6.2 above), and later a modified version of the Harvard predictive analysis technique (Konečna *et al.* 1966; Sgall & Hajičova 1966). The Czech synthesis program was based on the generative grammar model developed by Petr Sgall; and in this connection, considerable detailed research has been conducted on the formal linguistic description of Czech (Sgall & Hajičova 1966).

The theoretical foundation of the Czech group was a 'stratificational' approach (Ch. 3.10; cf. also 4.10). Four levels were recognised: graphemic, morphemic (concerned with word formation), formemic (roughly concerned with syntactic structures), and semantic (concerned with semantic relations, e.g. agency, and semantic representations). The assumption was that the semantic level approached language universality, and might function as an 'intermediary language'. Morphological analysis processed input text as far as the morphemic level; syntactic analysis as far as the semantic level. For their conception of an interlingua, the group adopted the Andreev approach (Ch. 6.4); i.e. not just "a net of correspondences" but "an individual language . . . specified by a generative grammar" (Konečna *et al.* 1966). The word order of the interlingua was to retain that of the input text, thus avoiding the need to look at intersentence relations to decide on topic–comment organisation (cf. the problems encountered at CETA, Ch. 10.1 below).

From the mid-1960s the group expanded its activities to many areas of computational and mathematical (particularly algebraic) linguistics, while still maintaining an interest in MT from the 'stratificational' approach (primarily in the form developed by Petr Sgall). No MT experimentation as such took place until 1976, however, when MT research was resumed (see Ch. 13.6 below).

6.11 HUNGARIAN ACADEMY OF SCIENCES

The MT research group at the Computing Centre of the Hungarian Academy of Sciences (Department for Theoretical Questions) was established in the summer of 1962 as a consequence of a conference on MT held in March that year (Kiefer 1964). At this conference, György Hell and György Sipöczy described their experimental word-for-word Russian–Hungarian system at the University of Technical Sciences. The first task of the small MT group at the Computing Centre was to test the algorithms (involving laborious machine coding). In September 1963, Ferenc Kiefer was appointed leader of the group. Apart from the work on Russian–Hungarian, the group also investigated English–Hungarian and German–Hungarian.

The group was considerably impeded by inadequate computer facilities for MT; above all, insufficient storage capacity. Consequently, the programs did not go beyond morphological analysis. The group devoted itself therefore to primarily theoretical work in the areas of syntactic analysis and semantics (Sipöczy 1964, Abraham & Kiefer 1966). Some research on mathematical linguistics applicable to MT was conducted in cooperation with Ferenc Papp and others at the University of Debrecen (Papp 1964). By 1966 research at the Computing Centre, now led by D. Varga (Kiefer had left Hungary), had turned to the development of parsing systems for language analysis in general, influenced to some extent by Mel'chuk's approach to semantic analysis (Varga 1967).

6.12 PROJECTS IN YUGOSLAVIA, POLAND, AND RUMANIA

There was considerable interest in MT at Belgrade University in Yugoslavia (*TA* 1(1) April 1960; *CRDSD* 8, May 1961; *CRDSD* 13, Nov. 1964). At the Institute of Experimental Phonetics, Djordje Kostić coordinated a large team compiling dictionaries and glossaries and conducting systematic studies of Serbian grammars. The original aim for a Serbo-Croat MT system was still being entertained in 1966, but evidently such ambitions came to naught.

The story was much the same in Poland. A group was set up during 1962 in the Research Centre for Applied Linguistics in the University of Warsaw. The aim was MT, but most work was of a theoretical nature in mathematical linguistics (*CRDSD* 10, May 1962; Josselson 1971).

Rather more progress was achieved in Rumania. Research began in September 1959 under the aegis of the Rumanian Academy of Sciences, and was directed by Grigore Moisil (Josselson 1971). Most work was of a theoretical nature by Moisil (1960) on systems for translating from French and Russian into Rumanian. There was, however, partial implementation by Erika Domonkos (1962) of an English–Rumanian 'direct' system. Tests of the system were conducted in 1962, evidently on a very small vocabulary.

There were no routines for resolving homographs, for dealing with pronouns or even for treating irregular English verbs.

6.13 RESEARCH IN EAST GERMANY

The East German Academy of Sciences set up its Working Group for Mathematical and Applied Linguistics and Automatic Translation (Arbeitsstelle für mathematische und angewandte Linguistik und automatische Uebersetzung) in 1960 under the leadership of Erhard Agricola. Its objective was the development of the mathematical and computational foundations of practical MT systems for translating from English and Russian into German. The group was engaged in extensive lexicographic activity, e.g. the compilation of reverse dictionaries, and on fundamental research on mathematical linguistics. By 1963 it was ready to test its ideas on an experimental English–German system, intended as a model for a practical system (Kunze 1966). The work was limited to a small corpus of just 22 sentences, but it was felt nevertheless that the practical adequacy of the approach and its formalism had been demonstrated. From 1963 until about 1966 the group directed its principal efforts to the development of a more extended experimental Russian–German system (Nündel *et al.* 1969). Most emphasis was placed on the algorithms for Russian analysis; it was believed that, at least in principle, the problems of German synthesis had been solved during the English–German experiment. Practical difficulties with computer facilities prevented the implementation of the system; algorithms had been formalised in detail but not programmed.

Both experimental systems were of the 'direct' bilingual, one-directional type. The main stages were described (Nündel *et al.* 1969) as follows: 1. lexico-morphological analysis (i.e. dictionary lookup and identification of grammatical categories), 2. idiom processing, 3. syntactic analysis (based on a dependency grammar approach) and homograph resolution, 4. selection of TL equivalents, 5. preparation of information for synthesis, 6. rearrangement (including the insertion of German articles), 7. syntactic synthesis, 8. synthesis dictionary (for German inflectional information), 9. morphological synthesis. The researchers acknowledged the absence of clearly separated stages of analysis and synthesis (stages 1 and 3 were analysis routines, stages 2, 4, and 6 'translation' and stages 5, 7, 8, and 9 synthesis), and also the limitation of the analysis procedures to structures which required treatment in German synthesis.

The methodology followed familiar patterns, e.g. alphabetical sorting of texts for dictionary searching, separation of stems and endings for Russian but not for English, a dictionary for general vocabulary and special technical microglossaries, the development of the group's own classification of verbs and adjectives, identification of fixed idioms for translation before syntactic analysis, the incorporation of syntax rules in the analysis algorithm (rather than in separate tables), and so forth. The deficiencies and limitations of the 'direct' approach were readily acknowledged by the end of the project, and the practical achievements were meagre, no working system having been implemented. Nevertheless there were substantial contributions by the group. These were primarily at a theoretical level, e.g. in the elaboration and rigorous formalisation of the dependency grammar model (cf. Kunze 1975) and in the investigation of syntactic ambiguity (Agricola 1967). As in many other groups, semantic problems were considered to be the greatest challenge for theoretical linguistic studies, but its members made only minimal contributions in this direction.

While this was clearly the principle East German MT project, it was not the only one. An intriguing example is the short-lived exploration at Jena by Fähnrich (1970) of a Georgian–German system; it was to be based on the MT research at the Georgian Academy of Sciences (Ch. 6.7 above). The argument for translating from Georgian was that numerous publications of scientific importance, in mathematics, mining, agriculture, and medicine, were being neglected because they were not accessible even in Russian summaries. A short text was selected for a manual simulation of a binary 'direct' system; Fähnrich's paper made no substantial contribution, it is of interest only as one of the few attempts to tackle the problems of a Caucasian language.

7

Projects and groups in Japan, China and Mexico (1956-1966)

7.1 PROJECTS IN JAPAN

Research on MT in Japan evidently began about 1956. The major groups up to the mid-1960s were those at the Electrotechnical Laboratory in Tokyo, at Kyoto University and at Kyushu University (Josselson 1970, Nagao 1982). Nearly all the research in this period was devoted to translation from English into Japanese. There were major inherent difficulties in the direct analysis of the Japanese character script, in particular, because of the lack in written Japanese of any indication of word boundaries.

Probably the best known of the earlier efforts in MT in Japan was the research on English–Japanese translation which began in 1958 at the Electrotechnical Laboratory in Tokyo, initially under H. Wada and later under R. Tadenuma (Takahashi *et al.* 1960, Nishimura 1970, Sakamoto 1970, *CRDSD* 5-15, 1959-69) There was a lack in Japan at that time of general-purpose computers with sufficent storage capacity for MT needs; the decision was made to build a special-purpose machine, the YAMATO, with a relatively large magnetic drum store but no multiplication or division mechanisms. As its corpus in the initial experiments the project selected textbooks for beginning students of English in Japanese junior schools. The deliberate simplification of these texts (just 2000 words, no relative pronouns, no relative adverbs, and no use of present perfect tense) was considered an advantage in the first trial. The system had four dictionaries: English word dictionary (arranged in frequency order), an idiom dictionary (also in frequency order), a syntax dictionary (a table of 20 groups of grammatical categories, referring to syntax subroutines), and a Japanese word dictionary. The inadequacy of direct word-for-word translation in the case of English–Japanese MT was to be solved by syntactic transfer routines. These were initiated by an iterative program for the identification of basic syntax patterns (i.e. category sequences such as noun + verb + noun).

Problems of homography had not been tackled. At a later date it was proposed to increase storage capacity by incorporating a photoscopic disc (Ch. 4.2). It would appear that the YAMATO system lasted until shortly after 1970.

There was also some work in the Electrotechnical Laboratory on Japanese–English translation, apparently on much the same lines. The problems of dealing with Japanese input were detailed by Yamada (1964), who had previously worked at CETA in Grenoble (Ch. 5.5). He described a program for segmentation and syntactic analysis of Japanese. The program scanned character by character identifying prefixes, roots, suffixes, etc. in a single pass, checking mutual compatibilities of adjacent elements and leaving complete resolution of structures until the Japanese verb was analysed at the end of the sentence (Japanese being a verb-final language.) The parser was modelled on the Harvard predictive syntactic analyser (Ch. 4.9).

Research at Kyushu University, Fukuoka, under Katsuo Ohno and Tuneo Tamati, also involved the construction of a special-purpose machine, the KT-1 (*Electronics Weekly* Sept 1960, Nagao 1982, *CRDSD* 8, May 1961). Initial research began in 1955, with experimental testing starting about 1960. The research was apparently mainly theoretical in nature, inspired in large part by the work at MIT under Yngve (Ch. 4.7). There was some investigation of a German–Japanese system but most emphasis was apparently placed on the foundations of an English–Japanese system (*TA* 2(4), Dec 1961), particularly the creation of an English–Japanese dictionary and on the formalisation of English and Japanese grammar (basically on the dependency grammar model). In essence, the system was of the 'syntactic transfer' type (as at MIT) with evident problems in the resolution of homographs and polysemes (Bruderer 1978).

A highly theoretical approach was adopted also by Itiroo Sakai, of the First Research Centre of the Defence Agency, who investigated a method of syntactic analysis based on algebraic operations (Sakai 1962). Intended to be universal, "applicable to any language of any syntactical nature" the method was somewhat akin to the categorial grammar of Bar-Hillel (Ch. 3.4). For example, the combination of the 'word categories' v-st (a verbal stem) and v-st/p/ (a possible suffix to a verb stem) yields p (a predicate); the combination of /n/n + p/ (an 'adjective predicate') and n (a noun) yields n. The basic mechanism was a matrix table lookup combining every category with all others in the sentence. Research on the model continued until about 1968 (*CRDSD* 15, 1969), and the approach was also investigated in the United States by Ascher Opler of the Computer Usage Company, New York, for a French–English system to be run on the IBM photoscopic machine (Ch. 4.13 above). It is not known whether there were in fact any implementations of Sakai's approach.

At Kyoto University MT research seems also to have been primarily of a theoretical nature. Josselson (1970) reports the work of Toshiyuki Sakai on a "translation procedure from English to Japanese, the principal feature of which is the use of four grammar tables. Analysis is done from the end of the sentence to the beginning, applying these four tables recursively". The most substantial work at Kyoto, however, was to begin about 1968 (Ch. 18 below).

As in many other countries, Japan witnessed a number of short-lived, small-scale projects during this period. There are reports of MT studies by Seiichiro Ohnishi at Nagoya University involving statistical analyses, by Osamu Watanabe at Niigata University on syntactic studies for English–Japanese and Japanese-English systems, and by T. Obonai and T. Sinohara at Nihon University, Tokyo, also on English and Japanese (*CRDSD* 13, Nov 1964). No doubt there were others.

In general terms, it is evident that up to 1965 Japanese MT research was pursued on much the same lines as in the United States. However, the shortage of powerful general purpose computers in Japan encouraged the investigation of special-purpose machines and perhaps the emphasis on theoretical studies. Research on the specific problems of dealing with Japanese script had been certainly started, but as yet results were still rather tentative.

7.2 RESEARCH IN CHINA

In the late 1950s and early 1960s there were apparently a number of MT groups active in China (*TA* 1(1), April 1960). Groups were set up in 1958 and 1959 at various Peking institutes of the Academy of Sciences of the People's Republic of China to investigate Russian–Chinese and English–Chinese systems. There were other groups elsewhere in China, one at Kharbin for the study of French–Chinese and German–Chinese translation. There is little information on the methods used by the groups, and naturally even less on their success or progress. The Russian–Chinese system was designed for translating mathematics texts and was apparently based on the approach of the Soviet group under Lyapunov at MIAN (Ch. 6.2) It would seem that at least a prototype was programmed and ran with a small dictionary.

7.3 NATIONAL UNIVERSITY OF MEXICO

A research group was set up in February 1960 under Sergio F. Beltran at the National University of Mexico (Universidad Nacional Autonoma de Mexico, Centro Electrónico de Cálculo). The first experiments were conducted on a Russian-Spanish system for translating titles of scientific and technical articles and books (*CRDSD* 7, Nov 1960). The project was later extended to investigation of systems for English–Spanish, French–Spanish, German–Spanish and Italian–Spanish. Most effort was devoted to the compilation of dictionaries, for which various statistical studies of the vocabulary of titles were undertaken. The project collaborated with the UNESCO Centro de Documentación Científica y Técnica, established in Mexico City to serve all Latin America. For the compilation of the Russian–Spanish dictionary the Mexican group established close links with the University of California group at Berkeley (Ch. 4.10). By November 1962 (*CRDSD* 11, Nov 1962) it was reported that the group had completed the adaptation of the Berkeley RUSDIC (Russian–English dictionary). The group continued until at least 1966 (*CRDSD* 14), with plans for "Russian–Spanish machine aided translation".

8

Expectations and criticisms: the decade from 1956 to 1966

The decade between the Georgetown-IBM demonstration in 1954 and the publication of the ALPAC report in 1966 may be characterised as one of initial widespread optimism of 'imminent' success followed by nearly equally widespread disillusionment at the slowness of progress. The turning point came roughly in 1960, marked by Bar-Hillel's influential survey (1960) and by changes of emphasis in the research strategies of many MT groups. In very broad terms, research in the earlier period from 1954 to 1960 concentrated primarily on semantic and lexicographic problems and research in the later period from 1960 to 1965 tended to concentrate more on syntactic problems and parsing strategies.

8.1 PERIOD OF OPTIMISM

In the first five years after the 1954 Georgetown-IBM demonstration (Ch. 2.5), MT research was pursued with great enthusiasm and optimism. Numerous groups were formed in many countries. In the United States, the five early centres of Washington, Georgetown, MIT, Harvard, and Los Angeles (RAND), were joined during the next five years by groups at Michigan, IBM, Ramo-Wooldridge, NBS, Texas, Berkeley (University of California), Wayne State, and numerous shorter lived projects. In the Soviet Union large scale projects were begun at three Moscow centres and in

Leningrad. Major projects were set up in Britain, Italy and Japan, and research was beginning in Czechoslovakia and France.

The mood of optimism is well captured in the book by Emile Delavenay (1960) completed in December 1958. This introduction of MT to the general public provided a brief history of the progress of MT, and a survey of the different approaches, the problems and the methods. From it we now have an invaluable picture of the way MT research was perceived at the time. "The translation machine . . . is now on our doorstep. In order to set it to work, it remains to complete the exploration of linguistic data . . ." Delavenay was aware of considerable problems; the complexities of syntax were only just becoming apparent. For Delavenay MT research in semantics and syntax was directed towards the refinement of basically word-for-word transpositions. Crude though they were, the achievements so far were believed to provide the foundations for future progress. "While a great deal remains to be done, it can be stated without hesitation that the essential has already been accomplished." Delavenay could even contemplate the translation of literature; it was just a matter of compiling the appropriate dictionaries to convey the local colour of the original. He went further. "Will the machine translate poetry? To this there is only one possible reply — why not?" Anything seemed possible with the awesome power of the new electronic machines. For Delavenay it was just a matter of time. "Translating machines will soon take their place beside gramophone records and colour reproductions in the first rank of modern techniques for the spread of culture and of science."

It is easy to smile indulgently at the naive optimism of Delavenay in 1958. He was not alone by any means. Bel'skaya in the Soviet Union, as we have seen (Ch. 6.1), shared his belief in the possibility of translating literary works. While most MT researchers did not agree on this point, they all believed in the ultimate success of MT, even though they differed, sometimes vehemently, about the best methods to be pursued.

8.2 VARIETY OF APPROACHES AND METHODS

There were first the differences between those groups who sought to produce a working system as soon as possible and those who held that fundamental research must be done before operational systems could be contemplated. Principal among the former were the Washington and IBM groups under Reifler and King. Also belonging to the pragmatists were Dostert and his Georgetown team, Booth at Birkbeck College, the Ramo-Wooldridge group, the ITMVT group in Moscow, and the ETL group in Tokyo. Those taking longer perspectives included the groups at MIT, Harvard, RAND, Cambridge, Milan, and the Soviet groups at MIAN in Moscow and at the University of Leningrad.

Within these broad divisions there were further differences. While the Washington and IBM groups developed essentially the word-for-word approach with refinements introduced through lexicographic information, the Georgetown and Ramo-Wooldridge approaches concentrated more on problems of syntax and structural manipulation. The IBM group and the Japanese ETL group were committed to the development of special-purpose machines, and Booth at Birkbeck inclined also towards hardware solutions.

Among the groups engaged in fundamental research there were differences between the 'empiricists' and the 'theorists'. Most committed to the 'empirical' approach was the RAND group, which distrusted traditional grammars and dictionaries and believed that MT must be based on actual usage.

The RAND group was also the strongest advocate of the 'cyclic' approach to MT system development, i.e. devising rules and programs for a particular text, testing them on another text, making amendments, testing on another text, and so forth, with the hope that eventually no further modifications will be necessary. Progressive modification was, of course, assumed to be necessary in the development of any operational system; what was particular to the 'cyclic' method was the explicit concentration on the corpus alone and the exclusion of any information from other sources, e.g. the analyst's own knowledge of the language and its structure. The cyclic method was adopted by the groups at Birkbeck and Ramo-Wooldridge, and in an extreme form by Brown at Georgetown (Ch. 4.3).

The Harvard group was also committed to fundamental empirical research, and, like the RAND group, believed in the need for careful preparatory work in order to achieve eventually MT of a high quality. As at RAND, the Harvard group concentrated in this period on the compilation of a large Russian dictionary.

The most theory-oriented groups were those at MIT, Cambridge, Milan, and Leningrad. The group at MIT stressed the need for fundamental linguistic studies, particularly in the area of syntax and was greatly influenced by the formal linguistics of Chomsky and his followers. The Cambridge and Leningrad groups were more interested in semantic approaches, both concerned with the construction of interlinguas, and at Cambridge investigating the thesaurus concept for semantic organisation. At Milan the emphasis was on a conceptual (i.e. non-linguistic) analysis of lexical and structural relationships.

Cutting across these various divisions were differences of MT system design. Most of the groups adopted the 'direct translation' strategy (Ch. 3.9), particularly those aiming for practical operating systems in the near future, e.g. Washington, IBM, Georgetown, Ramo-Wooldridge, Birkbeck. The most popular strategy among those with long term perspectives was the 'interlingual' strategy, e.g. Cambridge, Milan, and Leningrad. During this period emerged also the first versions of the 'transfer' strategy in the ideas of Yngve at MIT on 'syntactic transfer'.

To a large extent, however, MT research in this five-year period was often dominated by problems of computer hardware. Many of the groups, particularly in the Soviet Union but also, for example, the Cambridge group, had no access to computer facilities and much of their programming was simulated on punched card equipment. Even for those groups which did have computer equipment there were perennial problems of insufficient storage. Internal core storage was often very small, and external storage had to be on punched card or magnetic tape. Dictionary searching was therefore a major problem: for most the only real option at the time was sequential access to dictionaries on tape, and therefore preliminary alphabetisation of text words. The slowness of serial access prompted the development of the random-access photoscopic disk storage device by IBM (Ch. 4.2). Booth advocated the binary partition technique, but he had few followers.

It was the hope of most MT researchers that problems of text input would be solved in the near future by optical character readers. It was recognised that without much faster means of converting texts into machine-readable form the prospects of operational MT systems being economical were greatly reduced.

8.3 DOUBTS AND CRITICISMS, BAR-HILLEL'S REPORT

While optimism remained the prevailing mood, there were signs of some loss of confidence. Many groups had begun in the expectation of relatively quick success. There were not only problems of technical facilities and hardware, but also the complexities of the linguistic problems. These were becoming more and more apparent. The mood of optimism was now by no means universal within the MT community. Critics of MT were growing and becoming more vociferous year by year. There had always been those who were highly sceptical of any attempts to 'mechanise' language. Norbert Wiener (Ch. 2.2) was only the first of many who doubted that semantic problems could ever be resolved. For a long time those involved in MT research could ignore such objections; they could always claim that they were only at the very start of the enterprise, and that in any case most objectors did not understand and probably did not want to understand what MT research was really about. However, when criticism came from within, from one intimately familiar with MT research and its practitioners, then it could not be ignored so easily.

In February 1959, Yehoshua Bar-Hillel published his *Report on the state of machine translation in the United States and Great Britain*, prepared on the basis of personal visits to most MT groups in the US during October 1958 and on information received during the following months in response to a circular letter (Bar-Hillel 1959). One year later the report received wider distribution when it appeared in a revised form in the annual review journal *Advances in Computers* (Bar-Hillel 1960). The main addition in the later version was a survey of Soviet research based principally on a report by Rozentsveig (1958), the book by Panov (1960), and unpublished accounts by Oettinger and John W. Carr III of their visits to Soviet MT groups during 1958. (Probably Bar-Hillel also saw the survey by Oettinger (1958) before publication.) As far as the US projects were concerned, the later version did incorporate some updated information, but in essence it described the situation as Bar-Hillel saw it in late 1958. In particular, it should be noted that the wording of his forceful criticisms was not revised in any way.

The basic argument was that MT research was, with few exceptions, mistakenly pursuing an unattainable goal: fully automatic translation of a quality equal to that of a good human translator. Instead, it should be less ambitious and work towards the realisation of systems involving human collaboration.

In view of the later impact of this review it is well to keep in mind the stage at which MT research had reached in late 1958. Hardly any of the projects had been engaged on full scale research for more than two years. As we have seen (Ch. 4), the large Georgetown team was formed only in June 1956, the teams at Harvard and Cambridge received their first National Science Foundation grants in 1956, the RAND group was set up in March 1957, and research at NBS, IBM, Berkeley, Wayne State, and Texas did not start until 1958. Funded research had begun a little earlier, in 1955, by the relatively small-scale teams at Birkbeck College and Michigan University, but the only really long established large projects were those at MIT and Washington, and even there it may be noted that large scale funding started only in 1954 and 1956 respectively. The situation was much the same in the Soviet Union: only two of the Russian projects had been active for more than two years, and then only since 1955; others did not begin until 1956 or later (Ch. 6).

It is significant that Bar-Hillel did not cite any actual examples of translations produced by any of the projects, nor even allude to any particular linguistic or computational problems of their systems. Instead he concentrated his remarks explicitly on general questions of methodology. The thrust of his argument was that current methods could not conceivably produce fully automatic systems providing reasonable quality translations, either in the short or long term. The argument was based on highlighting the methodological shortcomings of individual projects and an abstract 'demonstration' of the impossibility of what he called 'fully automatic high quality translation' (FAHQT).

Bar-Hillel had become convinced that FAHQT was unattainable "not only in the near future but altogether". It was in fact a view he had expressed in his 1951 review (Ch. 2.4.2), before most MT projects had even been thought of. Now in 1959 he felt able to give a 'proof' in 'A demonstration of the non-feasibility of fully automatic, high quality translation' (Appendix III in Bar-Hillel 1960). His argument was based on the short sentence:

> The box was in the pen

in the context:

> Little John was looking for his toy box. Finally, he found it. The box was in the pen. John was very happy.

On the assumption that *pen* can have two meanings, a 'writing utensil' and an 'enclosure where small children can play', Bar-Hillel claimed that "no existing or imaginable program will enable an electronic computer to determine that the word pen in the given sentence within the given context has the second of the above meanings." This amounted to the very strong claim that in certain (not infrequent) cases no amount of context will suffice to resolve this type of homonymy. The reason is that we as intelligent human readers know "the relative sizes of pens, in the sense of writing implements, toy boxes, and pens, in the sense of playpens" and that this knowledge is "not at the disposal of the electronic computer". To put such information in a MT system would mean that "a translation machine should not only be supplied with a dictionary but also with a universal encyclopedia". For Bar-Hillel such a requirement was "utterly chimerical and hardly deserves any further discussion". Not only is human knowledge a vast store of facts, but it is also the infinite set of inferences which may be drawn from facts.

Bar-Hillel conceded that ambiguity can be resolved by the use of microglossaries and contextual clues. However, he thought that use of microglossaries increased the risk of mistranslation (meaningful but erroneous in a particular instance), and that contextual analysis can have only limited effectiveness. Resolution of some but not all ambiguities would not be good enough if the aim is 'high quality' translation.

Much of the point of his argument has now been somewhat blunted by achievements in computational linguistics and in AI semantic analysis (Ch. 15 below), but at the time Bar-Hillel's case against the FAHQT goal convinced many not involved in MT research that MT as such was doomed to failure, and it has continued to represent a challenge and point of departure for arguments about MT to the present day.

Bar-Hillel attributed the adherence of some MT groups to the FAHQT aim as a residue of the early initial successes in MT. In the first few years of MT there had been "a considerable amount of progress" in solving a large number of linguistic and computational problems and producing crude translations which expert readers could make some sense of. This progress had convinced many that "a working system (was) just around the corner". It had been realised only gradually that although "the problems solved until then were indeed many" they were "just the simplest ones" and "the 'few' remaining problems were the harder ones — very hard indeed." However, he did not condemn basic theoretical research as such, even if FAHQT was the distant aim, because it might be justified by "interesting theoretical insights", whether of benefit to practical MT or not.

As for operational MT he contended that researchers had either to sacrifice quality (low quality products were acceptable in many circumstances) or to acknowledge the necessity for post-editing. He advocated the latter aim, "high quality translation by a machine–post-editor partnership", as the most fruitful area of future MT development. The goal then should be partially automatic MT, commercially competitive with human translation, which could be gradually improved and refined with more and more of the post-editing operations carried out automatically. This goal required, however, the development of more reliable and flexible optical character readers, more attention to dictionary compilation, research on the efficiencies of different dictionary formats (full forms vs. stems and endings), and investigation of the need for pre-editing of input.

Not only did Bar-Hillel hold strong convictions about the aims of MT but he was also highly critical of two particular approaches: the 'empirical' approach, and the 'interlingual' approach. Adherents of the former distrusted traditional grammars and dictionaries and held that MT grammars and dictionaries must be built from scratch (often on the basis of statistical analyses of large text corpora). Bar-Hillel condemned it as both "wasteful in practice and not sufficiently justified in theory". Faith in statistics derived from earlier overestimations of the power of statistical theory of communication (Shannon-Weaver information theory), and there was no reason to reject normative grammars so completely, as they "are already based . . . upon actual texts of incomparably larger extension than those that serve as a basis for the new compilers".

As for the 'interlingual' approach, while he admitted that achievements in mathematical logic might reinforce the hope that the 17th century idea need not fail in the 20th century, he dismissed the idea for two reasons: one was the fallacy of the economic argument for multilingual systems, the other was the fallacy of what he saw as the basic assumption of adherents of the approach, namely that translation into a 'logical' interlingua was simpler than translation into a natural language. (The arguments for and against interlinguas will be taken up more fully below.)

With such a collection of strongly held views, it is not surprising that very few of the current MT systems escaped criticism, often harsh. In one way or another nearly all the US groups were found wanting. The only one to escape was that of Rhodes at NBS, praised for its efficient parser and its "practical aims" involving "no attempt . . . to obtain a FAHQT output." Specific criticisms were often harsh. For example, the work at MIT on the programming language COMIT was considered unnecessary, and the MIT group was censured for "reluctance to publish incomplete results." In similar vein, Harvard was accused of "strong distrust of the achievements of other groups". The Cambridge (CLRU) group's applications of lattice-theory were dismissed as "only reformulations . . . of things that were said and done many times before", and its conception of the thesaurus was too obscure for Bar-Hillel ("Since I could not persuade myself that I really understood the Cambridge group's conception (or conceptions?) of the thesaurus (or thesaurus-lattice) approach to MT, I shall say nothing about it", adding acidly: "Perhaps the reader will be luckier").

In general, Bar-Hillel's opinions were not based on a careful evaluation of the actual achievements of MT projects but they were already formed before the review was undertaken. He can be criticised for bias, prejudices, inaccuracies, and antagonisms, but the basic thrust of his main argument had some validity: "Fully automatic, high quality translation is not a reasonable goal, not even for scientific texts". The only reasonable goals were "either fully automatic, low quality translation or partly automatic, high quality translation". Both were considered to be technically (although perhaps not commercially) feasible at the time. Bar-Hillel did not think "great linguistic sophistication" to be either "requisite" or "helpful" for developing practical MT systems; basic linguistic research should continue with the long term improvement of MT in aim. However, there was a considerable overlap in linguistic research, resulting in "costly repetitions of achievements as well as, and even more often so, of failures". It was his opinion that much of this wastefulness was attributable to MT researchers' too long-lived adherence to FAHQT goals.

As one of the best known pioneers of MT, Bar-Hillel had written a report which was bound to influence public opinion, and it did. There is no doubt that it contributed to the disillusionment which steadily grew in the following years, and that it was held up as 'proof' of the impossibility of MT. To this day, Bar-Hillel's article is still cited as an indictment of MT research (not only for this early period, but in general). There can be few other areas of research activity in which one publication has had such an impact.

8.4 THE STATE OF THE ART IN 1960, AND NEW DIRECTIONS

Bar-Hillel's report had most effect on the external perception of MT; in most respects, it did not greatly affect the internal development of MT. Those groups which were not concerned with high quality MT (however defined) continued the development of systems to produce output needing a greater or lesser degree of post-editing; they would agree with Bar-Hillel that FAHQT was not achievable and so they would not attempt to achieve it. This was the essence of the Georgetown view (and of course also of the IBM group). On the other hand, those groups which did have FAHQT aims were spurred on to disprove Bar-Hillel's contention that it was impossible. They would probably agree with the Cambridge group that Bar-Hillel's criteria for high quality was too absolute and that his demonstration was not a 'proof'. (For CLRU the 'pen' problem could be resolved by thesaural methods, cf. Ch. 5.2) Bar-Hillel's arguments had, therefore, the unfortunate effect of polarising MT research between those who saw the need for more basic research in order to achieve successful MT and those who were concerned with the solution of practical MT problems.

Since the 1956 MIT conference (Ch. 2.6) there had been a number of important conferences at which contributions on MT had been made. For example, the international conference on 'Information Processing' organised by Unesco in June 1959 had included an important session on MT (Unesco 1960). Reports were made by Bel'skaya from the ITMVT in Moscow, Japanese speakers from the Electrotechnical Laboratory in Tokyo, as well as speakers from Cambridge, Harvard, MIT, and RAND. It was at this conference also that A. F. R. Brown of Georgetown gave the first public demonstration of an 'operational' system. Whether intended or not, the impression given was that Georgetown group was about to launch a commercial MT system. Some of those engaged in MT were highly critical; it was obvious that the quality of output was not good enough, and that promises of improvements could not possibly be fulfilled.

Although the Russians were making important contributions and there were also the groups in Britain, elsewhere in Europe, and in Japan, there is no doubt that at this time the main impetus for MT research was in the United States. The National Symposium on Machine Translation held in February 1960 at the University of California at Los Angeles (Edmundson 1961) brought together all the major (and most minor) active US groups: RAND, Ramo-Wooldridge, NBS, IBM, Georgetown, Texas, MIT, Berkeley, Washington, Wayne State, Harvard (cf. relevant sections in Ch. 4.). Some had only recently been formed (Texas, Berkeley, Wayne State) and were outlining future plans, but most had already a number of years' experience. This meeting was the first occasion at which a number of the new approaches and methods were publicly aired which were to characterise the next five years of MT research.

Principal among these were the descriptions of new methods of syntactic analysis: Hays (1961) gave the first public description of dependency grammar (Ch. 3.4); Garvin (1961) described the development of his 'fulcrum' theory, which he had begun at Georgetown and was to continue at Ramo-Wooldridge (Ch. 4.6); and Rhodes (1961) outlined the 'predictive analyser' under development at NBS, and which had previously been described only in an internal report (Rhodes 1959).

Up to this time, syntactic analysis had been seen primarily as providing data for the local manipulation of lexical items where SL and TL word orders did not match; for this all that was required was the determination of grammatical categories and sequences; the identification of groupings (in phrases and clauses) was not always considered necessary, since lexical information was sufficient to determine relationships of this kind. The main exponents of this attitude were the Washington group (and IBM) and, in a less extreme form, the Georgetown group. In general, syntax was considered less important than the problems of dictionary compilation, microglossaries, and lexical ambiguity. The only group to tackle syntax at an early stage was at MIT. For many researchers, however, the MIT concentration on 'abstract' formal syntax was too remote from the practicalities of MT; indeed, Bar-Hillel himself in his report (1960) had censured MIT commitment to Chomskyan grammar as "premature" (despite his own formalistic inclinations, as witness his categorical grammar, Ch. 3.4). From 1960, however, syntax became the dominant theme of much MT research. Symptomatic of the change was the switch at Harvard from dictionary work to the development of the NBS 'predictive analyser' (announced at this 1960 meeting by Oettinger & Sherry (1961)) and the attention devoted to syntax by groups which had previously tended to ignore it (e.g. the Cambridge group, Ch. 5.2). With the formulation of alternative methods of syntactic analysis there was confidence that this problem area, at least, could be conquered, and from this time on, the formalisation of syntactic theories and development of efficient parsers advanced rapidly.

Further evidence of future changes came in the presentation by Sydney Lamb of Berkeley of the first version of his 'stratificational' conception of language structure (Ch. 3.10 and 4.10). It marked the beginning of multilevel approaches, i.e. the separation of morphological, syntactic and semantic stages of SL analysis and TL synthesis, which though perhaps implicit in Yngve's 'syntactic transfer' approach (Ch. 4.7) had not before been formulated clearly. Lamb's model was itself to influence other MT groups (notably CETA at Grenoble, Ch. 10.1). For the present, however, the dominant strategy was to remain the 'direct' approach.

The new methods of syntactic analysis, the linguistic modelling of Lamb and the increasing formalism were characteristic, of course, primarily of the more theoretical inclinations of MT research. There was clear evidence at the conference of antagonism between those groups aiming for 'production systems' and those concentrating on basic research. Oettinger was particularly insistent that the Georgetown group should make its intentions plain: "In the last issue of the Georgetown Newsletter a statement was made that an automatic translation system would be operating as a production system within a year. I would like to know whether that is the system that was described today, in which the mean number of errors is 13.4% . . ." Dostert (of Georgetown) replied that all they intended was to have within a year a lexicon adequate for translating Russian texts in the narrow field of organic chemistry; he saw nothing wrong in developing systems which "produce inelegant but reasonably reliable text". But for Oettinger (and many others), the quality was just not good enough — little better than word-for-word translation — and it was considered intolerable that the public should be offered such error-ridden systems.

But how long would it be before MT research produced good quality translations? There were no clear ideas on how quality could be evaluated, but many knew there was much more linguistic work to be done — not only in syntax, but even more in semantics (which, as King (IBM) commented, "we haven't even begun to talk or think about seriously"). Oettinger was certainly not sanguine (prophetically, he commented "All of us who are dedicated to research have to face the prospects that our efforts may have been in vain"); but even he was surprised that Hays and Yngve should estimate "10 years' worth of problems" ahead. Although in retrospect even this was an underestimate, it was clear evidence that some MT researchers were in danger of becoming 'perfectionists' (Bar-Hillel thought some were already); and at the conference, Edmundson said "it is apparent to all of us that some of the MT investigators are not really concerned with production translation."

8.5 OFFICIAL SUPPORT FOR US RESEARCH

In the same year, MT research in the US received what was in effect an official seal of approval. It came in a report which was compiled by the Committee on Science and Astronautics of the US House of Representatives in June 1960 (US House of Representatives, 1960). The committee received reports and testimony from the funding agencies (Central Intelligence Agency, US Air Force, US Army, and US Navy) on the importance of MT to "the overall intelligence and scientific effort of our Nation" and for translations from English "for the exchange of cultural, economic, agricutural, technical, and scientific documents that will present the American way of life to people throughout the world." A survey was included to indicate US and foreign activity in MT (particularly the strong Soviet interest), and details were provided of the possible systems and of the current research methodologies. While recognising the dangers of duplicating effort, the committee believed that "all approaches are valid and should be pursued so that the Nation will benefit from an early interim capability while waiting for the long-term research to provide a highly accurate system." The committee was particularly impressed by the NBS research on syntactic analysis. In the "near future" it foresaw the establishment of a "national center for machine translation", and eventually a "national machine translation production program . . . operating on a full-time basis." In the long term it considered desirable the development of a "special-purpose computer, designed for translation." In the short term it approved the development "at an early date, of a limited machine translation with postediting (which) will provide the scientific community with a sample of things to come."

The committee's recommendations would have pleased all active US groups. Dostert of Georgetown would have found approval for his suggested national centres and early production prototypes; the theoretically inclined groups would have been encouraged to pursue the aim of high quality MT; those, like IBM, developing special-purpose machines would have been greatly reassured of continued support; and all would have liked the 'official' acknowledgement of the national importance of their efforts.

8.6 NATIONAL AND INTERNATIONAL CONFERENCES

In the few years since 1956, MT research had become, in Bar-Hillel's words (1960), "a multimillion dollar affair", with the major proportion of the effort in the United States. With so many groups active in the US, many researchers were becoming worried about duplication and lack of information about what others were doing. All the groups except MIT and Texas were engaged on investigations of Russian–English systems; and many were compiling large Russian dictionaries and lexical databases. Some groups were already cooperating, such as Washington and IBM, Harvard and NBS, Ramo and Wayne State, and RAND had long been making its dictionary information available; yet it was clearly felt that closer formal links were desirable.

As a result of informal discussions at the UCLA conference, a meeting was arranged later in the same year (in July 1960) at Princeton for all MT groups sponsored by US Federal agencies (NSF, CIA, USAF, US Army, US Navy). The participants included not only most of those US groups present in UCLA, with the exception of IBM, Ramo-Wooldridge and Harvard, but also the European groups at Cambridge and Milan, which were receiving US grants at the time (Wayne State University 1960). The success of the meeting in promoting frank exchanges of views led to a series of similar working conferences to be known as 'Princeton-type' meetings, all organised by the Wayne State group (Josselson 1970). The second conference of the series was held at Georgetown in 1961, and was devoted to 'grammar coding'; the third, again at Princeton, in 1962, was on the theme of 'syntactic analysis' (participants now included IBM and Ohio State); and the fourth devoted to 'computer-based semantic analysis' was held at Las Vegas in 1965 (where participation was extended to non-Federally funded groups). There may be some dispute about the amount of real cooperation at these meetings — Zarechnak of Georgetown believed little of tangible benefit resulted (Zarechnak 1979: 42) — but they did mark genuine steps towards the fully fledged discipline that MT was seen to be. As a further indicator of 'scientific maturity', it was at the third conference in 1962 that the Association for Machine Translation and Computational Linguistics was formally constituted.

Until about 1960, MT research had been concentrated in the large projects of the United States and the Soviet Union, with a significant contribution also from Great Britain. The period 1959–61 saw the appearance of numerous MT groups in many other countries: France (particularly the important CETA group), Belgium, Mexico, Czechoslovakia, Hungary, Rumania, East Germany, West Germany, China, and Japan (Ch. 5–7). In addition there was a new group in Britain at the National Physical Laboratory (Ch. 5.4), and among numerous new US projects the one at Ohio State (Ch. 4.13).

It was an opportune time for an international conference. In November 1961, the newly formed group at the National Physical Laboratory arranged a conference at its headquarters in Teddington, near London. Participants included representatives of all the major US and British groups, a French contingent, members of the Milan group, and a Japanese, Itiroo Sakai. There was unfortunately no Russian representation. The proceedings (NPL 1962) confirm increasing interest in syntactic analysis and in formal linguistic studies. Nearly all the contributions were concerned with some aspect of syntax; only the presentations from the Milan group, the Cambridge group, Wayne State, and IBM dealt with semantic and lexical problems in any depth. The contrast with the 1956 international conference, where only MIT and Georgetown were interested in syntactic questions, could not be more marked.

In the following year (in June 1962), the NATO Advanced Summer Institute on Automatic Translation of Languages was held in Venice (NATO 1966). Substantial contributions were made by Bar-Hillel, Brown, Ceccato, Vauquois, and others. Bar-Hillel's 'Four lectures' (also in Bar-Hillel 1964) were basically restatements of his views on the impossibility of FAHQT, backed up by demonstrations of the failure of contemporary AI experiments in 'learning' machines. The other contributors were all confident in their various ways of eventual success: Brown by empirical means, Ceccato by conceptual modelling, Vauquois by formal linguistics.

The NATO link was a sign of the growing international stature of MT. However, there were increasing doubts among outside observers. Basically, there were still no actual operative systems. There had been numerous promises, e.g. by Dostert (Georgetown) and Reifler (Washington), and there had been accounts of significant progress from numerous groups, which had sometimes been interpreted as promises by eager journalists. Why? The answer, many concluded, must be that MT was inherently impossible. A spokesman for this view, which he argued passionately, was Mortimer Taube.

8.7 TAUBE'S COMPUTERS AND COMMON SENSE

In 1961 appeared the book by Mortimer Taube entitled *Computers and Common Sense* (Taube 1961). Taube gave expression to a prevalent anti-computer view of the time, seeing mechanisation of quintessentially human processes as 'dehumanising' and ultimately and necessarily doomed to failure.

Understandably and justifiably, Taube began by looking for actual achievements in MT, and he found none. In support he quoted Oettinger (1960: 346) on the absence of working systems: "While several rules for producing smooth Russian–English automatic translations have been proposed in the literature, published experimental results have been conspicuously absent". However, Taube spoilt his case by exaggeration: "it can be stated categorically that twelve years after the Warren Weaver memorandum no practical, usable MT computer program exists . . . there does not even exist a practical or usable mechanical dictionary." In so far as there were no fully operational MT systems in evidence at this time he was, of course, correct. But he was wrong about their being no usable, working mechanical dictionaries; he had after all read about the most substantial one in Oettinger's book.

Taube's main argument was that MT is formally impossible. It is impossible because computers demand precise formalisation, and language cannot be formalised. Part of the argument rested on Gödel's theorem that consistent axiomatisation of mathematics is impossible: "Since, at the very least, language must include all mathematics and since there seems to be a proof that all mathematics is not susceptible to formal treatment, it would follow that natural language is not susceptible to formal treatment." Specifically in relation to translation, Taube denied the possibility of strict synonymy, echoing the contemporary arguments of the philosopher Quine (1960) on the indeterminacy of translational synonymy. Human translation is intuitive and "we assume that machines are not capable of intuition. Hence, if they are to translate at all, they must translate formally." The conclusion was inescapable: "mechanical translation in the formal sense is impossible because translation in the formal sense from one natural language to another is impossible."

Formal linguistic analysis, as exemplified particularly in the work of Noam Chomsky and Zellig Harris, was attacked by Taube as a misguided aberration which "has cast a mystique over the whole field of MT." His basic point was that attempts to define transformation rules and develop formal grammars without reference to notions of synonymy and significance were logically impossible. Taube's objection then was to formalism which neglected semantics.

For Taube there was just no point in continuing MT research. He noted that even practitioners could find no sound economic reasons. The University of Washington study (1959) had concluded that without optical character readers MT would be twice as expensive as human translation. Taube added sarcastically: "It seems that the main area of research should be print readers and not translating machines." He had no time for justifications based on prospects of the potential spin-offs (to linguistics or information retrieval), which were being mentioned increasingly by MT researchers, e.g. during the hearings for the House of Representatives report (8.5 above). Taube could find "nowhere in the literature of MT . . . a systems engineering study of its feasibility or practicality. In the absence of such a study and in the light of the known informality of language and meaning, research in MT takes on the character not of genuine scientific investigation, but of a romantic quest such as the search for the Holy Grail."

It matters little whether, in retrospect, Taube was right or wrong in some of his specific criticisms. McCorduck (1979), for example, points out that in his discussion of learning machines, Taube's "insistence on limiting what computers could do to a highly restricted sense of mathematical formalism meant he had to ignore those programs which did seem to exhibit learning, in particular, Samuel's checkers program." On MT Taube assumed that MT could only mean fully automatic systems producing translations as good as any human translator could do. Unlike Bar-Hillel, he did not even discuss the practical value of lower quality post-edited MT. Taube was also wrong in assuming that all MT research was based on the linguistic theories of Chomsky and Harris. As we have seen, many groups explicitly rejected such approaches: Washington, IBM, Milan, Cambridge, and Georgetown (to a large extent). Only at MIT had Chomskyan ideas been taken up at this time. On the other hand, he was right to reject an excessive attention to syntax which excluded semantics. Hidden in the polemics it is possible to read an argument for semantic as well as syntactic analysis in MT (McCorduck 1979); whether Taube would have agreed is doubtful. He would probably have dismissed the formalisation of semantics as yet another logical impossibility. His concern was to expose the formalist fallacies of determinism and to expose the mistaken idealism (or in some cases what he saw as wilful deceit) of those who were attempting the mechanisation of human thought processes, and MT was just one example.

In the MT community Taube's book seems to have been ignored as an irrelevant 'curiosity', as it was in AI circles (McCorduck 1979). But it must surely have had an impact on the public perception of MT research. Together with Bar-Hillel's article, it must have contributed substantially to the growing impatience about the evidently slow progress of MT.

Public perception would also have been influenced, at a more trivial level, by the frequently repeated stories of supposed MT howlers, such as the well known *invisible idiot* and *The liquor is alright but the meat is spoiled* versions (Ch. 1). It did not any longer appear surprising that the repeated promises of imminent working systems had failed to be fulfilled, and Taube had seemingly showed why MT would never come.

8.8 OPERATIONAL SYSTEMS, AND THE 'SEMANTIC BARRIER'

As it happens, in the next few years operational systems were put into full time service. In 1964 the Mark II version of the IBM system developed by King was installed at the Foreign Technology Division of the US Air Force (Ch. 4.2). Apparently, the earlier version, Mark I, had been used to translate Russian newspaper articles since 1959; but King did not reveal this until much later (King 1963). The Georgetown system for Russian–English translation was demonstrated during 1962 with some measure of success and, as a result, was delivered in 1963 to the EURATOM centre in Ispra (Italy) and in 1964 to the Atomic Energy Commission at the Oak Ridge National Laboratory. The output of both the Georgetown and the IBM systems was admitted to be of poor quality and usually in need of extensive post-editing, as the examples given in Ch. 4.2–3 above show. Nevertheless, the systems served a real need, many users expressing satisfaction with even unedited texts.

By this time, however, it was clear that research by more 'theoretical' groups was not succeeding. Intensive research on syntactic analysis had served only to show the intractability of syntactic ambiguity. Oettinger (1963) concluded from his own experience at Harvard with the predictive analyser that "the outlook is grim for those who still cherish hopes for fully automatic high-quality mechanical translation." Likewise Yngve (1964) confessed that the intensive research at MIT had shown that "Work in mechanical translation has come up against what we will call the semantic barrier . . . We have come face to face with the realisation that we will only have adequate mechanical translations when the machine can 'understand' what it is translating and this will be a very difficult task indeed."

It was already clear that sponsors were becoming less willing to support MT. In 1963, research at Georgetown was terminated, in circumstances which remain somewhat unclear (Ch. 4.3). In October of the same year, the director of the National Science Foundation requested that the National Academy of Sciences set up an independent committee to advise the Department of Defense, the Central Intelligence Agency, and the National Science Foundation itself on the future funding of MT research.

8.9 THE ALPAC REPORT

The National Academy of Sciences formed the Automatic Language Processing Advisory Committee (ALPAC) in April 1964 under the chairmanship of John R. Pierce of Bell Telephone Laboratories. The other members included two linguists, Eric P. Hamp (University of Chicago) and Charles F. Hockett (Cornell University); a psychologist, John B. Carroll (Harvard University); two MT specialists, David G. Hays (RAND Corporation) and

Anthony G. Oettinger (Harvard University); and one AI researcher, Alan Perlis (Carnegie Institute of Technology). The constitution is not without significance. Neither of the MT specialists believed in the continuation of MT research as such; at RAND, the emphasis had shifted since the early 1960s towards basic research in computational linguistics (Ch. 4.4), and at Harvard disillusion with the practicality of MT had been growing for many years, so that by 1964 active work in this area had virtually ceased (Ch. 4.9). Eric Hamp was a linguist of the Bloomfieldian school generally sceptical of mathematical and computational linguistics. On the other hand, Charles Hockett had been for some time an enthusiast for mathematical linguistics, and wrote a basic text on the topic (Hockett 1967); however before its publication Hockett underwent a "radical shift in point of view" between 1964 and 1965, and he became convinced that formal grammar of the Chomskyan kind was utterly misguided (Hockett 1968). Finally, Alan Perlis represented the emerging view of AI that linguistics-based (specifically syntax-based) approaches to language analysis were inevitably inadequate.

The committee undertook studies of the existing demand, supply and costs of translations, the demand and availability of translators, an evaluation of some MT output, and the costs of post-editing. ALPAC was concerned almost exclusively with translation from Russian and with economic considerations. From its surveys of US government translators and the provision of translations, it concluded that although poorly paid the "supply of translators greatly exceeds the demand", and that "all the Soviet literature for which there is any obvious demand is being translated". Indeed, it was concerned about "a possible excess of translation"; it thought that cover-to-cover translations of Soviet scientific journals "contain, in addition to much valuable information, many uninspired reports that the US scientist could have been mercifully spared." ALPAC concluded that "the emphasis should be on speed, quality, and economy in supplying such translations as are requested."

One solution was the provision of machine aids for translators. The committee had been impressed by developments of text-related glossaries by the Germany Army's translation service (later LEXIS), and of the automatic dictionary by the University of Brussels for the European Coal and Steel Community (DICATOM). The value of mechanised dictionaries had, of course, been recognised from the beginning of MT research, e.g. by Booth, and later by Oettinger, and machine aids of many kinds have now been developed, from the national terminolgy databanks to the personal glossaries. (They will be treated briefly in Ch. 17.6.) Increased support for the development of aids for translators was the least controversial of the committee's recommendations.

Machine translation, however, was most definitely not a solution. From its survey of the state of MT, ALPAC concluded that "there has been no machine translation of general scientific text, and none is in immediate prospect." In support, it drew attention to the fact that all MT output had to be post-edited. This was seen a 'failure': "when, after 8 years of work, the Georgetown University MT project tried to produce useful output in 1962, they had to resort to postediting". For some reason, ALPAC failed to acknowledge that most human translation, particularly when produced in translation agencies, is also revised ('post-edited') before submission to clients. The committee appears to have assumed that 'raw' MT output ought to be acceptable without editing.

The comittee sponsored evaluations of three (unspecified) MT systems by John B. Carroll, reported briefly in Appendix 10, and in greater detail by Carroll (1966), which showed conclusively that on ratings for intelligibility and informativeness all were significantly poorer than three human translations. It also received evaluation studies by the IBM Research Center and by Arthur D. Little Inc. of the IBM system at FTD (Appendix 11). The latter revealed that in a sample of 200 pages there were 7573 errors, of which 35% were omitted words, 26% wrong words, 12% incorrect choices, and 13% wrong word orders. The committee reached the general conclusion that although "unedited machine output from scientific text is decipherable for the most part . . . it is sometimes misleading and sometimes wrong . . . and it makes slow and painful reading". As examples of "recent [since November 1964] output of four different MT systems", the ALPAC report included passages from a Russian article on space biology translated by the systems at Bunker-Ramo, Computer Concepts, FTD, and EURATOM. The EURATOM system was, of course, as the report indicated, the Georgetown system (Ch. 4.3), and the Computer Concepts system was Toma's AUTOTRANS protoype of the later Systran (Ch. 4.13), also at this stage in most essentials the Georgetown system. The FTD system was the IBM Mark II (Ch. 4.2), and the Bunker-Ramo translations seem to have been produced by one of the earlier experimental versions (Ch. 4.6). Only the FTD and the EURATOM (Georgetown) systems were in fact operational systems; the others were still experimental, but this was not mentioned by ALPAC.

The MT output from these systems was obviously inadequate and unsatisfactory. Nevertheless, it was unfair of ALPAC to compare them unfavourably with the output of the 1954 Georgetown-IBM experiment (Ch. 4.3). For ALPAC, the work at Georgetown was typical of the progression from the "deceptively encouraging" early achievements to the current "uniformly discouraging" results. The committee failed to distinguish between a small-scale demonstration program working on prepared text and a large-scale working system dealing with unexamined texts.

More seriously, the committee failed to examine the theoretical research of other MT groups. The concentration on the Georgetown and IBM systems was probably understandable in view of the publicity these projects attracted, but it was surely amiss in neglecting to evaluate the projects at MIT, the University of California at Berkeley, the University of Texas, Bunker-Ramo, Wayne State University, and even Harvard University. It is true that the committee heard the testimony of Paul Garvin (Bunker-Ramo) and received the views of Victor Yngve (MIT). It is not known what these researchers had to say in substance, but the ALPAC report chose to emphasise Yngve's opinion that MT research had "come up against a semantic barrier" and that progress in MT required fundamental research in text understanding. This confirmed their belief that while support of MT research should be reduced since "there is no immediate or predictable prospect of useful machine translation" there should be support of basic research in computational linguistics.

The committee recognised the contribution of MT to the development of computer software and to theoretical linguistics. It acknowledged that computational linguistics had grown out of MT research, and it believed that "The advent of computational linguistics promises to work a revolution in linguistics", with implications for language teaching, psycholinguistics, and computer aids in information retrieval and translation. Given the recognition of the fruitful interaction between MT and computational linguistics it appeared perverse to many at the time and subsequently (e.g. Zarechnak 1979) that ALPAC should recommend increased funding for computational linguistics but no more funds for MT.

The ALPAC report was widely condemned as narrow, biased, and shortsighted. It was criticised strongly by Pankowicz of the Rome Air Development Center (one of the biggest sponsors) for its "factual inaccuracies . . . hostile and vindictive attitude . . . use of obsolete and invalid figures . . . distortion of quality, speed and cost estimates . . . concealment of data reflecting credit on MT . . . wilful omission of dissenting statements" (quoted by Josselson, 1971). MT researchers protested that improvements were imminent and that, in short, ALPAC's dismissal of MT was premature. But, whether the criticisms were valid or not, the damage had been done; MT research in the United States suffered immediate reductions and a loss of status which it has still not fully recovered. Whereas in 1963 there had been ten US groups (Georgetown, MIT, Harvard, NBS, Berkeley, Ohio State, Wayne State, Texas, Bunker-Ramo, and IBM) by 1968 there were just three (at Berkeley, Texas, and Wayne) and two of these suffered interruptions and reductions in funding (at Berkeley between 1965 and 1968 (Ch. 4.10 and 11.2), and at Texas between 1968 and 1970 (Ch. 10.3) The effect of ALPAC was also felt in other countries where quite different conditions prevailed: none of the three British groups were engaged in active MT research after 1968 (although the Birkbeck College group had stopped some time before ALPAC, in 1962); research in Japan and the Soviet Union continued at much reduced levels; only the French group CETA (Ch. 5.5 and 10.1) appears to have been relatively unaffected.

8.10 EXPENDITURE ON MT RESEARCH

Probably the most persuasive argument of ALPAC was that so little had been achieved despite huge investments of public money by the US government. As Roberts and Zarechnak (1974) put it, "from 1956 to 1965" MT research was being supported at "17 institutions to the tune of almost £20,000,000." These figures are frequently repeated, but they are in fact misleading. Appendix 16 of the ALPAC report lists expenditure under three headings: National Science Foundation (NSF) grants totalling $6,585,227,

Central Intelligence Agency (CIA) grants totalling $1,314,869, and Department of Defense (DOD) grants totalling $11,906,600. The DOD grants are broken down into grants by the USAF (mainly through the Rome Air Development Center), totalling $9,613,000, by the US Navy ($971,600) and by the US Army ($1,322,000); but no details are given of the recipients of the grants. The CIA grants went all to the Georgetown University project.

The NSF grants are listed under 17 recipients. This is the source of the "17 institutions" but it is an incorrect interpretation: three headings refer to grants for MT conferences (to MIT in 1956 and 1960, and to Wayne State in 1960 and 1962), and one to grants for ALPAC itself. The institutional recipients include the Cambridge Language Research Unit (a non-US group), the University of Pennsylvania (the group under Zellig Harris which was not engaged in MT research as such, cf. 4.13 above), and the University of Chicago (a grant to Victor Yngve to continue his MT work begun at MIT). There remain therefore ten US groups receiving NSF grants for MT research in the period 1956–65: Georgetown ($106,600, plus $305,000 transferred from the CIA, and in addition to the direct CIA grants), Harvard ($1,054,960, plus $206,500 transferred from RADC), MIT ($911,700), Berkeley ($722,400), Ohio State ($154,700), Wayne State ($444,000), Texas ($613,200), NBS ($221,200), Ramo-Wooldridge and Bunker-Ramo ($561,784), and Washington ($54,700). The total of direct NSF grants in the period is thus about $5,000,000.

Many of these institutions were also receiving grants from DOD sources, e.g. Washington from the USAF, Texas from US Army, and Wayne State from US Navy. It is known that the USAF supported the IBM project on a large scale, and that the Cambridge and Milan groups also received grants. However, there are good reasons to suspect that by no means all the huge DOD expenditure of nearly $12 million went to MT research.

In the report of the 1960 US House of Representatives mentioned earlier (8.5), details of USAF grants for 1960–61 are provided. Some support was being given to known MT research: the Milan project ($124,000), the Cambridge and Harvard projects ($125,000, via NSF), and the Ramo-Woodridge project ($130,000). Other grants went to MT-related research: to the MT evaluation project at the University of Washington (Ch. 4.1), and to Indiana University ($99,000, although this semantics research was only distantly relevant, Ch. 4.13). By far the greatest proportion of the total $3 million was going, however, to IBM for development of its photoscopic disk 'translator' ($1,787,000), to Baird Atomic Inc. for the development of an optical character reader to be used in conjunction with the IBM equipment ($381,000), and to Intelligent Machines Research Corp. for the development of ancillary computer equipment ($267,000). If we assume that, say, a third of the IBM grant went in fact towards the development of MT research as opposed to technical refinement of the Mark II equipment, then this still means that nearly two-thirds of the 1960 USAF grants for "mechanical translation" were in fact going on hardware development. It would be too great an assumption to extrapolate these proportions to the USAF total for the period 1956–65, but it may not be too inaccurate to suppose that the figure for MT research should be nearer $5 million than the $9,613,000 given in the ALPAC report.

A similar reduction should probably be made for the US Navy grants: the 1960 House of Representatives report again indicates that most US Navy contracts for MT activities were in fact for the development of hardware (character readers, pattern recognition, high density storage). Of the total $532,500 for the period 1953–60 less than a quarter ($115,900) went to 'pure' MT research (Wayne State). Only the US Army seems to have concentrated exclusively on MT projects as such in 1960 (supporting Texas and NBS). If these proportions are cautiously extrapolated for the whole period 1953–65 then perhaps the figure for US Navy and US Army MT research contracts should be nearer $1,500,000 than the $2,300,000 in the report.

These adjustments result in a total expenditure of approximately $13 million by the US government and military agencies on MT research at 11 US institutions and 2 foreign institutions during the period 1956–65. Although the figures are substantially smaller (by a third) than those given by ALPAC and repeated frequently in subsequent years, the level of financial support was nevertheless immense. There was a good deal of justification for sponsors to expect practical returns for their support.

8.11 THE SITUATION IN 1966

The ALPAC report may have dismissed solid achievements too readily, but it was probably quite right to call a halt to indiscriminate and wasteful expenditure on unrealistic projects. Unfortunately, it destroyed at the same time much of the credibility of MT research. After ALPAC few American researchers were willing to be associated with MT; indicative of the change was the deletion of Machine Translation from the title of the Association of Computational Linguistics in 1968.

In the decade of research since 1956, a considerable amount had in fact been achieved, not only in the United States but also in Britain, the Soviet Union, and elsewhere. As far as operating systems were concerned, there were after all two now in regular use: the IBM Mark II at the USAF's Foreign Technology Division at the Wright-Patterson Air Force Base, and the Georgetown systems installed for the Atomic Energy Commission at the Oak Ridge Laboratory and for the EURATOM Centre in Italy. Operating systems had also been tested at the National Physical Laboratory and in the Soviet Union. Admittedly, the achievement in this respect was far less than had been anticipated at the beginning of the decade; and furthermore, the quality of output was much poorer than would have been hoped for.

These operating systems were all products of the 'engineering' approach to MT, systems which started from fairly rudimentary foundations (often word-for-word systems) and were progressively refined on a trial and error basis. In the case of the IBM system the refinements were by lexicographic means (Ch. 4.2); in the case of the Georgetown and NPL systems, refinements also included addition of rudimentary syntactic analyses (Ch. 4.3 and 5.4). The system at Ramo-Wooldridge was also progressively refined by improved parsing and dictionary information (Ch. 4.6) although by 1967 it was not yet operational.

As opposed to the engineering approaches there were the numerous 'theoretical' approaches, many of which sought to perfect procedures and methods before implementation. Few of the groups taking the 'perfectionist' attitude succeeded in going beyond preliminary small-scale experimental tests. Prominent among the theoretical groups were MIT, Harvard, Berkeley, Cambridge, and the Soviet groups at MIAN and Leningrad. Typical of the attitude of these groups were the remarks of Lamb (Berkeley), who thought it "a very curious thing that so much of the work in the field of Russian-to-English MT has been devoted to writing translation programs instead of investigating the structure of Russian" (Lamb 1961).

There were, of course, many differences between the theoretical groups, as we have seen (Ch. 8.2). Some concentrated almost exclusively on semantic problems (e.g. Cambridge, Leningrad, and the Moscow Pedagogical Institute), but increasingly projects were concentrating primarily on syntactic approaches (Ch. 8.4): phrase structure grammar (MIT and Texas), dependency grammar (RAND and CETA), the fulcrum approach (Ramo-Wooldridge, Wayne State), and the extensive testing of the 'predictive syntactic analyser' (NBS and Harvard). Initial high hopes for syntactic approaches were in the end deflated by the problems of structural ambiguity, e.g. the prepositional phrase problem (Ch. 3.6), and by unexpected multiple analyses and parsing failures (Ch. 4.9). Nevertheless, foundations were laid for future advances in parsing techniques.

Problems of dictionary techniques were throughout subject to close examination. As we have seen (Ch. 8.2) the most popular method of dictionary access was the serial technique, but there were now alternatives: the binary partition method of Booth (Ch. 5.1) and the tree structure technique of Lamb (Ch. 4.10). In large part, dictionary searching was constrained by hardware deficiencies. There was, therefore, considerable interest in special-purpose equipment; not only the IBM photoscopic store, but also the Yamato machine in Japan (Ch. 7.1) and, according to Bar-Hillel (1960), they were also proposed in the Soviet Union. In the course of time, computer storage became less problematic and the notion of special 'translating machines' became largely irrelevant. Nevertheless, computer facilities were often unsatisfactory and many groups had virtually no chance to test their ideas on actual computers (Ch. 8.2 above).

The most characteristic MT system design of the period was the 'direct translation' approach, one-directional systems where SL analysis is directed explicitly towards the specific features of the TL, and where analysis and synthesis procedures are not separated (Ch. 3.9). This was the most common form, and is seen in the Washington, IBM, Georgetown, Birkbeck, NPL, and a number of the Soviet and Japanese systems. However, the advantages of separating SL and TL analysis were also recognised from the earliest days, e.g. by Panov in the Soviet Union (rudimentary 'transfer' systems can be seen in some of the Soviet systems), and most specifically in the 'syntactic transfer' approach at MIT (Ch. 4.7). This exploration of bilingual transfer mechanisms converting SL phrase structure analyses into TL phrase structure equivalents was to influence the development of the CETA and Texas approaches (Ch. 5.5 and 10.1; 4.11 and 10.3). Concurrently there emerged in both the Soviet Union and the United States the concept of multi-level analysis, the separation of stages of morphological, syntactic, and semantic analysis (Ch. 3.9). Its most explicit formulations appeared in the 'stratificational' theory of Lamb at Berkeley (Ch. 4.10) and in the theories of Mel'chuk (Ch. 6.3), later elaborated as the 'meaning-text' model (Ch. 10.2).

Most ambitious of all were the various proposals for interlingual systems. The idea of interlingual MT was put forward by Weaver in his 1949 memorandum. Researchers were both attracted by the centuries-old notion of a 'universal language' (Ch. 2.1) and by the practical advantages of translation via an 'intermediary language' in multilingual environments (Ch. 3.9). Richens was a strong advocate and at the Cambridge Language Research Unit his ideas of a basic universal set of primitive sense elements were tested in conjunction with the thesaurus approach (Ch. 5.2). The Milan group investigated in depth an interlingua which was intended to be a direct representation of 'conceptual' relations, independent of any languages, and was explicitly not based on universal or common linguistic features. Different conceptions of an interlingua were put forward by the Soviet researchers Andreev and Mel'chuk (Ch. 6.3–4). Mel'chuk proposed that an interlingua should be the sum of all features common to two or more languages. Andreev proposed an interlingua which would be a complete artificial language with its own lexicon and syntax, based on the most frequent common features in the languages under consideration. Other suggestions were the use of one of the artificial auxiliary languages, such as Esperanto or Interlingua (e.g. Gode 1955) — but, rather surprisingly, it is only recently that the idea has been taken seriously (Ch. 16.3). At the same time, Booth argued that the case for an 'intermediary language' was fallacious, firstly because in a multingual environment of *n* languages, the number of programs can be reduced even more than the 2*n* with an interlingua if one of the *n* languages itself is the mediating language (Booth *et al.* 1958). In fact Reifler (1954) and Panov (1960) had made the same proposal, suggesting English and Russian respectively as the best mediating languages. More pertinently, however, Booth argued that all SL–TL conversion involved abstract representations which could be regarded as 'intermediary'. In these remarks we may perhaps see the germs of the later ('deep syntactic') conceptions of the 'pivot language' of CETA (Ch. 5.5 and 10.1) and of the interlingual representations of the Texas group (Ch. 4.11 and 10.3).

In the face of the semantic complexities of MT, a number of researchers suggested limitations of vocabulary or grammar of input or output text. One line led to the development of the microglossary approach (Oswald 1957), the construction of specialised bilingual dictionaries to reduce the incidence of multiple meanings. The idea was taken up by many US projects (Washington, IBM, Georgetown, RAND), and in the Soviet Union. A second related line was the restriction of the MT system as a whole to one particular scientific field, which may be expected to have its own particular 'sublanguage': a popular choice was mathematics (e.g. Wayne State). Even more radical were Dodd's and Reifler's suggestions that writers should use 'regularised' language in texts (Ch. 2.4.3); but these ideas were not to be taken up in this form until later (Ch. 17.1–4). However, the notion of 'pidgin' MT languages did receive attention, by Reifler (Ch. 4.1) and in particular by the Cambridge group, which argued that 'low level' MT output could be made more understandable by the regular use of 'pidgin' variables (Ch. 5.2).

These were proposals prompted by the amount of post-editing that MT output evidently needed. Initially post-editing was seen as part of the feedback process of improving systems (e.g. at RAND, Ch. 4.4). Increasingly, it was realised that in the foreseeable future revision of MT text would be a necessity in operational systems, although many still hoped that eventually post-editing would wither away with 'higher quality' MT. However, there was surprisingly little discussion of what was meant by translation quality.

Miller & Beebe-Center (1958) were the first to suggest measures of evaluation. Judges were asked to rate human translations and simulated MT versions of a set of abstracts on a percentage scale (0% = "no translation at all", 100% = "best imaginable translation"). The results indicated that subjective scaling was a poor measure. More successful was a second evaluation on the basis of identifiable 'errors' of vocabulary and syntax. Finally the authors suggested comprehension tests as evaluative measures. Nothing more was attempted until output of actual MT systems became available in the late 1960s. In evaluations of the IBM system (Ch. 4.2), tests of 'reading comprehension' were used by Pfafflin (1965) and by Orr & Small (1967), and Pfafflin also used a measure of 'clarity' in preference to error analysis. In his evaluation studies for ALPAC, Carroll (1966) criticised the unreliability of comprehension scores, and used instead correlations of 'intelligibility' and 'informativeness' measures.

It is remarkable that quality evaluation should have been neglected, but it is perhaps symptomatic of the surprising failure of the US funding agencies to monitor the research they were sponsoring. One explanation is the wish to encourage as many different approaches as possible. A feature of most groups was the single-minded concentration on a particular method or technique. While MT was in these early stages (as it was still essentially at the time of ALPAC), this commitment was not necessarily bad; it meant, for example, that some approaches were tested to their limits. Examples are the thesaurus technique at Cambridge and the predictive analyser at Harvard. What was perhaps less excusable was the sponsors' failure to prevent duplication with so many groups doing basic investigations of Russian.

It is understandable in the 'cold war' climate of the 1950s and early 1960s (cf.the comments in the House of Representatives report above) that US research should have concentrated so heavily on Russian–English translation (all groups except MIT were involved), but the neglect of other languages is nevertheless remarkable. It is true that German–English MT was the main focus at MIT and Texas, and that Chinese–English translation was investigated at Washington, IBM, Georgetown, and (towards the end of the period) more extensively at Berkeley, Ohio State, and Ramo-Wooldridge. There were also studies of French–English (principally by Brown at Georgetown, but also at IBM) and of Arabic (at MIT and Georgetown). But Japanese, for example, was virtually neglected, except for a small study by Kuno at Harvard; and there was no MT research on Spanish within the US — a surprising omission in view of the US involvement in Latin America.

By contrast, Soviet research was far more diversified. There was again, for obvious reasons, a preponderance of work on English–Russian systems; but equal importance was attached to research on French, Hungarian, and languages of Soviet republics. In the rest of Europe also, the range of languages was more diverse: French, German, Italian, Latin, Czech, Rumanian. In Japan, research naturally concentrated on Japanese and English.

In 1966, research on MT had reached a low ebb. After a slow start, the decade since 1956 had seen a vigorous growth of activity. Initial encouraging results, based primarily on word-for-word experiments and early trials of 'direct translation' systems, were followed (after roughly 1960) by a gradual realisation of the immense complexities. The solutions looked for in increasing sophistication of structural analyses and syntactic formalism did not come readily; and the 'semantic barrier' seemed insurmountable. There were MT systems in operation, but the output was not satisfactory. It seemed that MT had been an expensive failure.

9

Strategies and methods since the mid-1960s

9.1 AFTER ALPAC

In the aftermath of the ALPAC report the reduction of research groups in the United States was dramatic: for a while there were just two groups (at Wayne and Berkeley), until the resumption in 1970 of the research at Texas and the beginning of a new group at the Logos Corporation. In Britain there were now no groups active: the Cambridge team had turned to other interests and the NPL project had ended. Elsewhere the picture was, however, less bleak. In the Soviet Union there had apparently been some reduction of activity (Roberts & Zarechnak 1974), but research continued on both theoretical projects, e.g. the 'meaning-text' approach of Mel'chuk (Ch. 10.2), and on practical systems, e.g. at the Patent Office in Moscow (Ch. 11.5). In France, work was continuing on the CETA project in Grenoble (Ch. 10.1), and in Italy EURATOM began MT investigations (Ch. 11.1). In Germany, there appeared a new group at Saarbrücken (Ch. 13.2), and Toma continued research which was to lead to the development of the Systran system (Ch. 12.1).

In the United States the main activity had been concentrated on English translations of Russian scientific and technical materials. In Canada and Europe the situation was quite different. The Canadian government's bicultural policy created a "demand for translation which far surpasses the capacity of the market, especially as far as technical translation is concerned" (Chandioux 1977). Shortly after ALPAC the Canadian National

Research Council sponsored three English–French projects at Saskatchewan (Ch. 12.5), Montreal (Ch. 13.1), and Cambridge (Ch. 5.2). In Europe the problems of translation were becoming equally acute: in addition to the needs of science, technology, engineering, medicine, and international trade and commerce there were now added the growing demand for translations of administrative, legal, and technical documents from and into the languages of the European Communities. As a consequence, the Commission of the European Communities installed Systran in its translation services and inaugurated a multilingual research project (Ch. 14).

In contrast to the aspirations of the first decade of research, the goals of MT researchers now became more realistic; no longer were translations expected to be stylistically perfect, the aim was readability and fidelity to the original. At the same time, there now emerged a number of linguistically more advanced systems based on 'indirect' approaches to system design and there was an increase in the variety of source and target languages. This chapter outlines the main developments since the mid-1960s.

9.2 DIRECT TRANSLATION SYSTEMS

Research has continued on 'direct translation' systems. One was the system developed by the Logos Corporation for the US Air Force which was used to translate American aircraft manuals into Vietnamese (Ch. 12.2). Another was the experimental Xonics system, a derivative of the Georgetown system (Ch. 12.3), and the recent PAHO system for Spanish and English, also based on the 'Georgetown' approach (Ch. 12.4). However, the best known was Systran, designed initially as a Russian–English system and later adapted for English–French translation for the Commission of the European Communities (Ch. 12.1). Systran may be regarded as essentially a greatly improved version of the Gerogetown system; linguistically there is relatively little advance, but computationally the improvements are considerable. The main ones lie in the 'modularity' of its programming, allowing for the modification of any part of the processes to be undertaken without risk of impairing overall efficiency, and in the strict separation of linguistic data and computational processes. In this way it avoids the irresolvable complexities of the monolithic Georgetown system (Ch. 4.3).

9.3 INTERLINGUAL SYSTEMS

The most innovative systems have been based on 'indirect' approaches. There were three major projects which investigated 'interlingual' approaches in depth; the Russian–French project by CETA in Grenoble (which had begun some time before ALPAC), the research in Moscow centred on the 'meaning-text' model (which also had its origins before 1966), and the German–English project of the Linguistics Research Center (LRC) at the University of Texas (Ch. 10). All were heavily indebted to current linguistic theories. Both the CETA and LRC groups were influenced by the

Chomskyan theory of transformational grammar (Ch. 3.5). It was argued that while languages differ greatly in 'surface' syntactic structures they share common 'deep structure' representations, which may be regarded as forms of 'universal' semantic representation. SL analysis passed through various levels ('strata') from 'surface' structures to 'deep' structures; and TL synthesis from 'deep' structures to 'surface' representations. In this conception, both groups were influenced also by Lamb's stratificational theory. At both CETA and LRC, interlingual representations were abstract formulas in terms of 'logical' predicates and arguments. However, in neither case were lexical items converted into interlingual representations, there was no attempt to decompose lexical items into semantic primitives. In brief, the CETA and LRC systems were interlingual in syntax, but not interlingual in semantics. By contrast, the 'meaning-text' model developed by Mel'chuk and others (Ch. 10.2) was an attempt to design a fully interlingual system. As in CETA and LRC, there were various levels of analysis and synthesis, from surface forms to 'deep' syntactic forms; but in addition there was a 'deep' semantic level where all lexical synonymy and ambiguity was resolved.

While CETA and LRC were quite thoroughly tested, the Soviet system was not implemented, mainly for external reasons. Even if it had been, it is doubtful whether it would have been more successful than CETA and LRC, neither of which went beyond the experimental stages. The basic fault was the rigidity of the processes: a failure at one stage of analysis corrupted all subsequent stages, and too often, too many structures were produced for a sentence which then had to be 'filtered out' later. It was largely as a consequence of disappointing results that the Grenoble group adopted a basically 'transfer' design for its new GETA system (Ch. 13.3), and that when the Texas group resumed MT research in 1978 it also adopted an essentially transfer strategy (Ch. 13.4).

9.4 TRANSFER SYSTEMS

In retrospect, these 'interlingual' systems were perhaps too ambitious at the time; the more cautious 'transfer' approach was probably more realistic as well as being more flexible and adaptable in meeting the needs of different levels and 'depth' of syntactic and semantic analysis.

In broad terms, the 'transfer' systems may be divided into those based on the MIT-type 'syntactic transfer' pattern and those in which syntactic analysis generally went further than 'surface' structures and more semantic analysis was incorporated. Examples of the former were the experimental Russian–English project at EURATOM (Ch. 11.1) and the Moscow Patent Office system which was installed for translating American patent abstracts into Russian (Ch. 11.5). The examples of the latter type were all to emerge since the mid-1960s. They included the POLA system at Berkeley (Ch. 11.2), Kulagina's system at MIAN (Ch. 11.5), and the TAUM project at Montreal (Ch. 13.1). The latter system may be seen in retrospect to have inaugurated the development since the early 1970s of techniques which have resulted in the advanced GETA system at Grenoble (Ch. 13.3), the SUSY system at Saarbrücken (Ch. 13.2), and the Eurotra project of the European Communities (Ch. 14.2).

In these newer transfer systems, the goal of analysis was the production of SL representations which resolve the syntactic and lexical ambiguities of the sentence in question, without necessarily providing unique representations for synonymous constructions and expressions (Ch. 3.9). Thus, while it might resolve homonyms such as *watch*, and equate lexical synonyms such as *expensive* and *costly*, it would probably not resolve certain prepositional phrase ambiguities or equate *buy* and *sell* constructions (Ch. 3.6). In comparison with 'interlingual' approaches there was more conservation of information about SL sentence forms and also greater reliance on bilingual dictionaries for providing information on SL–TL structural changes during the transfer stages. In sum, the 'depth' of analysis in transfer representations was less than in the representations of 'interlingual' systems.

One of the major theoretical justifications for 'transfer' systems is their extensibility to further language pairs in a multilingual environment (Ch. 3.9). Nevertheless, there are sufficient advantages in the inherent 'modularity' of such designs to warrant their adoption even when only a one-directional bilingual system is envisaged. The TAUM system was developed specifically for English–French translation, the POLA for Chinese–English, and the MIAN system for French–Russian. The SUSY and GETA systems were developed initially for a particular pair (Russian–German and Russian–French respectively), but have now been extended to other languages; and Eurotra has been designed *ab initio* as a multilingual system.

9.5 SEMANTICS–BASED SYSTEMS

At the same time as the more advanced 'transfer' systems were beginning to appear, MT research saw the introduction of the first semantics-based approach, inspired by methods and techniques of Artificial Intelligence (AI). This was the experiment by Wilks at Stanford University on an 'interlingual' English–French system.

Since the mid-1960s MT systems have been predominantly syntax based. This applies as much to the 'interlingual' and 'transfer' approaches as it does to the earlier systems. However much semantic information is included in interlingual and transfer representations, syntactic analysis is the central component: semantic features are attached to syntactic structures and semantic procedures operate primarily after syntactic structures have been determined. These systems are syntax based in another sense: their analysis and synthesis procedures are restricted almost exclusively to sentences. Features of discourse cohesion across sentences, such as pronominalisation and topicalisation (Ch. 3.7), have been neglected. The deficiencies have been recognised by many researchers, e.g. at LRC, TAUM, and GETA, but there are still only tentative suggestions for handling intersentential relations.

The importance of Wilks' MT research and of other AI projects which have followed, such as the Yale projects (Ch. 15.2), has been precisely in the exploration of semantics-based approaches to language analysis. Basic components of AI approaches are: semantic parsing, i.e. analysis of semantic features ('human', 'concrete', etc.) rather than grammatical categories; lexical decomposition into semantic networks (e.g. Schank's conceptual dependency model); and resolution of ambiguities and uncertainties by reference to knowledge bases. Initially, AI approaches were pursued as alternatives to 'traditional' syntax-based systems, but recently MT researchers are experimenting with AI methods in combination with linguistic analysis techniques, e.g. TRANSLATOR (Ch. 15.7), and some Japanese systems (Ch. 18.12).

9.6 INTERACTIVE AND RESTRICTED LANGUAGE SYSTEMS

One consequence of the ALPAC report was to convince many (if they were not already by Bar-Hillel) that fully automatic translation of good quality is unattainable. Some have explored the possibilities of interactive MT, in which man and machine collaborate in the production of translations; some have argued for systems based on restricted vocabulary and syntax; and others have exploited the computer's capacity to retrieve information from large databases by developing mechanised dictionaries to aid translators.

Interactive systems appeared in the late 1960s, with the experimental MIND project at RAND and the Chinese–English CULT system in Hong Kong (Ch. 17.8–9). As on-line processing became more generally available during the late 1970s, commercial organizations started to investigate the possibilities and, as a result, in recent years systems have appeared on the market place (Ch. 17). The amount of human interaction varies considerably from one system to another. Nearly all require human operators to assist in the analysis of SL text and in the compilation of dictionaries.

Imposing restrictions on the vocabulary and syntax of input texts remains attractive (Ch. 17.1–4). It is sometimes combined with interactive facilities, as in TITUS and Smart, and sometimes implemented on fully automatic systems, as in the case of Xerox's use of Systran.

9.7 THE DEVELOPMENTS AFTER THE MID-1970s

In the years since ALPAC the development of automatic dictionaries and terminology databanks has contributed in large part to the now increasing acceptability of MT. Until the 1970s practising translators were largely excluded from involvement in computer-based translation. MT was predominantly an affair for academics and government scientists. This has been changed by the development of machine aids for translators (Ch. 17.6). They have been created in response to the ever urgent needs of translators, particularly in large governmental and industrial units, for rapid access to up-to-date glossaries and dictionaries of terminology in science, technology, economics, and the social sciences in general. The potential of mechanised dictionaries was recognised from the very beginning of MT research, e.g. by Booth and by Oettinger, but it has only been realised as a result of recent technological advances, particularly in the availability of on-line access via public telecommunication networks and in the development of text editing and word processing equipment.

Equally important for the changing attitude to MT has been the decision by the Commission of the European Communities in the mid-1970s firstly to test and develop the Systran system for use in their translation services (Ch. 14.1) and then subsequently to approve a multinational MT research project for the development of the multilingual Eurotra system (Ch. 14.2). At the same time, the Commission organised a conference in 1977 under the title *Overcoming the language barrier* at which most contemporary MT groups presented accounts of their research (CEC 1977). In subsequent years the Commission has supported Aslib, the British organisation for special libraries and information services, in the organisation of a series of annual conferences which since 1978 have successfully drawn the attention of translators and business organisations to developments in MT and related activities (Snell 1979; Lawson 1982; Lawson 1985).

In retrospect the mid-1970s may prove to be a turning point for MT. It was not only in W. Europe that there was a renewal of interest. In 1975 for the first time since the mid-1960s an international MT conference was held in Moscow. It was organised by the All-Union Centre for Translations which since 1974 has assumed responsibility for the development of MT systems in the Soviet Union (Ch. 18.6). The conference was the first of a series held every four years. In the United States, the MT revival has been much more fitful. In March 1976 a seminar was organised in Rosslyn, Virginia, for the US government Foreign Broadcasting Information Service (FBIS 1976). The FBIS was translationg annually over a million words and was expecting demand to grow; it was "facing translation problems" and wanted to "reassess the state of the art" of MT and machine aids for translators. However, the general mood was pessimistic. Petrick, in his summary, concluded that "currently operational or projected machine-translation systems are only marginally different in their underlying organisation and design than their predecessors" and "I would not expect any current MT systems to compete with human translation except where low quality, unedited output suffices." On the other hand, Hays saw a future for interactive MT systems with text editing facilities.

In the event, US involvement has continued to be low. For many years only the University of Texas has been involved in fully automated systems (and they have been funded by a non-US company); however, in recent years there has been some increase in research interest elsewhere in the US, indicated by the conferences in August 1985 at Gerogetown University (*LM* 25, Oct. 1985) and at Colgate University (Nirenburg 1985). Much of the renewed 'academic' interest is centred on AI approaches (Ch. 15), and is small-scale experimental research. Since the mid-1970s the main US activity has been in the commercial developments of interactive MT systems, where there has been considerable progress, although these systems are often marketed as adjuncts to office automation systems, and avoid the tainted name 'machine translation' in favour of 'computer assisted translation.'

9.8 COMPUTATIONAL AND LINGUISTIC TECHNIQUES AND ISSUES

Whereas in the early 1960s, the main advances in language processing took place within the context of MT research, since 1966 most innovations have occurred outside this environment. In part this was a result of ALPAC's recommendation that support should concentrate on computational linguistics rather than MT projects. However, there was already a considerable growth of natural language processing activity outside MT before ALPAC, notably on question-answering and information retrieval systems. Above all, artificial intelligence research was turning increasingly towards problems of language understanding and text analysis, e.g. Weizenbaum's ELIZA, Winograd's SHRDLU, Schank's conceptual dependency model, etc. (Boden 1977).

The particular relevance of AI methods and techniques will be discussed later (Ch. 15 and 19.3). The next sections summarise relevant issues and developments of the late 1960s and early 1970s in general parsing and analysis techniques.

9.9 SEPARATION OF LINGUISTIC DATA AND ALGORITHMS

In the earliest systems, programs included procedures which combined linguistic information and specific actions. For example, the ITVMT English–Russian program (Ch. 6.1) consisted of a succession of searches for specific English words; and the Georgetown algorithm (Ch. 4.3) was driven by specific lexical items. The advantages of separating algorithmic procedures from linguistic data (and not only lexical but grammatical as well) were argued particularly by Yngve of MIT (Ch. 4.7) and Lamb of Berkeley (Ch. 4.10). The result was a tripartite design for parsing: a dictionary (with grammar codes), a processing algorithm, and a store (table) of grammar rules. It enabled the linguists to concentrate on linguistic analysis, and programmers to concentrate on efficient algorithms; and it meant that rules could be changed or modified without changing the processing algorithm. Garvin (1972), on the other hand, argued that computationally more efficient programs were possible in a 'bipartite parser' where the algorithm searches for linguistic patterns as directed by grammar rules embodied in the algorithm itself. Although there is general agreement on separating lexical data from algorithmic routines, there are still differences of opinion regarding the desirability of separate grammar rule tables and abstract algorithm routines (see, e.g. Ch. 13.4 on the latest Texas system). In the 1970s, however, strict separation was widely adopted. It is seen most clearly in the development of 'abstract' tree transduction procedures (below).

9.10 MODULARITY

Modular design is most apparent in the subdivision of syntactic analysis programs. During the 1960s a number of projects developed parsers which consisted of a series of 'passes' to identify groups and phrase structures (noun phrases, verb groups, clauses, etc.); a typical example was the 'fulcrum' analyser of Garvin at Ramo-Wooldridge (Ch. 4.6). The disadvantage of the monolithic complexity of the Georgetown system was that particular procedures (e.g. to deal with adjective–noun congruence) could not be changed without affecting other parts of the system. The advantage of dividing procedures into relatively independent subroutines is that parts can be modified and tested without running such risks (and, of course, such modularity is easier if grammar rules and algorithms are separated). Since the mid-1960s modularity has become the norm, even in systems of the 'direct translation' type such as Systran (Ch. 12.1).

9.11 TRANSFORMATIONAL PARSING

'Given Chomsky's demonstration of the inadequacies of phrase structure grammars (Ch. 3.5) and the disappointing experience (both within and outside MT) with parsers based on equivaent formalisms (e.g. dependency parsers and predictive analysers), it was natural that researchers should investigate transformational parsers. There was a further reason why the transformational theory was attractive. This was the claim that while languages may differ conisderably in 'surface' structures they all share the same 'deep structures' (Chomsky 1965: 117ff). The theory seemed to offer a way of dealing with syntactic equivalencies between languages, and it proved a stimulus to research on 'interlingual' approaches to MT, as already indicated.

It was soon found, however, that the Chomskyan formulation of transformational rules could not be easily implemented in syntactic analysis program. In fairness to Chomsky, it needs to be pointed out that he has never suggested that his model could be applied in computational systems for language analysis; indeed, he has written in relation to the intellectual climate of the 1950s: "As for machine translation and related enterprises, they seemed to me pointless as well as probably quite hopeless" (Chomsky 1975: 40).

The basic reason why transformational analysis does not work easily is that Chomsky's model is conceived as a generative grammar; it accounts for structures by describing how they may be formally derived from an initial node S by rules such as S → NP + VP, NP → A + N, VP → V + NP, etc., and by transformational rules which convert and merge phrase structures. It does not describe how structures can be recognised; i.e. it does not supply a mechanism for parsing. Researchers such as Petrick (1971) and the MITRE group (Grishman 1976, King 1983a) discovered that parsers based on procedures with reverse transformational rules are inordinately complex; many different sequences of transformational rules may have applied in the generation of any surface structure; each possibility must be tried and each potential 'deep structure' must be tested for well-formedness. Furthermore, many transformational rules, such as those forming coordinate structures (Ch. 3, Fig. 5), and there is no way this information can be reconstructed with certainty. Much ingenuity was devoted to transformational parsing, but the general conclusion is that the methods work well only on very restricted domains (King 1983a).

9.12 FILTERING

Many analysis programs incorporate 'filters' which check for well-formedness of derived structures. For example, a surface structure analyser determines which sequences of grammatical categories (assigned by dictionary lookup or morphological analysis) are legitimate parsings. A 'deep' structure parser then tests each putative surface structure, either in terms of possible 'deep structure' sources (as in transformational parsing) or in terms of semantic coherence. The semantic criteria may include 'selection restrictions' or valid 'case' relationships (Ch. 3.6 and below). Such a model of analysis adopts, therefore, a multi-level or 'stratificational' conception of language structure: morphological, syntactic, semantic (Ch. 3.10); and each stage of the analysis program acts as a 'filter' for structures accepted by the previous stage. The basic difficulties of the 'filtering' approach are the risks, on the one hand, of rigidity and, of eliminating unusual (but valid) structures and, on the other, of allowing too many structures of doubtful validity. Both faults were present in the analysis programs of CETA and LRC (Ch. 10).

9.13 AUGMENTED TRANSITION NETWORK (ATN) PARSING

The ATN parser developed by William Woods (1970, 1973) was the outcome of research he undertook with Kuno in the Harvard Computation Laboratory on improvements to the 'predictive syntactic analyser' (Ch. 4.9). Woods' parser differs in two important respects from the finite state 'grammar' of the Harvard analyser. Firstly, the arcs of one finite state network may be labelled with the names of other networks; thus, in the extremely simple 'grammar' of three networks displayed in Fig. 12 below, transition to state 2 requires the first word of a sentence (S) to be an aux(iliary verb), while transition to state 1 or from state 2 to 3 requires the satisfactory completion of the NP network, i.e. testing for the categories 'pron(oun)', det(erminer)', 'n(oun)' and reaching state 7 or state 8. The optional PP network — its optionality indicated by an arc looping back to the same state — requires the testing for a 'prep(osition)' and again the satisfactory completion of the NP network. As such, this parser would still be no more powerful than a phrase structure grammar. It can in fact be made equivalent to a transformational grammar.

Its 'transformational' capability is achieved by adding tests and conditions to the arcs and by specifying 'building instructions' to be executed if the arc is followed. Thus, for example, transition of arc 'aux' to state 2 would specify the building of the first elements of an interrogative (phrase) structure, which could be confirmed or rejected by the conditions or instructions associated with other arcs. Likewise, the transition of an arc recognising a passive verb form would specify the building of elements of a passive construction to be confirmed or rejected as later information is acquired. As a consequence, Woods' parser overcomes many of the difficulties encountered by previous researchers in attempting to devise parsers with reverse transformational rules (9.11 above).

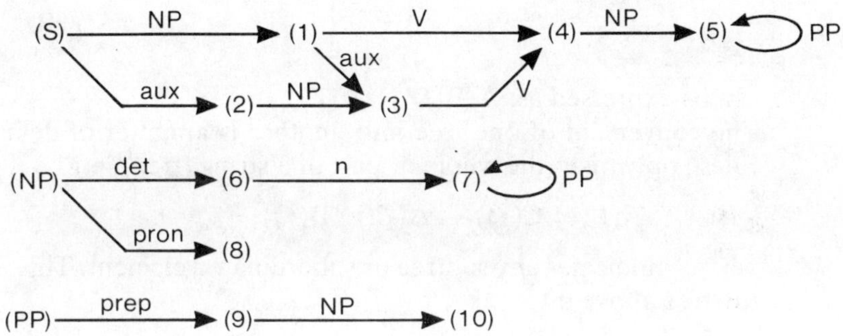

Fig. 12 — Partial ATN grammar.

One of the principal attractions of ATN parsers is that they are by no means restricted to syntactic analysis. Indeed in AI systems they are commonly used for deriving semantic representations (e.g. Simmons 1973). Conditions may specify any type of linguistic data: thus, arcs can test for morphological elements (suffixes and verb endings) and for semantic categories ('animate', 'concrete', etc.); and instructions can build morphological structures and semantic representations. Furthermore, because the arcs can be ordered, an ATN parser can make use of statistical data about the language and its grammatical and lexical structures.

Normally ATN parsers operate top-down (cf. Ch. 3.4), with all the disadvantages that entails, principally in wasteful reiterated analyses of lower level constituents (e.g. simple noun phrases in multiple analyses of sentence structure). However, it is also possible for ATN parsers to be implemented breadth-first, exploring all possible paths 'in parallel', and thus minimising backtracking routines (see Johnson 1983 for an introduction to ATN parsing).

9.14 TREE TRANSDUCERS

Analysis and synthesis programs involve the transformation of one structure (e.g. string of elements or phrase structure tree) into another. In earlier systems (and in many later 'direct' systems) such transformations were implemented by routines specifying both constituent elements and their interrelationships. As a consequence of separating linguistic data from algorithmic data, there evolved the notion of 'abstract' tree transduction algorithms. Within MT research, they appeared first in the Q-system of the TAUM project (Ch. 13.1).

Such algorithms are based on the fact that any tree can be expressed as a string of bracketed elements, thus the tree:

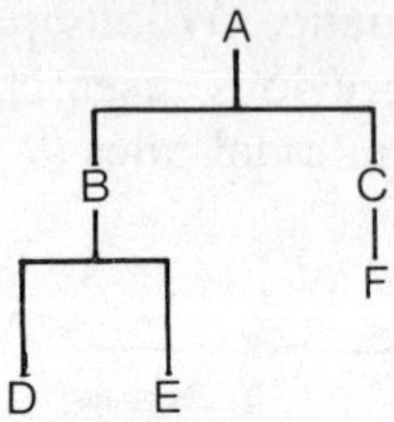

can be expressed as: A(B(D,E),C(F))
The conversion of one tree into another is a matter of defining rewriting rules applying to the whole or part of a string (tree), e.g.

$$A(B(*),C(*)) \rightarrow A(C(*),B(*))$$

where * indicates any subtree or subordinated element. This would convert the tree above into:

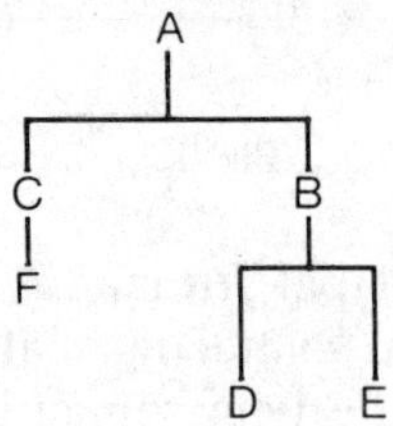

Tree-transducers are able to deal with the occurrence of optional elements in trees or sub-trees which are not affected by the conversion rules, e.g. the occurrence of an unspecified string or tree '?' between B and C at the same level. (For example, B and C might be elements of a phrasal verb *look . . . up*.) The rule might then be written:

$$A(B(*),?,C(*)) \rightarrow A(C(*),?,B(*))$$

They can also be applied in the conversion of strings of elements or subtrees into trees or into other strings of elements or subtrees, e.g.

$$A(*)+B+C(*) \rightarrow D(A(*),B)+C(*))$$

i.e.

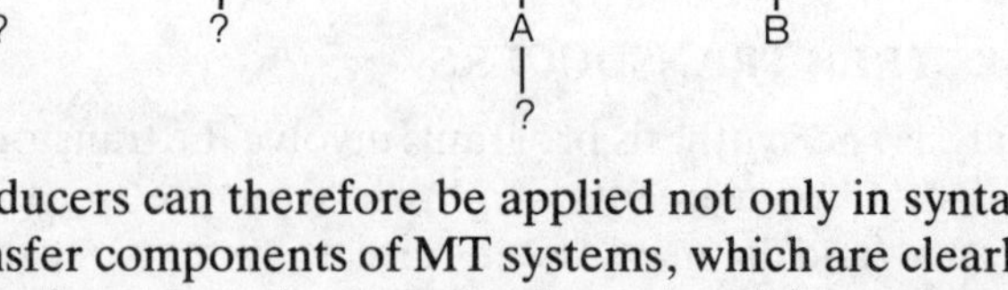

Tree-transducers can therefore be applied not only in syntactic analysis and in the transfer components of MT systems, which are clearly their most obvious applications, but also in procedures involving strings and loosely structured representation (e.g. in morphological analysis, cf. example in TAUM, Ch. 13.1). Applied in syntactic analysis tree-transducers operate as bottom-up parsers (Ch. 3.4), building upwards from strings of grammatical categories to phrase structure trees (NP or VP) and to sentence structure trees.

9.15 CHARTS

Natural language analysis involves typically the computation of a large number of possible partial analyses, many of which, notoriously, lead to dead ends. (This was amply demonstrated in the finite state and phrase structure parsers of the first MT decade.) Charts have been developed as means of keeping track of partial analyses and providing data for the selection of the 'best' parsings (Varile 1983).

The basic principle of the chart is that tree structures can be represented as labelled graphs. For example, the tree:

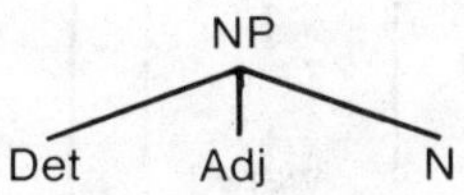

(where the dominance relations are explicit and the linear (precedence) relations are implicit, cf. Ch. 3.4). As a chart this appears as:

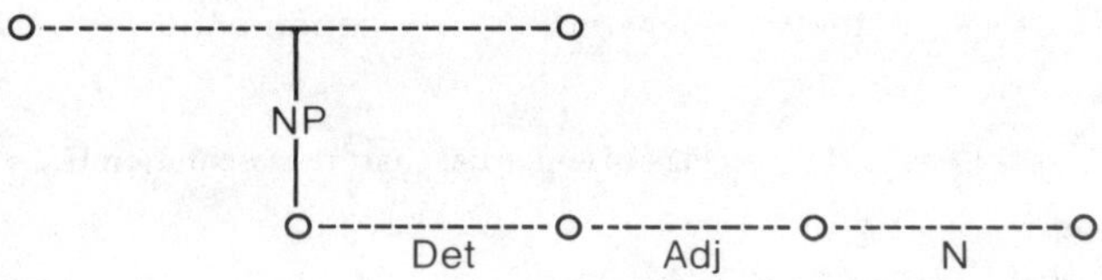

(where the linear relations are explicit and the dominance relations implicit).

Alternative analyses can be easily accommodated. Suppose, for example, two analyses of *The peasants were revolting*: one in which the VP (*were revolting*) is interpreted as Cop + Adj, and the other in which it is interpreted as Aux + PrPt (i.e. a present durative form). The two interpretations can be included on the same chart (Fig. 13).

The interpretation of charts in parsing involves the creation of arcs which subsume sequences of arcs, i.e. the replacement of complete analyses for partial analyses. In the process, some arcs for partial analyses are not subsumed, they represent failed analyses. For example, the analysis of the sentence *They were condemned prisoners* might start from the chart in Fig. 14.

The next stages are illustrated in Fig. 15: an arc enclosing Adj(condemned) and N(prisoners) is drawn, i.e. NP (Adj(condemned), N(prisoners)); and an arc enclosing Aux(were) and PstPt(condemned) is also drawn, i.e. the passive construction: VP (Aux(were), PstPt(condemned)).

The parser now looks for complete structures. In the lower part of the chart, there is no arc which can subsume VP and N; there is one which could subsume Pron and VP but this would leave N(prisoners) unaccounted for.

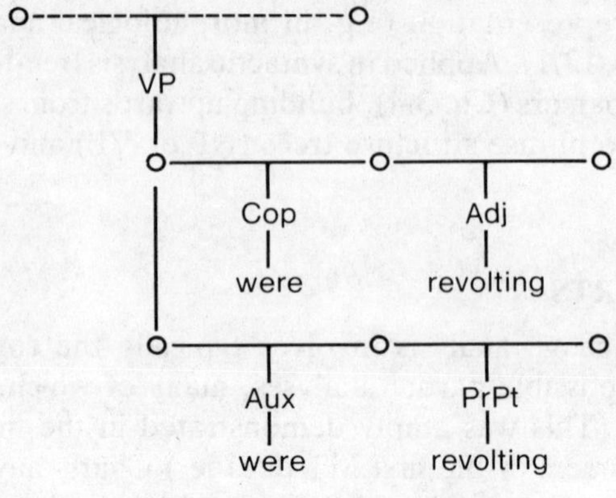

Fig. 13 — Partial chart representation I.

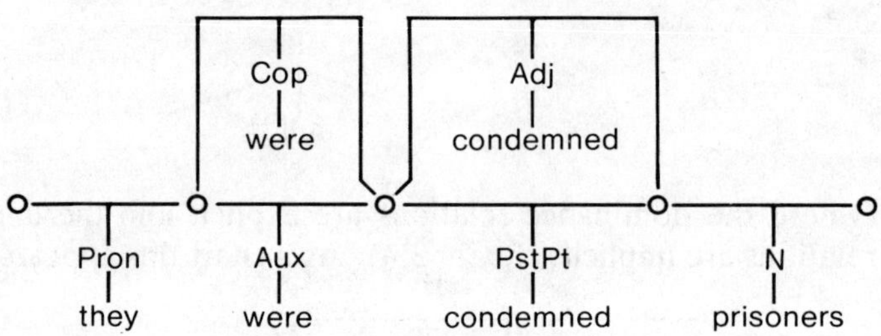

Fig. 14 — Partial chart representation II.

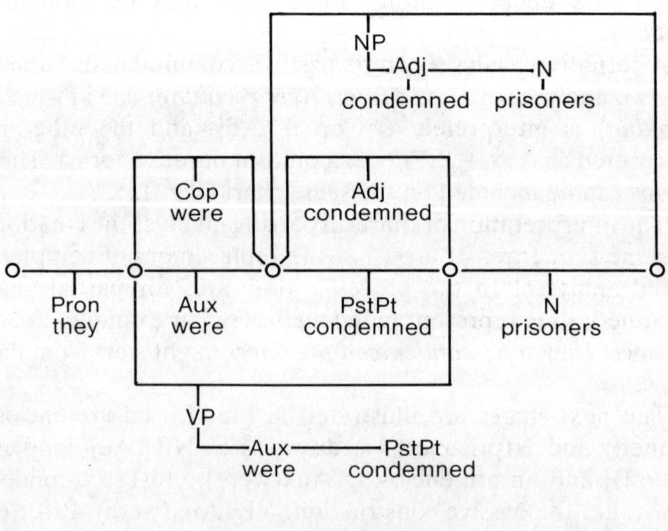

Fig. 15 — Chart representation III.

As a result the only successful parse joins Cop and NP as a VP, and then Pron and VP as S, producing the final complete arc: S (NP (Pron(they)), VP(Cop(were), NP(Adj(condemned), N(prisoners))).

Charts made their first appearance in MT systems in the TAUM project (13.1), and in the context of the MIND project (Ch. 17.8), where they were developed by Martin Kay and Ronald Kaplan. Subsequently, charts have been used in GETA, SUSY, METAL, and Eurotra. The flexibility of the chart method of handling parsing data is indicated by the fact that they have been used with a number of different types of parsers.

9.16 SEMANTIC ANALYSIS

Before the late 1960s the analysis of sense relations among lexical items in sentences and texts tended to be divorced from the analysis of syntactic relations. The thesaurus approach of the Cambridge group and the correlational anlysis of the Milan group were conceived essentially as alternatives to syntax-based approaches. Semantic information was incorporated in word-for-word and syntax-oriented systems in the form of semantic features (e.g. 'human', 'mass', 'quality') attached to lexical entries in order to resolve ambiguities of structure and to aid selection of TL forms. The use of semantic features and 'selection restrictions' has remained a standard method since the 1960s (Ch. 3.6).

Analysis of semantic relations as such was not practised until the appearance of 'interlingual' systems. These systems (e.g. CETA, LRC) introduced the analysis of logical relations (predicates, arguments, attributes), which has continued to be employed in later 'transfer' systems and in other MT approaches. On the other hand, the analysis of lexical sense relations (synonymy, paraphrase, causation, etc.) and lexical decomposition has generally appeared only in systems adopting AI approaches (Ch. 15 and below).

The most popular type of semantic analysis has been the use of 'case frame' analysis, adopted in many systems ('direct' as well as 'transfer') during the 1970s and now established as a standard proven technique. The notions of 'case' and 'case frame' were introduced during the late 1960s primarily from the work of Charles Fillmore (1968). The intention was to capture the equivalence of semantic roles in sentences such as:

John sold the car to Mary
The car was sold to Mary by John
Mary was sold the car by John

where it can be said that in each one *John* is the 'agent' of the transaction, *Mary* the 'beneficiary' (or recipient) and *the car* the 'object' (or 'patient'). Agent, Beneficiary, and Object (or Patient) are case relations; others are Instrument, Source, Goal, etc. In English they are often expressed by prepositions (*by* for Agents, *to* for Beneficiaries, *with* for Instruments, etc.); in other languages by 'surface' case markers (e.g. in Latin or Russian: accusative, dative, or ablative case endings). The 'case frame' for a verb is the specification of those case relations which may (optionally or obligatorily) occur with it. In this respect case frames are an extension of the notion of valency (Ch. 3.4). Cases are widely assumed to be 'universal' and language-independent; but there is remarkably little agreement on what the 'universal cases' are! Although originally formulated in the context of generative grammar, cases and case frames have been applied in many different contexts; they are particularly popular in Japanese MT projects (Ch. 18.2) and in AI approaches, where cases are frequently basic constituents of semantic grammars.

9.17 SEMANTIC PARSING

Parsers and analysis programs in MT, as in most computational linguistic processing, have been based on the sentence as the unit of analysis. Syntactic theory developed primarily as a description of sentence structure (cf. Chomsky's definition in 3.5 above). It does not account for the choice of specific sentence structures in context, e.g. selection of a passive instead of an active, nor for relationships between sentences within texts, e.g. selection of pronouns to refer to antecedent nouns. And it is not only syntactic analysis that has been confined to sentence structure. Most of semantic analysis has been restricted to resolving ambiguities within sentences.

Semantic parsing was developed within the context of AI research as a means of overcoming the well known inadequacies of sentence-based syntactic parsing and as a method of deriving cognitive representations for language understanding systems. In its 'pure' form, semantic parsing is based on the recognition of semantic features (of lexical items in text) either in sequences and patterns, or in 'conceptual' frameworks. An example of the former is Wilks' parser which looks for semantic 'templates', such as the sequence of 'primitives' MAN HAVE THING (Ch. 15.1). An example of the latter is Roger Schank's conceptual dependency approach in which the occurrence of a lexical item activates predictions of semantically (or conceptually) compatible items. Thus 'drink', as an item of INGEST(ation), predicts an actor, a liquid object, and an optional container, within a specific network of relationships (cf. Ch. 15.2). Both approaches may be regarded as extensions of the 'case frame' notion beyond the sentence, since both templates and predictions can act across sentence boundaries. Although semantic parsing has been employed most frequently in AI approaches to MT, the basic notions are being incorporated increasingly in otherwise essentially syntax-based systems (cf. GETA and Eurotra).

9.18 OUTLINE OF PROJECT DESCRIPTIONS AND GENERAL SOURCES

The next nine chapters deal with the many MT systems which have been developed since the mid-1960s. The arrangement is primarily according to system design, with chronological divisions also applied as appropriate.

Interlingual systems immediately after ALPAC are described first (Ch. 10), followed by other 'indirect' systems of the period (mainly of the 'syntactic transfer' type) in Ch. 11. The 'direct translation' systems since the mid-1960s are treated in the next chapter: Systran, LOGOS, PAHO, and others. This chapter is followed by extensive treatments of the important 'transfer' systems TAUM, SUSY, GETA, and METAL, and also the more recent Logos system and Czech research. Chapter 14 deals with the systems associated with the Commission of the European Communities, the various Systran systems, and the Eurotra project. The increasingly significant work on Artificial Intelligence approaches is described in the next chapter. This is followed by accounts of various other 'interlingual' projects since the mid-1970s; and in Ch. 17 by descriptions of restricted language and interactive MT systems. Lastly, Ch. 18 describes research in the Soviet Union since 1975 and the recent important MT activity in Japan. The final chapter of the book attempts to summarise the present situation and point to possible future prospects.

The main bibliographic sources for the systems are given in the appropriate sections. Major sources for the period as a whole are the surveys by Bruderer (1978), Hutchins (1978), Josselson (1971), Kulagina (1976), Lehmann & Stachowitz (1972), Locke (1975), Roberts & Zarechnak (1974), Slocum (1984a), Tucker & Nirenburg (1984), and Whitelock & Kilby (1983). All contain substantial bibliographies (particularly Bruderer's handbook), but in addition the excellent bibliography by Mel'chuk & Ravich (1978) covering the period 1964–70 must be mentioned.

10

Interlingual systems, 1965–1975

10.1 CENTRE D'ETUDES POUR LA TRADUCTION AUTOMATIQUE (CETA), UNIVERSITY OF GRENOBLE (1961–1971)

As we have seen (Ch. 5.5), the group at the University of Grenoble was set up in 1960 under the sponsorship of the Centre Nationale de la Recherche Scientifique, initially in conjunction with a MT group in Paris. In the following ten years it developed the interlingual approach in a system for Russian–French translation of mathematics and physics texts, which was tested from 1967 to 1971 on a corpus amounting to 400,000 words. In addition some trials were made with the system on SL texts in German and Japanese. (The definitive source for CETA is Vauquois 1975).

The central feature of CETA was a 'pivot language' (Veillon 1968), Vauquois 1969, Vauquois *et al.* 1970, Vauquois 1971), an artificial language free of the morphological and syntactic constraints of natural languages. An early description of the formalism was given in 1962 by Vauquois (1966), but full elaboration did not commence until 1966. (The mathematical properties of the formalism were described at length by Veillon *et al.* 1967.) The formalism was designed primarily as an interlingua for syntactic structures, i.e. as the common 'deep syntactic' base of the languages in the system. (In fact, CETA's deep syntax went further than Chomsky's notion of 'deep structure' and represented semantic relationships, as we shall see.) Its lexicon, however, did not represent a common base; instead the pivot language conjoined the lexical units of whichever two languages were being processed (usually Russian and French). In other words, while the CETA pivot language was a true interlingua in syntax, it was a bilingual 'transfer' mechanism in lexicon. Further, it was not intended that all sentences with the same meaning would be analysed as (or generated from) one unique pivot language representation. Nevertheless, although there were thus as many 'pivot languages' as there were SL–TL pairs analysed, all shared the same syntax and in this respect CETA considered their formalism as a first step in the direction of a 'universal language' (Vauquois 1975).

Analysis and synthesis in CETA proceeded in clearly separated stages. After pre-editing, Dictionary lookup (based on Lamb's approach, Ch. 4.10) identified word-stems and affixes. The next stage, Morphological analysis, eliminated unacceptable stem-affix groupings, e.g. the segmentetation of *habilité* as HABILIT+É would be accepted (past participle of HABILITER) but not as HABIL+ITÉ, since the dictionary would record -ETÉ as the nominalisation suffix for HABILE. Morphological analysis was defined formally as a finite state grammar (cf.3.4), and in addition, analysis rules were coded directly into the program, i.e. not located in separate tables; consequently, as in all programs which embed grammar rules in algorithms, the morphological analysis programs of CETA were difficult to change; however, their merit was much faster processing (Vauquois 1975).

Syntactic analysis was in two stages. The first stage was a phrase-structure analysis (a context free grammar, using the Cocke parser). It produced the familiar structures of nominal and verbal phrases, and it included identification of discontinuous elements (e.g. *look . . . up, take . . . away*) triggered by information attached to the particles (*up, away*). As an example, a partial phrase structure analysis of *Le remplacement des tramways par des autobus a permis un développement rapide de la circulation dans les rues de la ville* (from Vauquois 1971) is shown in Fig. 16.

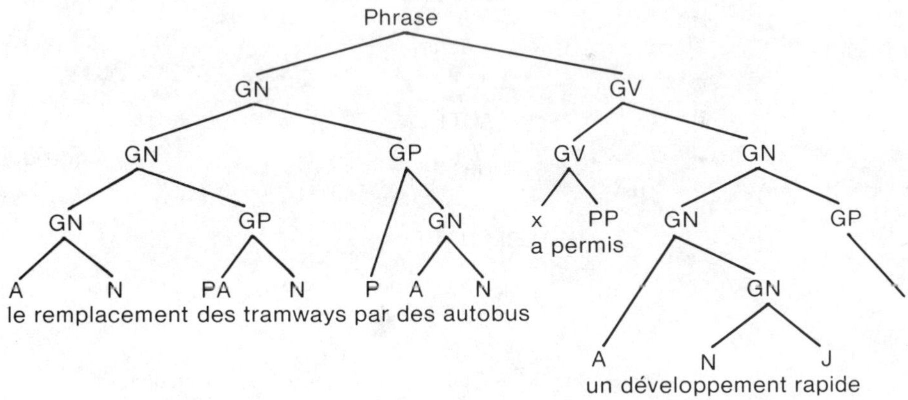

Fig. 16 — CETA surface syntactic analysis.

In the second stage, the 'surface syntactic' structure was augmented by dependency relations, e.g. in a clause the verb was marked as 'governor' and the noun phrase as 'dependent'. Where a sentence could have two or more syntactic interpretations, the system produced a 'surface syntactic' analysis for each. In this dependency tree representation, analyses entered the

Transfer stage where they were converted into 'pivot language' representations. These representations were in propositional logical form, consisting of predicates and their arguments or (in Tesnière's terminology 'actants'). To this end, lexical units were classed as either predicatives or non-predicatives: predicatives included adjectives and adverbs as well as verbs, and non-predicatives were nouns and articles. In the 'pivot language' representations the arguments of predicatives could be either non-predicatives or other predicatives. Transformation into pivot language syntax involved therefore the 'semantic' (propositional logical) analysis of dependency relations and the removal of word-classes (GN (=noun phrase), GV (=verb phrase), N, J (=adjective), etc.), resulting in the production of abstract tree representations, such as Fig. 17 (Vauquois 1971) for the sentence above:

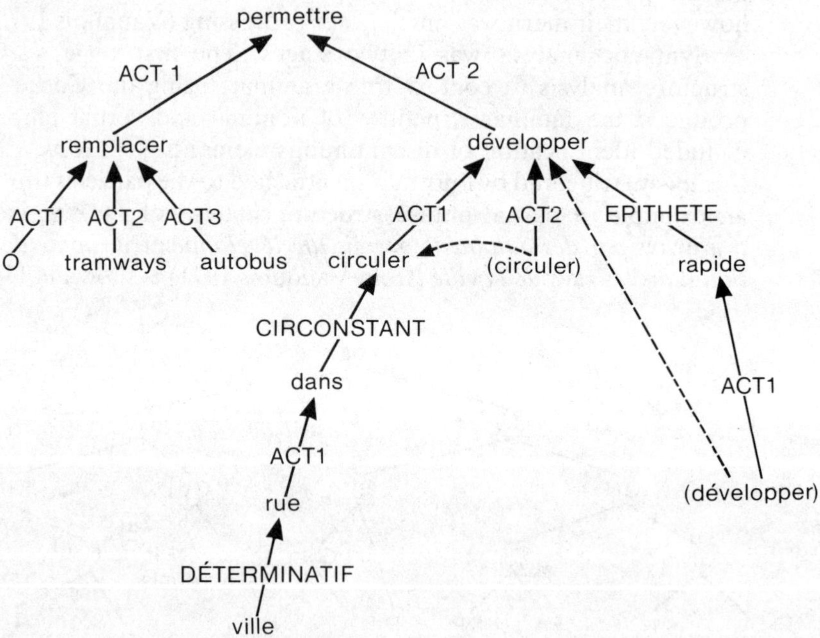

Fig. 17 — CETA 'pivot language' representation.

(where *circulation* is regarded as both what is developing (agent, ACT1) and what is being developed (object, ACT2), and *rapide* is both modifier and predicative of *développer*). At the same time the semantically anomalous analyses were 'filtered out' by checking the compatibilities of the constituent SL lexical components on the basis of information in the SL dictionary.

Such a tree was the source for TL synthesis. It began with the substitution of SL lexical units in the pivot language representation by their equivalent TL units. In syntactic synthesis, units were examined for their potential word-classes and for dependency relations with other word-classes. First, a predicative was located and its arguments checked as possible NP dependents. If one argument was itself a predicative, e.g. DEVELOPPER in the tree above, the possibility of a clause structure was also investigated (i.e. . . . *que la circulation se développe rapidement* . . . as well as NP *développement*). Then the argument nodes (Act 1, Act 2, etc.) were replaced by appropriate categories (V, NP, Adj, etc.), elements were reordered to conform to TL surface syntax and the synthesis of TL words was begun (e.g. Act 2 (DEVELOPPER) became either V(DEVELOPPE) or NP(DEVELOPPEMENT)). Morphological synthesis completed the process by producing the correct surface forms (including the editing of variants, e.g. *le* → *l'* before *a, e, i, o, u*).

An appraisal of the system in 1971 revealed that only 42% of sentences were being correctly translated and that readers found only 61% comprehensible. Although over half the incorrect sentences were caused by input errors, insufficient computer capacity or defects in programs which could be easily amended, it was found that the remainder lay beyond the system's capabilities. The main trouble was the rigidity of the levels of analysis; if morphological analysis failed because the dictionary had no entry for a word or did not record all homographic variants, then this affected all subsequent processes; if syntactic analysis failed to parse any part (however small) of a sentence, it was rejected. In addition, the parser was inefficient: it attempted too many partial analyses which came to nothing, and it produced too many analyses which had to be 'filtered out' later. What was needed was a parser which did not use its full armoury of analysis for every simple phrase structure but reserved the more complex parts for only complicated sentence structures. Finally, it was concluded that better synthesis would be possible if information about the 'surface' forms of SL sentences was also transferred; in the existing system information on choice of subject noun, use of passive, subordination of clauses, etc., was largely lost during conversion to pivot language representations, but such information could help considerably the selection of appropriate TL expressions.

A change in computer facilities in 1971 encouraged the Grenoble team to rethink the design of their MT system. From this date, the group, now called Groupe d'Etudes pour la Traduction Automatique (GETA), has worked on a system based on the 'transfer' approach (Ch. 13.3 below).

10.2 MEL'CHUK'S 'MEANING-TEXT' MODEL (1965–1976)

The syntactic representations of CETA were clearly influenced by the dependency grammar of Tesnière (1959), as the use of the term 'actant' reflects. However, the most direct influence on the CETA approach to MT system design was the 'meaning-text' model of the Russian linguist Mel'chuk (Mel'chuk & Zholkovskii 1970, Mel'chuk 1973), as the CETA researchers have acknowledged (Vauquois 1975, Vauquois *et al.* 1970). Mel'chuk's model is stratificational in conception, like the analogous but nevertheless distinct and independent theory of Lamb (1966). Mel'chuk's model was developed for an English–Russian system in collaboration with Olga Kulagina and others (1967, 1971), although it was not implemented for internal political reasons (Ch. 11.5 below). In the course of years, since its original formulation in 1965 by Zholkovsky and Mel'chuk it has grown into a fully fledged linguistic theory no longer specifically designed for MT application (Mel'chuk 1981). Nevertheless, it has remained more firmly rooted to the practicalities of MT analysis than Lamb's more theoretical speculations.

In Mel'chuk's 'meaning-text' model there are six levels or 'strata' of linguistic representations: phonetic, phonemic, morphemic, surface syntactic, deep syntactic, and semantic. (For MT purposes the first two are unimportant.) Surface syntactic representations include such grammatical dependency relations as 'subject-of', 'complement-of', 'auxiliary' and 'determinant', and the structure of nominal groups. Its elements are the 'actual lexemes' (words) of the language. Deep syntactic representations are tree structures indicating valency relations among root lexical elements ('generalised lexemes'), such as 'agent', 'instrument', and 'location'. Semantic representations are abstract networks of semantemes (meanings of generalised lexemes) or of elementary semantic units (semes). For any given SL sentence there could be a number of different semantic representations each corresponding to a number of possible interpretations. As in CETA, every strata would 'filter out' any syntactically and semantically anomalous representations from lower levels.

One important feature of the 'meaning-text' model is the incorporation of discourse indicators at both syntactic and semantic levels. Representations include links between pronouns and their antecedents, and they include an indication of which elements are the topic (or 'theme') of the sentence ('what it is about') and which are the comment (or 'rheme') of the sentence ('what is said about the topic'). At the deep syntactic and semantic levels there appear in addition indications of which elements are 'new' in the text, i.e. have not been mentioned in previous sentences, and which are 'given' (known or inferrable from earlier text, or which readers may be presumed to be familiar with already, i.e. can be presupposed).

A second important feature of the 'meaning-text' model was the extensive treatment of semantic relationships. The researchers established a set of some 50 'lexical functions' which linked generalised lexemes at the deep syntactic level. These lexical functions include, as one would expect, such relations as: synonymy, e.g. *shoot* and *fire*, antonymy, e.g. *victory* and *defeat*, and conversives, e.g. *fear* and *frighten*. They include also many other relations rarely (if ever) formalised in MT, and only recently considered in AI (and even in that field, rarely in the thoroughness of the 'meaning-text' model.). For example, a verb and an agentive noun, (*write* and *writer*, *prevent* and *obstacle*); and a verb and its causative form (*lie* and *lay*). They include also phraseological and idiomatic constructions, such as indications of the typical or 'idiomatic' verb for expressing particular relations to a given noun, e.g. the inceptive verb for *conference* is *open* but for *war* it is *break out*. Likewise, the causative verb for *dictionary* is *compile*, for *foundations* it is *lay* and for a *camp* it is *set up* or *pitch*. Finally, as a last example of a lexical function: the realisational or implementative verb for *order* is *fulfill*, for *law* it is *observe*, for *promise* it is *keep* and for *obligations* it is *discharge*. (In many respects, the notion of lexical function was a conceptual forerunner of AI notions of semantic representations, Ch. 15 below.)

The lexicographic aspect of the model was explored in depth. It resulted in the elaboration of the concept of an 'explanatory–combinatorial' dictionary, designed for the automatic generation of texts from a given semantic representation (Apresyan *et al.* 1969). The basic principles were that it must be "fully sufficient for a smooth, idiomatic and flexible expression of a given meaning", i.e. it must provide explicitly all the information necessary for the correct choice and usage of words in a given context. It was combinatorial in the sense that it showed the combinability of lexical items in utterances; and it was explanatory in the sense that through the lexical functions it provided semantic interpretations of combinations. Fragments of dictionaries were elaborated for a number of semantic 'fields', e.g. words for emotions (Iordanskaya 1973).

In the description of the CETA system it was made clear that it was not a fully interlingual system. It is true that CETA could deal with some syntactic equivalences, e.g. the structure dominated by *développer* in Fig. 17 above could represent either a subordinate clause with *développer* as finite verb or a noun phrase with *développement* as a verbal noun. In this respect CETA corresponded to the 'deep syntactic' level of Mel'chuk's model. However, CETA lacked much of the detailed paraphrasing operations present in Mel'chuk's model, which were made possible by the indication of complex semantic relations.

The interlingual features went far beyond those of CETA. Not only were its representations genuinely interlingual, and not restricted to syntactic equivalences, but Mel'chuk also recognised the importance of retaining SL 'surface' information about theme and rheme, the choice of subject noun, the use of passive, subordination of clauses, etc., which could help substantially in the selection of appropriate TL forms. It is only to be regretted that no actual implementation was possible, although whether it would have been in fact any more successful must be doubtful.

10.3 LINGUISTICS RESEARCH CENTER (LRC), UNIVERSITY OF TEXAS (1970–75)

Research on MT was revived at Texas by a contract from the USAF Rome Air Development Center for research on a German–English system. The project was established in 1970 with Rolf A. Stachowitz as principal researcher, while Winfred Lehmann continued as overall director of the Linguistics Research Center (LRC). The main sources for information on this project are the reports by Lehmann and Stachowitz (1970, 1971–75, 1972a).

Some work had continued intermittently on the earlier German–English model (Ch. 4.11), although mainly it seems on expansion of the dictionary: by 1970 the German dictionary contained 40,000 items and the English 77,500 items (Lehmann and Stachowitz 1971), very little more than in 1965 (although additional information for a further 47,000 English items was available from the Russian Master Dictionary, which had been deposited at LRC, Ch. 4.11). The new system was, however, to be on a larger and more ambitious scale: a fully automatic 'interlingual' system.

At an early stage of the project, during 1970 and 1971, the Linguistics Research Center held a series of study conferences and individual consultations involving prominent linguists and MT researchers. The results were summarized in a 'feasibility study on fully automatic high quality translation', to which were appended a number of papers by participants and consultants (Lehmann & Stachowitz 1971). There was certainly no uniformity of opinion about the future prospects and direction of MT, but the LRC group felt able to conclude that their research was on the right lines. The major problems of MT were no longer computational but linguistic. Theoretical research in linguistics supported the 'universal base' hypothesis: "the surface structures of any language can be related to such a universal base. Since the universal base in turn can be used for deriving the surface structure of any language, the universal base can serve as the intermediary language between any source language and any target language." In other words, the 'interlingua' approach to MT presented a feasible model. The earlier LRC model had been essentially a syntactic 'transfer' model (Ch. 4.11), now structural analysis was to go to a universal 'deep' level common to any SL and TL. The project's aim was, therefore, to be the development of methods of analysis and formalisms of representation which could be applied to any pair of languages.

In fact LRC had further ambitions. MT was to be just one part, albeit important, of a general system, the Linguistics Research System (LRS), later to be renamed METAL (Mechanical Translation and Analysis of Languages). LRS was to be of sufficient generality for application to other aspects of natural language processing; there was particular interest in applications in information retrieval. The ultimate goal was a system which could recognise and produce synonymous sentences, by deriving 'canonical form' (i.e. semantic interlingual) representations from sentences and generating all 'surface' realisations of such representations (Stachowitz 1971).

Unfortunately, most linguistic theory was inadequate for MT purposes: linguistic research had dealt "primarily with syntactic analysis of individual sentences, and hardly at all with semantic problems and discourse analysis." Transformational grammar had proved to be inefficient as a model (Ch. 9.11); more hopeful were dependency grammars and grammars based on the string analysis model which Harris had developed at the University of Pennsylvania (Ch. 3.5 above). The latter formed the foundation of the LRC procedures. However, while syntactic problems seemed tractable, the neglect of semantic problems hindered advances in MT; in particular, there were the differences of 'world views' reflected in the vocabularies and semantic relationships of languages. Nevertheless, it could be assumed that "closely related languages, like English and German, are similar in expressing their semantic distinctions overtly and covertly, and even in their surface structures; accordingly, they are relatively easy to translate into each other." The LRC group were encouraged to concentrate on these two languages: "for the development of the technology of machine translation, systems designed for related languages are accordingly recommended at this time as an immediate goal. Medium-range goals (Russian–English) and long-range goals (Chinese–English) should also be planned." In fact, LRC did start up again research on Russian using as a foundation the Russian Master Dictionary. A Russian–English project was therefore established in parallel to the German–English one, based on the same methodology and approach to MT system design and using the same computational techniques (Roberts & Zarechnak 1974).

As in the contemporary CETA project, which had also adopted the 'interlingual' approach, the basic stages of the LRC system were: analysis of SL texts into an intermediary representation, and synthesis of TL texts from the intermediary representation. But, also like the CETA 'pivot language', the LRC interlingua was not a genuine interlingua. It was restricted to syntactic structures ('universal' deep structures); there was no attempt to decompose lexical items into (universal) semantic primitives, for example. Tosh's earlier suggestions of 'universal' numerical semantic codes were not pursued; nor were his ideas of using Roget's *Thesaurus* to establish interlingual codes (Ch. 4.11). The lack of semantic analysis meant that the system could not, for example, handle such semantic equivalences as *He talks a lot* and *He is loquacious*. Conversion of vocabulary from German into English was consequently made through a bilingual dictionary operating essentially at the lexical level.

Analysis was performed by three separate 'grammars' working in sequence. After morphological analysis and dictionary lookup, the 'surface sentence' was converted by a 'surface grammar' into one or more tentative 'standard strings'. In this process certain elements discontinuous in the surface form (e.g. verbs such as *look . . . up*) would be brought together. In the second stage, the tentative standard strings were tested by a 'standard grammar' for syntactic well-formedness and each string accepted by the standard grammar was then provided with one or more phrase-structure representations, called 'standard trees'. The result of such an analysis for the sentence *An old man in a green suit looked at Mary's dog* is illustrated by the standard tree in Fig. 18 (Lehmann and Stachowitz 1972a).

The third stage, 'normalisation', filtered out semantically ill-formed standard trees by testing the semantic compatibility of syntactically related lexical items (referring to information provided in dictionary entries). Each standard tree was then converted into a 'normal form' (or several 'normal forms' if the sentence was genuinely ambiguous). In this 'deep structure' representation relationships between items were expressed in terms of

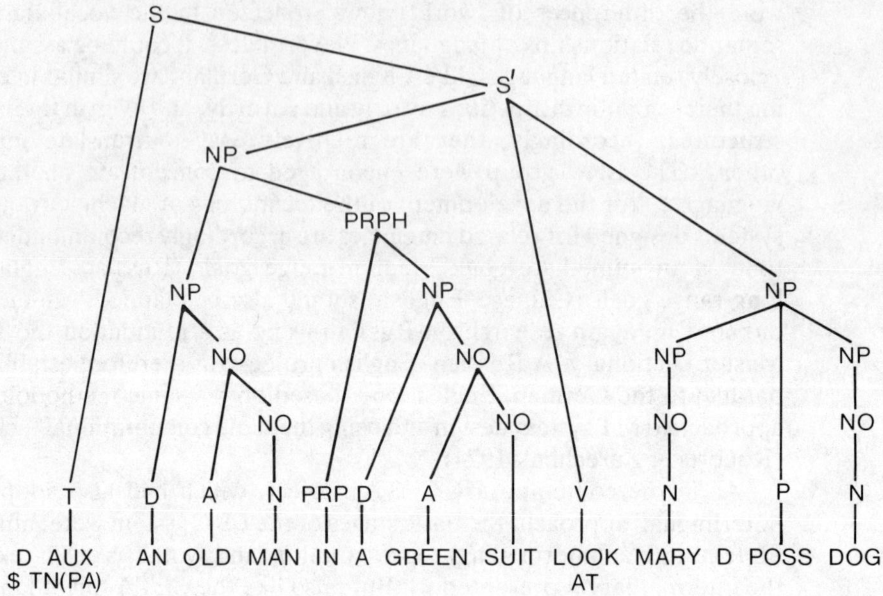

Fig. 18 — LRC standard tree representation.

'predicates' and 'arguments' or, alternatively, 'entities' and 'attributes' (much as in CETA representations, Ch. 10.1). From the standard tree above would be derived the normal form in Fig. 19.

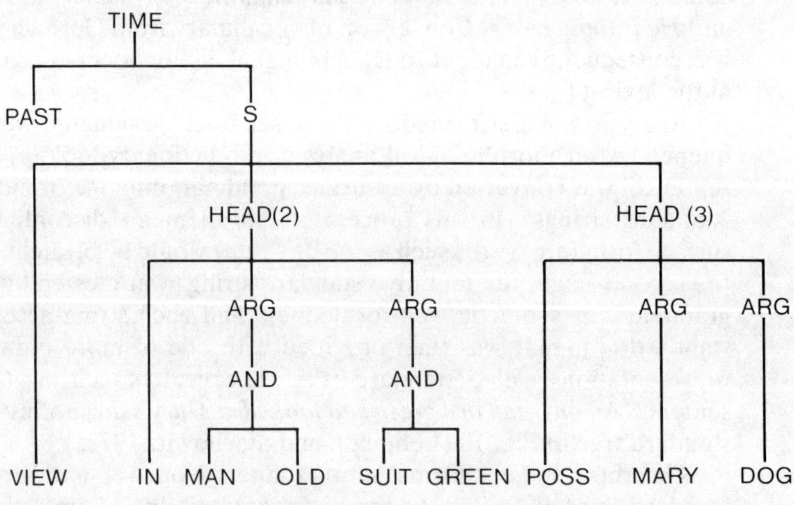

Fig. 19 — LRC 'normal form' representation.

The conversion from the standard tree into this normal form involved the identification of *in* as the predicate element of a tree with *the green suit* and *the old man* as argument elements; and the recognition of the adjectives in these noun phrases as arguments of their respective head nouns. The result is a dependency-style semantic representation intended to be independent of language-specific surface and phrase structure forms. It could not be completely language independent, however, because the system lacked semantic decomposition of lexical items. (The conversion of 'normal forms' into 'canonical forms' would have been the next stage of analysis.) Consequently, such semantic equivalences as *He ignored her* and *He took no notice of her*, could not be indicated since these sentences would have different 'deep syntactic' structures.

Synthesis of TL (English) sentences proceeded first by the substitution of TL lexical elements in the 'normal form', then the conversion of 'normal forms' into 'standard strings' and finally the conversion of strings into 'surface sentences'.

The LRC system suffered, like CETA, from an inadequate method of syntactic analysis. There were obvious problems if parsers failed to produce a structure for a given input at some stage of the analysis. But there were equally problems with too many analyses. For example, the 'context-free' (bottom-up) parser in the 'standard grammar' component often produced too many phrase structure analyses, e.g. for nominal constructions with prepositional phrases (cf. Ch. 3.6 above). The absence of intersentential and discourse semantics also allowed multiple 'normal forms' to be produced for a single 'standard tree'. Furthermore, since a single normal form could obviously be the source of many different (but semantically equivalent) surface forms the problems of synthesis were also multiplied. In the end, the complexities of the procedures became too great for a workable MT system.

However, from the beginning LRC projects were conceived as general-purpose systems designed also for other automated language processes. At the theoretical level, for example, the possibilities of 'language comprehension' systems were investigated. These would have included not only a semantic analysis component but also logical components and (AI-type) 'real world' knowledge and "awareness" components (Stachowitz 1971). The research on information retrieval in the later years of the project were part of this activity. Most emphasis was consequently placed on the system's ability to produce single 'normal form' semantic representations from a great variety of surface forms, which had potentially much relevance for automatic indexing and abstracting (Lehmann & Stachowitz 1972a).

Funding for the project ended in 1975, and there was again a hiatus in MT research at LRC, until a new project was started in 1978 (Ch. 13.4 below).

10.4 FORSCHUNGSGRUPPE LIMAS, BONN (1964–76)

Founded in 1964 by Alfred Hoppe the LIMAS (Linguistik und maschinelle Sprachverarbeitung) research group in Bonn pursued lines of theoretical MT research similar in a number of respects to those of the Milan group (Ch. 5.3). The basic premise was that computer language processing, including MT, must be based on a language-independent semantic syntax, a 'communicative grammar' expressing content elements and their relations (Hoppe 1966, 1967; Lehmann & Stachowitz 1972). A classification of content elements or 'semantic factors' (i.e. essentially semantic features such as 'place', 'location', 'interior', 'product', 'producer') was developed; every lexical item was coded positively or negatively for each of the finite set (about 80) of 'factors'; translation from English to German involved the comparison and matching of matrices of coded 'factors' both between languages and within languages. For example, German *nach* is either a preposition coded for 'time' or a preposition coded for 'place'; the selection of English *after* (coded for 'time') or English *to* (coded for 'place') depends on the coding of the associated nouns, i.e. *nach dem Mittagessen: after lunch; nach Köln: to Cologne* (Schweisthal 1967). Semantic constraints were also expressed in terms of 'case frames', although Hoppe did not use this terminology. For example, he referred to a 'Geschehensziel' appearing as a subject (*der Hund wird gefüttert*), as accusative object (. . . *füttert den Hund*), as the specifier in a compound (*Hundefütterung*), or a genitive attribute (*Fütterung des Hundes*) (Hoppe 1966). Clearly, Hoppe's 'communicative grammar' was a variant of semantic syntax. As in the case of Ceccato's similar approach, the LIMAS group was anticipating the development of 'interlingual' semantic grammars within the AI framework (Ch. 15).

The LIMAS programme of research consisted therefore primarily in the laborious establishment of a lexicon of semantic factors, the construction of factor matrices for English and German vocabulary, the determination of analysis rules for deriving factor formulas, the development of matrix matching and conversion procedures, and the establishment of synthesis rules for deriving output text. The system was intended to be fully reversible, and potentially extendable to other languages (Zint 1967). From the late 1960s the emphasis turned much more to theoretical explorations of general text analysis (e.g. for information retrieval), and so not surprisingly the practical results were meagre: a 1975 demonstration of the LIMAS content analysis program was devoted to a short text of just 400 words (24 sentences). The LIMAS group was funded by the Deutsche Forschungsgemeinschaft until 1976 (Hoppe 1984).

11

Other indirect systems, 1965–1975

11.1 EURATOM, EUROPEAN SCIENTIFIC DATA PROCESSING CENTRE (CETIS), ISPRA (ITALY) (1967–75)

When EURATOM (the European Atomic Energy Community) acquired the Georgetown Russian–English system in 1963 (Ch. 4.3) the primary purpose was to provide scientists at Ispra and other EURATOM research centres with a rapid and economic translation service. Translations were delivered without post-editing and, although it was accepted that the quality was not high, for the purposes of 'current awareness' and quick information users were satisfied to receive some form of translation rather than none at all (Perschke 1968).

The secondary purpose of the acquisition was to use it as the basis for research at the European Scientific Data Processing Centre, CETIS (Centre Européen pour le Traitement de l'Information Scientifique), which had been set up by EURATOM at Ispra in 1959. The Centre came under the aegis of the Commission of the European Communities in 1967, when the European Communities were formed from a merger of EURATOM, the European Coal and Steel Community, and the European Economic Community. The research at CETIS was conducted under the direction of Sergei Perschke. The first step was to extend the application into the field of documentation by the development of a system for the automatic indexing and abstracting of Russian documents (Perschke 1969). Its software was based on the SLC-II macro-assembler programming system, an improved version of the system developed by A. F. R. Brown to run the Georgetown (GAT) translation programs (Ch. 4.3); and after subsequent enhancements and improvements it became from 1972 the fully automatic information retrieval system FAIRS (Perschke *et al.* 1974).

Support had earlier been given to the development at the University of

Brussels of a Russian–French system, latterly based on the Georgetown system (Ch. 5.6). Work began at CETIS in 1967 on a Russian–English system, now based on SLC-II, and designed for the IBM 360/65. The principle problems with the Georgetown system were seen as the poor handling of homographs and the lack of full syntactic analysis. In the CETIS system SL analysis was to produce a full 'surface syntactic' representation with some semantic markers. The syntactic model adopted was Ceccato's correlational analysis (Ch. 5.3). Perschke had been a member of the Milan group before going to CETIS, and Ceccato's research had received funds from EURATOM in earlier years (Ceccato 1967). In the spirit of Ceccato, Perschke (1970) included as a long-term objective the introduction of semantic analysis of lexical items and of "a system of associations, i.e. the formal description of general knowledge about the relation of things to each other." More immediately, the CETIS project was to be the basis for a multilingual system, designed to cope with the pressing needs of the European Communities translation services (Ch. 14). Although research would begin with Russian–English the intention was to add other TLs soon afterwards (Perschke 1970a). The system was designed therefore on the 'transfer' model, with separation of SL analysis and TL synthesis. In fact, the system was modelled on the 'syntactic transfer' approach advocated earlier by Yngve (Ch. 4.7), initially operating "at a very low level of semantic analysis" (Perschke 1968), but capable of progressive refinement "because of its open-ended design" (Perschke 1970a). There were five stages: pre-editing (as in the Georgetown system), dictionary lookup and morphological analysis (rather similar to the Systran approach), transfer (which combined SL syntactic analysis and SL–TL converstion into TL tree representations), and morphological synthesis (Perschke *et al.* 1974). However, only the analysis programs were developed in any detail as most activity concentrated on the information retrieval applications, and so the full system did not reach a prototype implementation.

In effect, the CETIS research was overtaken by events. For its practical Russian–English MT needs, EURATOM installed Systran at Ispra in 1970 (Ch. 12.1). By 1975 there were far more advanced MT projects under way within the European Communities, the Leibniz group was laying plans for collaborative research on a multilingual system and there were beginning to emerge ideas for a European multilingual system based on the most advanced linguistic and computational developments (Ch. 14).

11.2 UNIVERSITY OF CALIFORNIA, BERKELEY (1967–75)

Research on Chinese-English MT began at Berkeley while Lamb was still director, under C. Y. Dougherty (Ch. 4.10). Around 1967 there was the beginning of a certain amount of cooperative work with the centres at Bunker-Ramo and the University of Texas (Wang *et al.* 1973) Berkeley was to be responsible for a large machine-readable dictionary and the development of an automatic parser and grammar; Texas (Ch. 4.11) joined in the lexicographic work and Bunker-Ramo (Ch. 4.6) undertook to apply its fulcrum technique in the development of "interlingual mapping rules for Chinese to English" (taking as input the structural trees provided by the Berkeley parser), and also the development of an English synthesis program (cf. Chai 1968). However, in 1967 MT research at Bunker-Ramo ceased, and since the Berkeley parser was also only at an initial stage of experimentation, "no fruitful results came out of the cooperative venture."

In 1968, US research on Chinese–English MT was consolidated at Berkeley, under the direction of William S. Y. Wang who had previously been on a Chinese MT project at the Ohio State University (Ch. 4.13). Closely linked to the MT research was the Dictionary on Computer (DOC) project concerned primarily with Chinese historical phonology. The MT project itself, the Project on Linguistic Analysis (POLA), continued the earlier emphasis at Berkeley on the problems of analysing and parsing Chinese. There was also considerable research on a Chinese–English dictionary (70,000 entries in 1973) and on comparative analyses of Chinese and English syntax, but almost no work was done on programs for the synthesis of English output. Details of POLA are to be found in Wang *et al.* 1973, 1974, 1975, Wang 1976).

The POLA system QUINCE was based on the 'transfer' approach: "Chinese sentences constitute the source language input. This is submitted to the parser and analysed into structural trees. Interlingual processes then apply to these structures to map them into the appropriate English structure. These structures are then used for synthesis into the target English output by applying the necessary surface structure rules" (Wang *et al.* 1973). The translation process had six stages: Input, Segmentation, Lexicon, Grammars, Transfer, Extract.

The input of Chinese text characters causes problems for all MT projects: POLA experimented with a number of systems for coding into Standard Chinese Telegraphic Code (including the one developed at IBM and the Itek Corporation, Ch. 4.2, but it was found generally unreliable and difficult to operate). A large part of the POLA research effort was devoted to this task before the project ended in 1975.

The next stage after input (segmentation) dealt with one of the problems peculiar to Chinese, namely the lack of sentence-delimiting and word-delimiting symbols. Using punctuation marks, prepositions, and conjunctions it derived a preliminary segmentation of Chinese texts into tentative sentences and 'subsentences'. The stage of dictionary lookup (Lexicon) could then search for the longest matching sequences of Chinese characters. By 1975 the Chinese–English dictionary comprised over 82,000 entries (30% general vocabulary, 60% physics, 10% chemistry).

The parsing of Chinese ('Grammars') was performed by a battery of five 'subgrammars', which acted on tree and subtree structures. Syntactic analysis of Chinese is made difficult by the absence in Chinese of surface markers for tenses, gender, cases, and grammatical roles. With most Chinese words having multiple syntactic functions, it was necessary to include semantic markers in dictionary entries which could be referred to during analysis for homograph disambiguation.

In the next stage, Transfer, the synthesis of English-like structures was begun. Structural transfer rules were formalised as generalised tree transducers (cf. 9.14), e.g. converting:

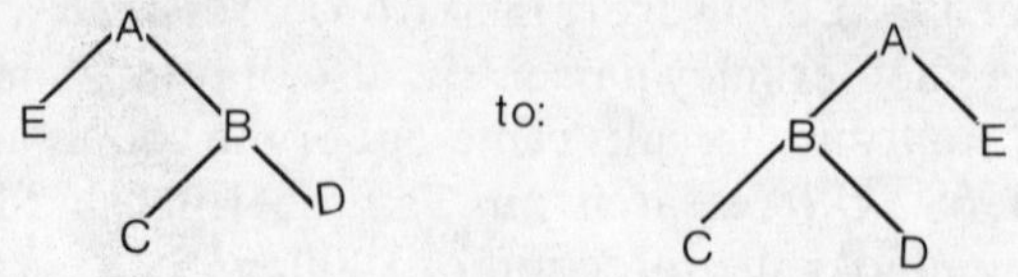

For example, these rules (applied recursively) could transform the Chinese structure shown in Fig. 20.

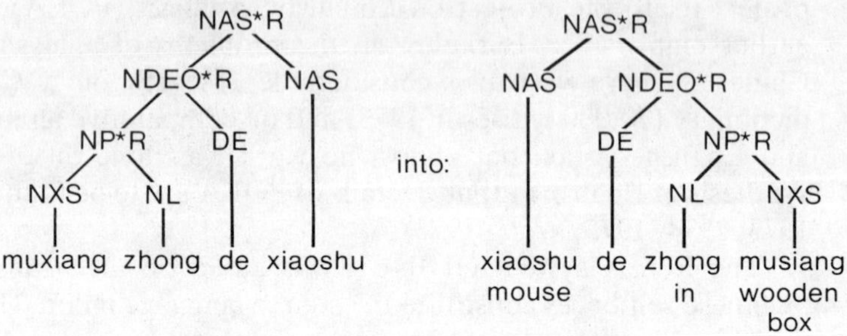

Fig. 20 — POLA structural transfer.

Subsequent parts of transfer would substitute TL (English) lexical items, delete *de*, insert *the*, and (since the grammar code NAS indicates a plural noun) change *mouse* to *mice*. In the final stage ('extract'), the English sentence string would be stripped from the TL tree structure, and appropriate morphological adjustments performed for English output.

On the computational side, QUINCE had a number of features in common with other experimental systems at the time (in particular CETA and LRC, Ch. 10.1 and 10.2). It followed the sound practice of distinguishing clearly between linguistic data and algorithmic procedures, and programming complexity was avoided. At an earlier phase of the project, it had become apparent that the monolithic grammars were growing unmanageable, and in 1973 the system was redesigned on 'modular' lines (reaching final implementation in May 1974.) The grammar was divided into a flexible sequence of 'subgrammars' (formulated as phrase-structure grammars) allowing linguists to rewrite small areas of the grammatical program without fear of impairing the system as a whole. It was intended that some of these subgrammars could incorporate heuristic techniques (presumably on lines indicated by Garvin, Ch. 4.6 above), although at the close of the project in 1975 none had in fact been implemented. There was also some interest in introducing intersentential analysis, particularly since written Chinese itself does not indicate sentence boundaries. Finally, The POLA project attempted to make the system 'portable'. The whole program was written in a 'structural programming language' (GASP), apparently with similarities to Pascal, which it was claimed (or hoped) made the system "highly machine independent" and easily adaptable to any large-scale third generation computer (Wang *et al.* 1975).

11.3 OTHER US PROJECTS

Bruderer (1978) reports a project by Nitaya Kanchanawan of the Ramkhamkaeng University of Bangkok on an experimental Thai–English MT system. Research began at the Florida State University, Tallahassee, in 1974 and transferred to Texas in 1975. It was a strictly limited system on simple intransitive sentences, with a dictionary of just 345 Thai entries. Apparently, the parser combined a Backus-Naur formalism of a context-free grammar with transformational rules. The analysis was oriented towards TL (English) structures producing 'deep structures' for TL synthesis; however, there was no semantic analysis and therefore no resolution of polysemes. The MT design would appear to have had little or no connection with the major LRC project at the time (Ch. 10.3).

Equally tentative was the research at the Dropsie College for Hebrew and Cognate Learning, Philadelphia, by James D. Price. In 1969, he submitted a doctorate dissertation which described work on a context-sensitive phrase-structure grammar of Hebrew in preparation for a projected Hebrew–English MT program, apparently on the 'syntactic transfer' model (Price 1969).

11.4 UNIVERSITY OF MÜNSTER (1966–1969)

The research by Klaus Brockhaus (1971) at the University of Münster was devoted to the design of a small-scale system for reciprocal translation of English and German. A primary objective of this research, completed in 1969, was the development of methods of phrase-structure analysis for English and German and of generalised algorithms for syntactic transfer. The system was tested on a very small corpus of deliberately limited nature. The partial syntaxes for German and English did not, for example, treat adverbs or conjunctions, or the English progressive present form of verbs; and the partial vocabularies excluded all instances of homography. The aim was solely to test the adequacy of the syntax program; problems of semantics were deliberately ignored. Although obviously limited, the work represents an early attempt to generalise syntactic transfer algorithms in the form of abstract tree-transduction rules (Ch. 9.14). Brockhaus moved subsequently to Heidelberg where he directed the SALAT project (Ch. 16.1).

11.5 BULGARIAN ACADEMY OF SCIENCES (1964–76)

Research in Bulgaria was stimulated by preparations for the 5th International Congress of Slavists held in Sofia in 1963 (Ljudskanov 1966). At this time began studies by Leskov on problems of applied linguistics with reference to

MT between Slavic languages; and the theoretical research by Alexander Ljudskanov on Russian–Bulgarian MT.

In 1964 the section 'Automatic translation and mathematical linguistics' was established in the Mathematical Institute of the Bulgarian Academy of Sciences, Sofia. Its aims were the compilation of a Russian–Bulgarian dictionary for mathematics, the construction of a general algorithm for lexical analysis, and the commencement of work on a Russian–Bulgarian MT system, initially a word-for-word and dictionary system.

Ljudskanov's main contributions were his theoretical studies of human translation and MT strategies (Ljudskanov 1972). One of his arguments was that translation does not necessarily require full ('deep') understanding of the subject matter being translated. What is required is knowledge of how to select the appropriate TL expressions for a given SL text. Even in cases where apparently the translator refers to extra-linguistic knowledge in order to understand the text, "the referential approach is aimed not at establishing information about the real world for its own sake but at using the real world to establish information about the corresponding devices of the language" (Ljudskanov 1968). He introduced the idea of 'necessary translation information' consisting of the basic lexical information and the additional contextual information necessary for interpretation. The problem for MT is to determine what this information is to be in particular cases. The contextual information will vary according to the language pairs involved; it is not essential always to analyse to the 'deepest' semantic levels; MT can work sometimes at more superficial levels. His conclusion was that MT requires a different type of model to the general linguistic models developed by CETA and by Mel'chuk, for example. His inclination was, therefore, away from abstract interlingual approaches and towards a practical 'transfer' approach.

Some results were achieved after 1970 on an experimental Russian–Bulgarian system for mathematics texts, implemented on a Minsk-32 machine. The system was apparently of the 'syntactic transfer' type, based on dependency grammar. A basic assumption was the isomorphism of separate linguistic levels, permitting standard forms of analysis at morphological, syntactic, and semantic levels (Zarechnak 1979: 63). Certain parts of analysis and synthesis programs were, therefore, to be worked out as 'universal' algorithms, i.e. much as tree transducers may be regarded. It is unclear how much of the system was programmed; a large part of the research programme was devoted to quantitative and statistical studies of Bulgarian. The project appears to have ended before Ljudskanov's death in 1976 (Bruderer 1978).

11.6 PROJECTS AND RESEARCH IN THE SOVIET UNION (1966–76)

Reactions to the ALPAC report by MT researchers in the Soviet Union were highly critical. In 1969 Kulagina and a number of colleagues wrote (Locke 1975):

> We wish to declare decisively that this view has no real support: it is founded upon a failure to understand the problem in principle and confusion of its theoretical, scientific and practical aspects. The fact that machine translation has been ineffectual in practice to the present should, in our opinion, lead to an increase rather than a decrease in efforts in this area, especially in exploratory and experimental work.

Evidently, Soviet researchers were coming under as much pressure as their US colleagues to deliver working systems. As in the United States, those responsible for funding research began to lose interest and an era of lower MT support began (Roberts & Zarechnak 1974). There is then evidence of some decrease in Soviet research activity after the mid 1960s, but it is clear that MT did not suffer the virtual eclipse that occurred in the United States: research continued on both the theoretical and the practical fronts. The systems of this period were based on both 'indirect' strategies; the more theoretical being interlingual, the practical systems being transfer.

The most important example of advanced theoretical MT research was the work of Igor A. Mel'chuk on the 'meaning-text' stratificational model, which has been described above (Ch. 10.2). Research on this approach was pursued by workers at a number of Moscow research institutes until Mel'chuk was dismissed from his post for political reasons in 1976 (Mel'chuk 1981; *Survey* 23(2), 1978, p. 126–140). Mel'chuk emigrated to Canada, where since 1977 he has continued his research in the Department of Linguistics of the University of Montreal; two years later his co-worker Alexander Zhol'kovsky, emigrated also. His other principal collaborator, Yurii Apresyan, has apparently been able to continue some experimental work on a French–Russian system based on the 'meaning-text' approach at Informelektro, the information centre for the Institute of Electrotechnology in Moscow (Kulagina 1976, Bruderer 1978, Marchuk 1984). MT activity at the Moscow State Pedagogical Institute for Foreign Languages, where the Laboratory for Machine Translation had latterly been the principal focus for work on the English–Russian 'meaning-text' model, was limited by 1977 to partial algorithmic simulations, according to Marchuk (Bruderer 1978: 158). Olga Kulagina, another of Mel'chuk's principal collaborators, was evidently able to remain active on the development of the French–Russian system at the Institute of Applied Mathematics (Ch. 6.2), until research on this 'transfer' system was transferred to the Centre for Translation (see Ch. 18.6 below). Other researchers of the group have apparently dispersed, with some able to maintain an interest in MT (e.g. Shalyapina 1980).

In the late 1960s and early 1970s there was research at a number of other Soviet institutions. By 1969 an operational English–Russian system had been developed at the Central Scientific Research Institute for Patent Information and Techno-Economic Research (Tsentral'nyi nauchno-issledovatel'nyi institut patentnoi informatsii) by A. L. Vasilevskii, L. G. Kravets, V. A. Moskovich, G. A. Tarasova, and others (Kulagina 1976). Research on the system for translating patents had began in early 1963, and the first experimental version was tested between 1964 and 1966, initially on the 'Strela-3' and later on the 'Ural-4' (Kravets *et al.* 1967). Development on later versions continued until 1969, when the operational system was implemented (Vasilevskii *et al.* 1971). The Moscow Patent Office system was a bilingual 'transfer' system designed specifically for translating the artificially structured texts of patents. Built on the 'syntactic transfer' approach, English texts were analysed as dependency structures (using methods developed earlier by Mel'chuk); in the Transfer stage, dependency trees were converted into equivalent Russian 'surface' structures and Russian lexical units substituted, involving familiar methods of distinguishing homographs and resolving problems of multiple equivalents by reference to syntactic contexts and semantic compatibilities (using semantic features such as 'concrete', 'abstract' etc.); finally the stage of Russian synthesis produced morphologically and syntactically correct output. However, it appears that a substantial burden was carried by dictionary information rather than grammar routines (Lawson 1983), thus the system may have been more like 'direct translation' systems than a true 'transfer' type. The first dictionary was compiled for texts on internal combustion engines (Vasilevskii *et al.* 1971). Development continued until about 1977 according to Marchuk (Bruderer 1978: 158), and it was also installed at Atominform, the Information Centre for Nuclear Energy, Moscow, under V. M. Kalinin.

Research in Leningrad continued during the 1960s and early 1970s at the Laboratory of Mathematical Linguistics on an English–Russian system under S. Y. Fitialov, G. S. Tseitin and B. M. Leikina (Ljudskanov 1972: 187; Bruderer 1978). Work on the experimental 'syntactic transfer' system (with dependency structure analysis) began in 1966, but apparently progressed very slowly; Kulagina (1976) reported that only a very limited number of trial translations had been completed by 1976, and it would seem that research ended shortly afterwards. Evidently the interlingual research led by Andreev (Ch. 6.4) had already ceased in the late 1960s; although Andreev himself has continued to contribute to MT theory.

12

Direct translation systems since 1965

12.1 SYSTRAN SYSTEM OF LATSEC INC./ WORLD TRANSLATION CENTER (1964–)

Although involved in the installation of the Georgetown sytems at the Oak Ridge National Laboratory and at EURATOM in Ispra, Italy (Ch. 4.3), Peter Toma had already set up a company to pursue MT research (Ch. 4.13). This was Computer Concepts Inc. based in Los Angeles. By April 1963 he reported the development and operational implementation of AUTO-TRAN a "fast efficient and accurate" MT system for Russian–English translation with a dictionary of 100,000 stem entries in the fields of atomic energy and medicine, programmed on the IBM 7090 (*CRDSD* 10–11, 1962; 13, Nov. 1964).

Shortly afterwards in 1964 Toma moved to Germany, where he was able to continue his research with the support of the Deutsche Forschungsgemeinschaft (DFG). Here, on the IBM 360/50 at Bonn University, Toma was able to begin the development of the Systran Russian–English system (again working mainly at nights, according to his own account, Toma 1984) A detailed description of this prototype, showing clear signs of its GAT-SERNA ancestry, has been given by Janda *et al.* (1970). In 1967 the DFG had put forward a proposal to develop a Russian–German version at the University of the Saar; the proto-Systran Russian–English system was thoroughly evaluated, but eventually the Saarbrücken group decided to develop its own system (Ch. 13.2 below).

In 1968 Toma founded his own company Latsec Inc. in La Jolla, California, in order to continue development (now also supported by the US Air Force) and by early 1969 Systran was ready for testing at the Wright-Patterson Air Force Base (Dayton, Ohio). From July 1970 Systran took over from the IBM Mark II system (Ch. 4.2), where it continues to provide Russian–English translations for the USAF's Foreign Technology Division to this day. Subsequently, Systran was used by the National Aeronautic and Space Administration (NASA) during the joint US–USSR Apollo–Soyuz space project (1974–75), and in 1976 it replaced the Georgetown system at EURATOM.

For NASA Latsec Inc. developed an English–Russian version, apparently within one year (Bruderer 1978). At the same time, other language pairs were being prepared. A Chinese–English version was demonstrated in 1975 to representatives of the American government, and a German–English version to the US Army.

The most significant development, however, was to prove to be the English–French system (started in 1973). This version was demonstrated in Luxembourg in June 1975 to representatives of the Commission of the European Communities (Bruderer 1978). As a result, the Commission concluded a contract with the World Translation Center (the 'commercial' branch of Toma's company), to develop versions for translation between languages of the European Communities. The English–French version was delivered in February 1976, followed by the French–English version in 1978 and the English–Italian version in 1979. All three systems have been under continuous development and expansion by staff of the European Communities at Luxembourg, and all came into full production in March 1981 translating internal documents of the European Communities on an ever increasing scale (see Ch. 14.1 below).

There are now a number of other users of these versions: e.g. the French–English system at the Centre for Nuclear Research (Kernforschungszentrum) in Karlsruhe (Habermann 1984) and Aérospatiale in Paris; the English–French system at General Motors of Canada (Sereda 1982), Xerox (Elliston 1979, cf. 17.2 below), and Aérospatiale; and the English–Italian system at General Motors of Canada. There will certainly be others. Subsequently, Systran has also brought to operational status an English–Spanish system (purchased by General Motors of Canada and Xerox, among others) Other versions are said to be at an "advanced stage of development": English–German, German–English, English–Portuguese, English–Arabic, German–French, and German–Spanish; and plans are said to be under way for Spanish–English and Japanese–English (Van Slype 1983, Pigott 1984).

In 1978 the World Translation Company Canada was established to market Systran II (a system integrating MT programs, word processing, and photocomposition systems) in the United States, Canada, and parts of Europe. In 1979 the Systran Institut was set up in Munich to promote Systran in Europe, since when a number of contracts with companies have been concluded. Finally, a Systran service bureau has been established in Luxembourg (after an abortive attempt in 1980 to open one in Canada (Van Slype 1983)) which can provide translations to companies which cannot purchase their own system. Having started as a project for US military purposes, Systran is now a commercial product.

General descriptions of Systran are to be found in Toma 1977, Whitelock & Kilby (1983) Van Slype & Pigott (1979), Pigott (1981), and briefer descriptions by Toma (1974, 1976a, 1976b). For the Russian–English system the basic material is in the technical reports (Toma *et al.* 1970, 1972, 1973, 1974).

In many respects, Systran may be regarded as essentially a greatly improved descendant of the Georgetown 'direct translation' system. Linguistically there is little advance, but computationally the improvements are considerable, resulting in the main from the 'modularity' of its programming design. The monolithic complexity of the Georgetown system is overcome and the modification of any part of the processes can be undertaken with much greater facility and with much reduced risks of impairing the system's overall efficiency. Modularity is reflected in the following features. There are two main types of programs: (i) system programs, written in assembler code, which are independent of particular languages; these are control and utility programs, such as those responsible for dictionary lookup routines; and (ii) translation programs which are broken down into a number of stages, each with separate program modules. Translation programs for SL analysis and TL synthesis are to some extent independent of particular SL–TL pairs, although there are still a number of procedures during SL analysis which are determined by the needs of a particular TL. Nevertheless, the modularity of the translation programs has enabled the relatively straightforward introduction of new techniques of analysis wherever they seem appropriate.

However, the main component of the system remains the large bilingual dictionary containing not only SL–TL lexical equivalences but also grammatical and semantic information used during analysis and synthesis. Much of this information is formulated as algorithms to be invoked during various stages of the translation processing. As in 'direct' systems (like Systran's ancestor, the Georgetown system), these SL–TL dictionaries are of great complexity, and so consistency and regularity is difficult to maintain. While it is therefore true to characterise Systran as a partially 'transfer' system in that programs of structural analysis and synthesis are largely independent, the main translation processes are driven by the SL–TL dictionaries, as in 'direct' systems. Systran may therefore be regarded as a hybrid 'direct-transfer' system (Fig. 21).

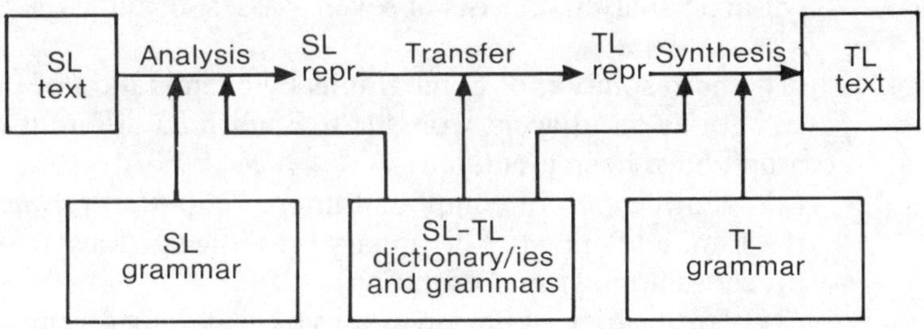

Fig. 21 — Hybrid 'direct-transfer' system.

Toma's (1977a) claims that Systran is a multilingual system are true, therefore, only with respect to the generality of the programming for structural analysis and synthesis. New versions of Systran are developed by incorporating SL and TL specific procedures in analysis and synthesis and by compiling new SL–TL bilingual dictionaries. Work on dictionaries does not, however, have to always start from scratch as in many cases there need be only minor differences in the coding of SL lexical items when coupled with a new TL (Pigott 1983).

The dictionary database for Systran comprises two bilingual dictionaries, one of single-word entries and one of multi-word expressions. From these are derived the dictionaries used during translation: a High Frequency dictionary including prepostions, conjunctions, irregular verb forms, etc., and the first words of idiomatic expressions; a Limited Semantics dictionary for idioms and compound nouns to be treated as lexical units; a Conditional Limited Semantics dictionary for dealing with semantic compatibilities and valencies; and the Main dictionary divided into stems and endings (except in the case of English). Dictionary entries include codes indicating: morphological class (verb and noun paradigms), part of speech, government and valency, agreement, transitivity, noun type (animate, mass, abstract, etc.), semantic markers ('physical property', 'food product', etc., — 450 such codes are available), any TL preposition governed by the item, and TL equivalents with morphological and syntactic information for synthesis.

In Systran there are five basic stages (Whitelock & Kilby 1983, Van Slype & Pigott 1979): Input, Main dictionary lookup, Analysis, Transfer and Synthesis (Fig. 22).

The Input program loads the text (in Roman transliteration, in the case of Russian) and checks each word against the High Frequency dictionary. In the next stage, the remaining words of the text are sorted alphabetically and searched for in the Main Stem dictionary. The words are then sorted back into the original text sequence and passed to Morphological analysis (in the case of languages like Russian and French) before going to the Analysis program proper. When English is the SL in question, there is no morphological analysis as the dictionaries contain full forms; but for Russian and French stems and endings are entered separately.

Syntactic analysis consists of seven 'passes' through the SL text:

(1) The resolution of homographs by examination of the grammatical categories of adjacent words (for English 83 different types of homograph have been identified).
(2) Identification of compound nouns (e.g. *blast furnace*) by checking the Limited Semantics dictionary (in some versions of Systran this pass precedes homograph resolution).
(3) Identification of phrase groups by searching for punctuation marks, conjunctions, relative pronouns, etc. (i.e. a rudimentary phrase structure analysis).
(4) Recognition of primary syntactic relations such as adjective–noun congruence, noun–verb government and noun–noun apposition; this pass is performed in a right-to-left scan.
(5) Identification of coordinate structures within phrases, e.g. conjoined adjectives or nouns; this pass makes use of semantic markers to

establish acceptable linkages e.g. in *smog and pollution control*, the coordination of *smog* and *pollution* rather than *smog* and *control*.
(6) Identification of subjects and predicates, principally by searching first for a finite verb and then for a (preceding) noun not already marked as an 'object' or 'modifier'.
(7) Recognition of prepositional structures, searching first right-to-left for a preposition and then left-to-right for its dependent noun phrase.

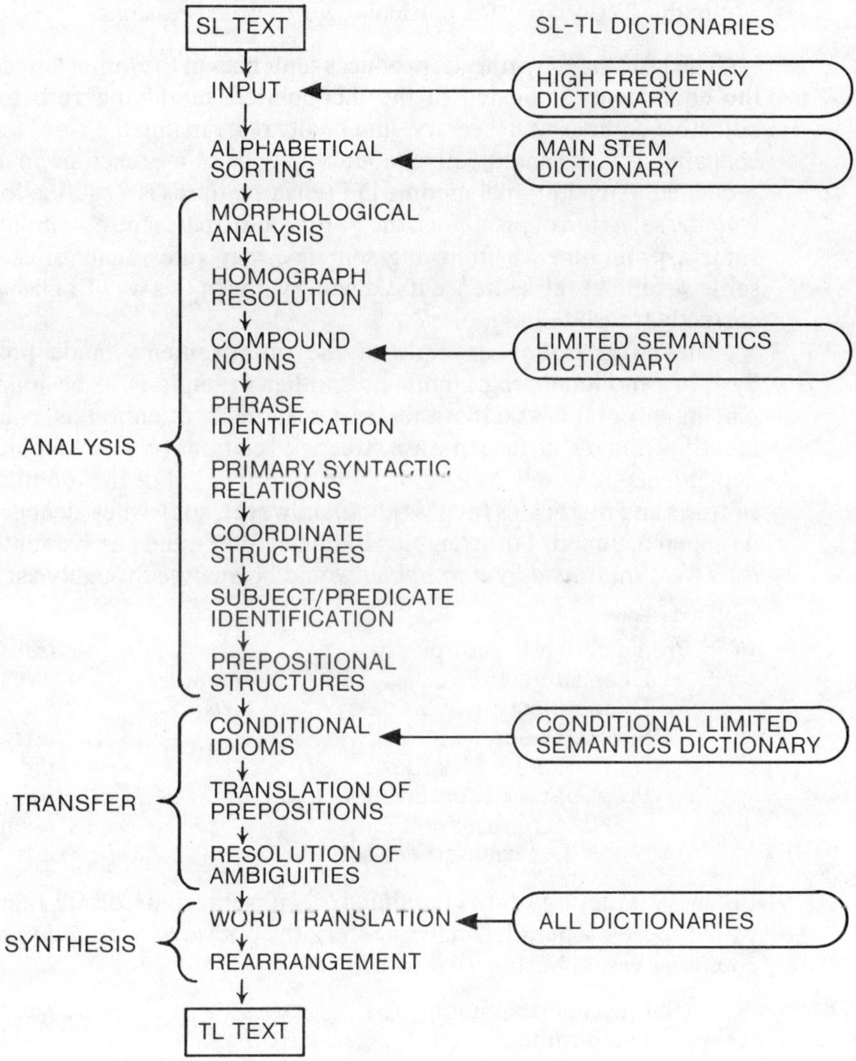

Fig. 22 — Systran stages of translation.

The Transfer program has three parts:

(1) Search for words with idiomatic translations under certain conditions (e.g. if *agree* is in the passive, it is translated as French *convenir*, otherwise it appears as *être d'accord*), by reference to the Limited Semantics Dictionary.
(2) Translation of prepositions, using the semantic information assigned to words which govern them and which are governed by them.
(3) Resolution of the remaining ambiguities, generally by tests specified in the dictionaries for particular words or expressions.

The last stage, Synthesis, produces sentences in the target language from the equivalents indicated in the dictionaries, modifying verb forms and adjective endings as necessary, and finally rearranging the word order, e.g. changing an English adjective–noun sequence to a French noun–adjective sequence. An additional module in French synthesis is a routine for dealing with the selection of pronouns; the routine anticipates the possibility that the subject pronoun of a following sentence may refer anaphorically to the subject noun of the sentence it is dealing with. In this way English *it* may be correctly translated as *il* or *elle*.

The latter is one example of the improvements made possible by Systran's modular programming. Another example is to be found in the parsing program. As in other systems, most attention is paid to the identification of 'surface' phrase structure relations (e.g. noun phrases) and dependency relations (e.g. nouns and adjectives). For the identification of subjects and predicates (at pass no. 6), however, somewhat 'deeper' analysis has been included. For example (Billmeier 1982), the passive sentence *The texts were translated by a computer* would be analysed roughly as:

Sentence
  Predicate: verb, past passive . . . . *translate*
    Deep subject: . . . . *computer*
    Deep object:. . . . . *texts*
    Subject: noun . . . . *texts*
      Determiner: def.art . . . . *the*
    Prep. phrase 1: preposition . . . . *by*
      Noun phrase: noun . . . . *computer*
        Determiner: def.art. . . . . *a*

Likewise, a noun phrase containing 'deep' subject–predicate relationships would receive a parallel analysis. Thus, the phrase *the translation of texts by computer* would be analysed roughly as:

(Subject): verbal noun . . . . *translation*
  Deep subject: . . . . *computer*
  Deep object:. . . . . *texts*
  Determiner: def.art . . . . *the*
  Prep. phrase 1: preposition . . . . *of*
    Noun phrase: noun . . . . *texts*
  Prep. phrase 2: preposition . . . . *by*
    Noun phrase: noun . . . . *computer*

Consequently, Systran is producing analyses which mix 'surface' and 'deep' structure information (rather similar indeed to analyses in TAUM and GETA in this respect, see Ch. 13.1 and 13.3 below); however, as Billmeier (1982) points out, Systran's incorporation of such features is selective, partial, and not based on a coherent linguistic model.

The description of Analysis and Transfer as separate stages may be a little deceptive, in that it is not only during Transfer that TL selection takes place; in particular the second pass which treats 'idiomatic' compounds decides on TL forms, which in turn determine later stages of analysis. The distinction between analysis and transfer is less clear-cut in Systran than in 'purer' examples of 'transfer' systems, cf. 3.9 above (Whitelock & Kilby 1983).

The main burden of the translation process rests, as pointed out earlier, with the large bilingual dictionaries. The information which is assigned to SL lexical data is restricted to that which is found necessary for facilitating conversion into one specific TL. Any information about either the SL or TL lexicon or grammar is included, in any mixture which seems convenient. As a consequence, there seems to be no uniformity, methods are inconsistent, coverage and quality are uneven, and modifications of one section of the dictionary can often have unexpected consequences.

Some examples of the mixture of SL and TL information can be found in the Russian–English system. The routine for inserting definite and indefinite articles combines syntactic information about the Russian text (e.g. whether the noun is qualified by a following genitive noun, a prepositional phrase or a relative clause), some semantic information (e.g. whether the Russian is an ordinal number), and information on English equivalents (e.g. an English 'mass' noun such as *water* usually requires a definite article). The methods of determining English syntactic forms are varied: in some cases, they are controlled by codes in Russian lexical items, e.g. *esli* includes a code to change a Russian infinitive construction ('if to examine . . .') to an English finite form (*if we examine . . .*) (Toma *et al.* 1970); in other cases the English syntactic form results from a manipulation of the output, e.g. Noun + *of* + Verbal noun + *of* + Noun (*result of treatment of burns*, from RESUL6TAT LECENI4 OJOGOV) becomes Noun + *of* + Gerundive + Noun (*result of treating burns*) (Toma *et al.* 1973).

The bilingual dictionaries make use of semantic categorisation, both as indicators of subject fields (to assist the resolution of polysemy) and as indicators of semantic compatibilities. However, the system of 'semantic classification' is so complex that at times it appears to be *ad hoc*. Examples of the use of 'semantic classes' from the Russian–English version are, e.g., the translation of Russian prepositions according to the 'semantic class' of adjacent verbs or nouns: *DO* is translated as *up to* if the preceding verb or noun is '+increase' and as *down to* if it is '+decrease', *PO* is translated as *along* if the following noun is '+linear', as *over* if '+nonlinear' and as *using* if '+metal tool' (Toma *et al.* 1974). Similarly, Russian 'noun + genitive noun' structures may be translated as English 'noun + noun' (where the first noun modifies the second and corresponds to the Russian genitive) only if the 'semantic class' of the Russian genitive is COMP(osition), MATH(ematics), MEAS(ure), MOTION, OPTICS, QUAL(ity), etc. (Toma *et al.* 1973). Clearly, these 'semantic classes' have nothing to do with the semantics of Russian, they are *ad hoc* labels (some indicating 'components of meaning', others subject fields) designed solely to overcome difficulties with the English output. Similar problems with Systran semantic classification was encountered in the development of the English–French system by the European Communities (see Ch. 14.1).

The Russian–English version has been in regular use by the US Air Force since 1970. It is reported that at the present time, over 100,000 pages are being translated every year, more than 2 million words in 1980 (Van Slype 1983). Most texts are used unedited, mainly for 'information scanning', only 20% receiving 'light editing'. There is said to be "considerable user satisfaction" and a 90–95% accuracy level is claimed.

It is only recently, however, that the Russian–English version has been evaluated at all systematically. The 1972 report by Leavitt *et al.* (1972) was concerned mainly with cost analysis and the optimisation of post-editing and recomposition functions. Sinaiko (1971) compared a 1964 Mark II translation and a 1971 Systran translation of the same Russian text (itself a good translation of an English article), finding that Mark II left 1.2% of the words untranslated and Systran 2.3%, and that Mark II provided alternative translations for 6.3% of the words and Systran for 5.3%. He concluded that "little progress has been made in recent years" on MT systems.

Later output from Systran has shown, however, that this conclusion was too harsh, as a comparison of the following (perhaps untypically good) Systran output with Mark II translations (Ch. 4.2 above) will show (Bruderer 1978:

> THE SWISS PUBLIC IS WORRIED, THE BASEL NEWSPAPER "NATIONALZEITUNG" WRITES IN ONE OF THE LAST ISSUES. RECENT AMERICAN STATEMENTS ABOUT THE FACT THAT THE USA CAN USE FORCE IN THE NEAR EAST, THE NEWSPAPER EMPHASIZES, CAUSE ALARM ALL OVER THE WORLD. AS CONCERNS SWITZERLAND, THEN, IF THIS COURSE CONTINUES, IT WILL EXAMINE THE QUESTION CONCERNING AN EXIT FROM THE RECENTLY CREATED ON THE INSISTENCE OF WASHINGTON INTERNATIONAL ENERGY AGENCY, WHICH UNITES A NUMBER OF THE CAPITALIST COUNTRIES — THE GREATEST USERS OF OIL.

A thorough evaluation of the Russian–English system by Knowles (1979) was based on translations produced during tests in 1977 conducted by the Gesellschaft für Mathematik und Datenverarbeitung in Bonn (1977). The corpus comprised a pedagogic grammar of Russian written for German students (2000 sentences), and four Russian technical texts on scales and weighing, airports, helicopters, and eyesight (500 sentences) taken from Great Soviet Encyclopaedia. Some of the translations from the grammar were undoubtedly odd: *We heard, as a door was discovered and as someone entered into an adjacent room* (i.e. 'We heard a door opening and someone entering the next room'), *They speak, as if it left* (i.e. 'They say he has gone') — there were particular problems with pronouns because of the lack of context. Results from the technical texts were somewhat better:

> A HELICOPTER, A FLIGHT VEHICLE HEAVIER THAN AIR WITH VERTICAL BY TAKEOFF AND LANDING, LIFT IN WHICH IS CREATED ONE OR BY SEVERAL (MORE FREQUENT THAN TWO) ROTORS . . . A HELICOPTER TAKES OFF UPWARD VERTICALLY WITHOUT A TAKEOFF AND IT ACCOMPLISHES VERTICAL FITTING WITHOUT A PATH, MOTIONLESSLY "WILL HANG" ABOVE ONE PLACE, ALLOWING ROTATION AROUND A VERTICAL AXIS TO ANY SIDE, FLIGHT IN ANY DIRECTION AT SPEEDS IS PRODUCED FROM ZERO TO THE MAXIMUM . . .

Although Knowles found that errors were occurring on average every four or five words, many of these could be easily rectified by additional entries in the dictionaries or by additional grammatical information (particularly on valency relationships). Knowles also suggested that further improvements might be possible with a Wilks-type 'semantic calculus' to identify anaphoric relations (Ch. 15 below), and by more sophisticated ambiguity routines. In his view, greater consistency and perserverence would overcome many of the errors, since with Systran's modularity and open-endedness it should be possible to incorporate enhancements without undue difficulty.

The USAF Russian–English system has been under constant development since its installation in 1970 (Bostad 1982). During a five-year period, the number of homograph routines doubled and stem entries in dictionaries increased by 30,000. Although there was evidence of improvements in the quality of translations, there was also a growing concern that "a certain degree of degradation was occurring"; after 'improvements' had been introduced, errors were appearing in other parts of the system where none had occurred before. Monitoring changes revealed that, on average, the "improvement/degradation ratio was consistently around 7:3". On aggregate there was progress, but it was not uniform and there were substantial losses. The answer was to take greater care; every proposal is checked against a library of Russian input texts (*ca.* 50 million words), and accepted only if there is no degradation. Improvement of the USAF system is therefore now a matter of "fine tuning" the quality, not of making large scale modifications.

In many respects, the Systran Russian–English system dates back to the early 1960s in conception. The later Systran versions for English–French, English–Italian, and other pairs, incorporate improvements resulting from experience with Russian–English (Ch. 14.1). Whether, as a consequence, these newer versions can avoid (or at least delay for a longer period) the quality degradation experienced by the US Air Force model has yet to be seen.

12.2 LOGOS DEVELOPMENT CORPORATION (1969–78)

The Logos Development Corporation was founded in 1969 by Bernard E. Scott in order to continue research under the sponsorship of the US Air Force for an English–Vietnamese MT system. He had begun preparatory work on the system in the Spring of 1965 at Computer Technology Inc. In June 1970 a public demonstration of the system (LOGOS I) was given on a small corpus of just 1300 words, which was considered sufficiently satisfactory for the US Air Force to commence the translation of training manuals and to recommend further development. Nevertheless, the designers described it as an "initial capability system. . . not yet sufficiently developed for a large scale machine translation of technical material" and emphasised that LOGOS output required considerable post-editing (Byrne *et al.* 1970).

LOGOS I maintained complete separation of SL analysis and TL synthesis and of computer programming processes and linguistic data and rules. It was claimed that "in theory" the system could be "applied to translation problems between most language pairs." This was because the "programs are entirely language-independent" even though the procedures themselves and the dictionaries were specifically designed for one particular SL–TL pair, English and Vietnamese. In brief, LOGOS I was a hybrid 'direct-transfer' system (Fig. 10), in which bilingual dictionaries are coupled with separate defined stages of analysis, transfer, and synthesis.

No pre-editing of the English text was necessary. The program automatically detected word and sentence boundaries and identified parenthetical sequences. There were two dictionaries, one of high frequency words loaded into computer memory at start up, and a large dictionary on tape searched sequentially (eventually containing some 100,000 entries). Entries were in base forms, with separate tables of endings. After Dictionary lookup, the syntactic parser, working first from the end of the sentence (right-to-left) and then from the beginning (left-to-right), resolved word-class ambiguities, recognised noun phrases, subjects and predicates, agreements, coordination, and resolved some semantic ambiguities. There was, however, no attempt to produce complete phrase structure analyses (the grouping of constituents evidently went no further than recognition of noun phrase boundaries). Analysis went only as far as was needed to obtain enough information to transform English structures into acceptable Vietnamese syntactic forms. A particular point was made of the mixture of syntactic and semantic information in the analysis routines. In essence the procedures were much like those of Systran at this date.

In the transfer phase, English structures were transformed into types found in Vietnamese; thus adjective–noun groups were inverted to give Vietnamese noun–adjective groups, complex verbs were simplified ("Vietnamese tense indicators are very simple"), genitive nouns became *of*-forms (*pilot's compartment: compartment of the pilot*), and passive constructions were changed into active ones (since Vietnamese has no passive voice), e.g. *Wires can be disconnected upon removal of clip* became: *(You) can disconnect wires when you have removed clip*. The final stage replaced English lexical forms by Vietnamese.

The system produced output sentence by sentence (examples in Bruderer 1978: 308-313). The limitations of the syntax-oriented system were freely acknowledged and post-editing was essential; because of the "inherent ambiguity of English" it would be possible to remove the many mistranslations only by semantic analysis or by reference to pragmatic information (Byrne *et al.* 1970).

LOGOS I was the subject of a thorough evaluation by Sinaiko & Klare (1972) on the basis of an Air Force manual translated by the system in the autumn of 1970, only a few months after the public demonstration. 172 Vietnamese student pilots with knowledge of English were tested on their comprehension of the manual in the original English, a Vietnamese human translation, the LOGOS translation unedited and the same LOGOS translation after revision. Scores for comprehension were best for the human translations, next for revised MT and worst for unedited MT; but for clarity, revised MT scored better than human translation, with unedited MT worst. The most surprising result, however, was that the Vietnamese students' comprehension scores for the English original texts were slightly higher than for the best human translations; and that, furthermore, Vietnamese who had been in the United States for five or six months did almost as well in English comprehension tests as an American control group. Similar tests with a US Navy manual confirmed the results (Sinaiko & Klare 1973). The investigators concluded that "perhaps the best way to help Vietnamese use US manuals is to improve the readability of the English text itself", which "could provide the considerable bonus of helping American users as well." The results were naturally rather unencouraging, but in any case the need for aircraft manuals in Vietnamese was shortly to come to an end.

In subsequent years the Logos Corporation continued developments of its system. By 1973 an English–Russian version of LOGOS III had been developed, and later experimental work was being pursued on systems for translating from English into French, Spanish, and German (Locke 1975, Bruderer 1978). In the mid-1970s the Logos Corporation received a contract from the Iranian government to develop a multilingual system for translation into Farsi (Persian). Initially just English–Farsi, it was later to be expanded to embrace Russian, German, French, Spanish, and Arabic as source languages; but, as before, Logos' plans were to be overtaken by history. No more was heard of Logos until the launch of the 'Logos Intelligent Translation System' in 1983 (Ch. 13.5).

12.3 XONICS CORPORATION (1970–76)

A demonstration of a small-scale Russian–English MT system was given at the FBIS seminar in 1976 (Chaloupka 1976). It had been developed "in the last 6 years" by Bedrich Chaloupka (who had worked in the Georgetown project since 1956), Giuliano Grugnoli, and Allen Tucker. The program was written in PL/I for an IBM 370 computer. The system could operate either in batch mode (for large volumes of text), sentence by sentence (for abstracts and titles) or interactively (for dictionary updating). There were separate SL and TL dictionaries, each containing "rudimentary" grammatical information and amounting to about 25,000 items of physics and chemistry vocabulary in either stems or full forms. No special skill or linguistic training was required to work with the dictionaries. The system was said to be "not styled on any specific linguistic theories"; it would appear to be essentially a 'direct' system of the Georgetown type, capable of "properly translating prepositions and semantic units and rearranging participle and nested structures". It is possible that experience with the Xonics system contributed to the development of the PAHO system.

12.4 PAN AMERICAN HEALTH ORGANIZATION (1976–)

The Pan American Health Organization (PAHO) is an intergovernmental agency dealing with health matters in the Americas and also serving as the World Health Organization's regional office for the western hemisphere. Its translation services deal primarily with Spanish and English, with some demand for translations into Portuguese and to a much lesser extent into French. The feasibility of developing a MT system was considered in the mid-1970s, and in 1976 PAHO contracted consultants to build an in-house system, initially for Spanish–English translation (Vasconcellos 1984, 1985). The consultants were Bedrich Chaloupka, Giuliano Gnugnoli, and Allen Tucker of the TABOR company (who had worked on the 'Georgetown-type' Xonics system). At PAHO the project has been the responsibility of Muriel Vasconcellos, who in the late 1950s had been an administrative assistant in the Georgetown project (*LM* 4, 1984); in 1979 she was joined by a full-time researcher, Marjorie Leon.

Development of the Spanish–English system (SPANAM) continued until 1979, by which time the basic software had been written (in PL/I) and dictionaries comprising some 48,000 SL entries had been compiled. The system has been designed for an IBM mainframe computer, and (since 1979) integrated with a Wang word processor, enabling direct text input, on-line revision of MT output, and dictionary updating at the terminal. SPANAM has been operational for internal users at PAHO since summer 1980. The first major task for the new system was the PAHO biennial budget document, and by September 1983 a total of over a million words had been translated for PAHO and WHO users. A cost and quality evaluation was made on the MT output in 1981 by Macdonald and Zarechnak from Georgetown, as a result of which improvements were made to SPANAM procedures and work began on the development of an English–Spanish system (ENGSPAN).

For its MT model, not surprisingly, "the approach decided on was originally quite similar to that developed at Georgetown University in the late 1950s and early 1960s" (Vasconcellos 1984), i.e. the GAT 'direct translation' system (Ch. 4.3 above). There are some differences: rather than a single SL–TL dictionary, there are two separate dictionaries linked by 'lexical numbers' assigned to a pair of SL and TL forms (and the TL dictionary is in numerical order); there are also no preliminary alphabetical sorts before dictionary searches.

The SPANAM program passes through the following stages (Vasconcellos 1984, 1985, Tucker 1984, Leon 1984). On input, SL words are checked against a High Frequency dictionary, then the Main SL dictionaries (with entries as either stems or full forms), and finally an idiom dictionary. The analysis program begins with a routine for homograph resolution, based on the grammatical categories of adjacent words; then, alternative translations for prepositions are considered (also according to the grammatical categories of preceding and following SL words). The next routine handles rearrangements of direct and indirect objects. Then follows a routine for handling reflexive verbs and negation (e.g. Spanish *no ha* becomes English *has not*). The next pass rearranges adjectives, conjunctions, and nouns within Spanish noun phrases into appropriate English patterns (i.e. a series of SL–TL structural transformation rules). Finally, SPANAM looks up the English (TL) dictionary and a morphological synthesis routine produces TL output.

SPANAM is clearly a representative of the 'direct translation' MT model, with no separate modules of SL analysis and TL synthesis, with procedures designed specifically for the pair Spanish–English (and not vice versa). It has virtually no disambiguation (beyond distinguishing syntactic homographs), primarily because 'syntactic analysis' is limited and does not identify subjects, agents, or actions (Tucker 1984). Polysemy is therefore handled by the use of 'microglossaries' for special disciplines (Vasconcellos 1985). Any semantic analysis would require additional dictionary information beyond basic syntactic data. Post-editing is essential, and was in fact assumed and planned for from the beginning. There were no perfectionist inclinations and there are still none. SPANAM is seen as a purely practical machine aid.

Development of the English–Spanish system (ENGSPAN) began in 1982, supported by a grant from the US Agency for International Development (Leon 1984). Its basic dictionary has been compiled by reversing the SPANAM dictionary, amending entries and adding more English terms. It was soon realised that analysis of English demands more extensive parsing than Spanish, particularly with regard to noun phrases. For this it is intended to augment dictionary entries with information about verb valency (preferred subjects, direct objects, and indirect objects, etc.) and with semantic markers (i.e. 'human', 'animate', 'mass', etc.) — which may also be done in the SPANAM dictionary eventually. Stages of analysis and transfer are the same as in SPANAM, i.e. dictionary lookup, verb string analysis and rearrangement, homograph resolution, noun phrase rearrangement, morphological synthesis of Spanish verbs, synthesis of Spanish nouns (Leon 1984). For English morphological analysis a program has been written by Macdonald. There are plans to develop an ATN-type parser for English syntactic analysis, making selective use of semantic coding, and giving improved treatment of homographs, coordination, and eventually perhaps anaphora. As with SPANAM, there is no expectation of high quality output; the project concentrates on frequent problems of English syntax and ignores fine details. It is intended also that ENGSPAN parsing wil be 'fail-safe'; some kind of translation will be produced even if part of the analysis is unsuccessful.

The PAHO system is unusual in that the same organisation is involved as the developer of the MT software, as the translation service using the system, and, through its members, as the end-users of the translations produced. The level of satisfaction seems to be high: there has been a steady rise in the use of SPANAM (over half a million words translated in 1983), all types of texts have been handled (with "best performance on long technical documents and reports"), unedited MT output has been acceptable sometimes, and the postediting rate has been high (6500 words a day). Vasconcellos concludes that "it is conservative to estimate that the gain in terms of time and cost is at least threefold".

Both systems were demonstrated at the 1985 Georgetown conference (*LM* 25, Oct. 1985), and delegates were apparently impressed by their ability to handle all types of texts, even those falling outside the fields of medicine and public health. Some evidence of the quality of Spanish–English translations is to be found in the following 'raw' output (from Vasconcellos 1985):

> The extension of the coverage of the health services to the underserved or not served population of the countries of the Region was the central goal of the Ten-year Plan and probably that of greater scope and transcendence. Almost all the countries formulated the purpose of extending the coverage although could be appreciated a diversity of approaches for its attack, which is understandable in view of the different national policies that had acted in the configuration of the health systems of each one of the countries.

12.5 UNIVERSITY OF SASKATCHEWAN (1965–72)

One of the projects set up by the National Research Council of Canada in the late 1960s (Ch. 9.1) was the English–French MT project at the University of Saskatchewan under Kathleen Booth, who had previously worked on MT at Birkbeck College with her husband, A. D. Booth. This 'direct translation' system consisted essentially of a bilingual dictionary compiled on the basis of statistical analyses of a 20,000 word corpus (from the *Canada Year Book* 1962). From this were determined the most probable grammatical categories for English entries and their most frequent French equivalents (K. Booth 1967; K. Booth 1970). The stages of the system were: dictionary lookup (using Booth's binary cut method, Ch. 5.1); identification of categories and assignment of French forms; and 'translation' (rearrangement of verb phrase sequences, inflection of nouns, adjective–noun inversion, and output). No attempt was made to select from alternatives, e.g. *from* was given as *de/depuis/d'après*; and coordinate structures of the form 'Adj N and N' were analysed always (on the basis of probabilities) as '(Adj N) and N' and never as 'Adj (N and N)' (K. Booth *et al.* 1971). An evaluation of the system was conducted in 1970 in which 'post-editors' with no knowledge of English were asked to correct 39 sentences of French output. An example extract (from Booth et al. 1971):

> L'AMERIQUE NU NORD COMPREND SIX R1EGIONS PRINCIPALES NATURELLES/PROPRE/ QUI SONT 2A LA FOIS/ AUSSI BIEN QUE/ PHYSIOGRAPHIQUES ET GEOLOGIQUES PARCE QUE LES 3AGES, LES SORTIES ET LES STRUCTURES DES ROCHES SOUS JACENTES/ FONDAMENTAL/ D1ELIMITENT/ D1ECIDER/ LES TERRAINS/ NATURE/ DES TERRES DE SURFACE.

Despite the obvious shortcomings, it was felt, nevertheless, that reasonable results were feasible after post-editing by specialists with access to the original English text. After Booth moved to Lakehead University, Thunder Bay, in 1972, no further research seems have been done.

12.6 OTHER DIRECT TRANSLATION SYSTEMS

Two other, mainly short-lived, projects to produce 'direct translation' type systems are known. It is very well possible that others have also been constructed during the period.

During the early 1970s there was another English–Vietnamese MT project at the Xyzyx Information Corporation at Canoga Park, Menlo, California. The system had apparently been first developed for English–French translation of aeronautics texts on an IBM 360. The MT stages were apparently much the same as in Logos and the 1970s versions of Systran. Bruderer (1978) reports that in 1975 the dictionary comprised just 12,500 English entries; considerable post-editing was necessary. It was claimed to have been in use at some time in Canada.

An experimental program for Russian–English MT was written in FORTRAN by T. D. Crawford at University College Cardiff (Crawford 1976). Analysis was evidently restricted to phrase structure only, no resolution of homography being attempted. The BABEL system apparently produced some translations for internal use, employing a small dictionary of some 17,500 words. The project ended in 1977.

13

Transfer systems since 1970

13.1 UNIVERSITY OF MONTREAL, TAUM (1965–1981)

Research on MT in Canada began in 1965 with the sponsorship by the Canadian Research Council of projects at the University of Saskatchewan, at the Cambridge Language Research Unit, and at the University of Montreal. The Saskatchewan project concentrated mainly on a statistical approach to a 'direct translation' English–French system (Ch. 12.5), and the CLRU project investigated the possibilities of an interactive approach (Ch. 5.2 above).

At Montreal, the Canadian Research Council set up CETADOL (Centre de Traitement Automatisé des Données Linguistiques) in November 1965, under the direction of Guy Rondeau. MT research began slowly; initially the group was concerned mainly with general problems of natural language processing, studies of English morphology, syntax, and grammatical classification, but from 1967 access to the Kuno-Woods' parser encouraged serious MT research (Chandioux 1977). In 1970 the group was renamed TAUM (Traduction Automatique de l'Université de Montréal), with an operational English–French system as its goal. The first prototype was constructed under the leadership of Alain Colmerauer (making particular use of Colmerauer's Q-system software) and first tested in 1971 (TAUM 1971). Research continued until 1977 on the development of the TAUM prototype under Richard Kittredge as director. Since 1973 the TAUM group had been funded by the Translation Bureau of the Canadian Secretary of State; and in May 1975 the group was contracted to develop a system for translating public weather forecasts: TAUM-METEO was delivered the following year and has been in daily operation since 1977. The success of TAUM-METEO led to a contract for a more ambitious project, the translation of aircraft maintenance manuals from English into French. The TAUM-AVIATION project, under the direction of Marcel Paré, was the principal activity of the group from 1977 until 1980. In that year, an independent evaluation of the project (Gervais 1980) concluded that there was little prospect of a cost-effective production system in the near future, and the sponsors brought the TAUM project to an end in 1981. A general retrospective overview of the whole TAUM project has been given by Isabelle (1984); a comprehensive bibliography by Bourbeau (1983); and a detailed description and critical evaluation by Whitelock & Kilby (1983). Reports of the prototype system are to be found in TAUM 1971, 1971a, 1973a, 1973b, and Kittredge 1972; the principal documentation for METEO is Chevalier *et al.* 1978; and that of TAUM-Aviation is Baudot *et al.* 1977, Isabelle *et al.* 1978, Bourbeau 1981, and Isabelle & Bourbeau 1984.

13.1.1 System design

The TAUM team developed its basic design in close cooperation with other research groups, particularly the Grenoble group (Chandioux 1977). The experience of CETA convinced the Montreal group that the best prospect for adequate realistic and practical MT in an operational setting was a system based on the 'transfer' approach. The TAUM system represents a typical example of the 'transfer' approach in perhaps its purest form, having five basic stages: Morphological analysis of English, Syntactic analysis of English, Transfer, Syntactic generation of French, Morphological generation of French.

The other major lesson was the desirability of separating strictly the algorithms from the linguistic data and processing. As its computational metalanguage, TAUM adopted the Q-systems formalism developed by Colmerauer (1971), and which subsequently influenced the design of the Prolog programming language by Colmerauer and others at Marseille and at Edinburgh in the early 1970s (Kowalski 1985). Q-systems (Q=Quebec) are computer programs for the manipulation of tree structures and strings of trees irrespective of the labels attached to the nodes of trees. A tree may be fully articulated as in a phrase structure representation, e.g. PH(SN(IL), SV(V(MANGE), SN(LA, CHOUCROUTE))), or it may represent a list (items separated by commas), e.g. L(A,B,C,D), where each item may itself be a tree, or it may represent a categorisation, e.g. PREP(TO), or a single node, TODAY. A string of trees is defined as a sequence of trees separated by plus signs, e.g. SN(PAUL) + V(VIENDRA) + DEMAIN + CHEZ + PRON(MOI). A Q-system rule converts strings (of one or more trees) into new strings, it may apply to the whole or to only a part of a string, and may include variables for labels, list or trees. For example, in the rule PREP(A*) + SN(X*) → OBJIND(P(A*), SN(X*)) the A* is a variable for a label (TO, FROM, . . .) and the X* is a variable for a list (of nouns). Clearly, the Q-system formalism is very powerful, capable of handling morphological and syntactic representations within any formal model, and also suitable for application in dictionary lookup procedures. However, it does have its drawbacks: the formalism does not permit easy copying of features from node to node, or specifying sequences of constituents,and as "the only method of passing control between Q-systems is to chain them" the formalism does not permit conditional applications of grammars, with consequential wasteful invocations of inapplicable routines (Whitelock & Kilby 1983).

Whereas TAUM-METEO was written entirely in the Q-systems metalanguage, other computational procedures were also developed for TAUM-AVIATION. For certain applications the generality of Q-systems was too powerful; greater efficiency was needed for certain specialised tasks. SISIF was a finite-state automaton for pre- and post-processing of texts; LEXTRA was designed for lexical transfer; and for syntactic analysis Stewart (1975) developed REZO, an adaptation of Wood's ATN parser (Ch. 9.13 above).

The first stage of linguistic processing was Morphological analysis. This involved the assignment of category labels, e.g. prepositions: WITHIN → P(WITHIN), including prepositional phrases: IN THE PROCESS OF → P(INTHEPROCESSOF); segmentation of prefixes, e.g. UNDERSTOOD → UNDER + STOOD); regularisation of irregular forms, e.g. STOOD → SW(STAND) + ED(PST); restoration of prefixes, e.g. UNDER + SW(STAND) → SW(UNDERSTAND); identification of suffixes, e.g. TRIED → TRI + ED, PUTTING → PUTT + ING; construction of potential base forms (TRI → TRY, PUTT → PUT). Dictionary lookup searched for both segmented forms (TRY + ED, SERIE + S, FLY + S) and full unsegmented forms (TRIED, SERIES, FLIES), rejecting those not located (SERIE, TRIED). It included the assignment of category labels (ADJ, N, . . .) and 'features', e.g. ANImate, CONCrete, ABSTract, for nouns, features of admissible arguments (subject nouns, objects, etc.) for verbs, and obligatory prepositions, such as TO with *listen*.

Syntactic analysis was in two phases. The first included the recognition of noun phrases and complex verb forms and the rearrangement of constituents as needed, e.g. DET(V*) + N(X*) → NP(N(X*), DET(V*)). The second established the 'canonical forms' of sentences. It incorporated both phrase structure rules and transformational rules: input strings of trees were formed into single complex trees and reordered (or deformed) as 'deep structure'-type representations. Thus, verbs were placed before their argument noun phrases, passive constructions were made active, extraposed *it* forms were transformed (e.g. It be ADJ that S → S be ADJ) and relative pronouns were replaced by REL and the head noun copied into its argument position in the subordinate clause. An example analysis is shown in Fig. 23.

Each arrow line represents a step in the analysis (i.e. the application of a replacement rule) working upwards from the 'surface form' at the bottom to the final form at the top. The example shows the inversion of article and noun in a noun phrase formation: DET(ART(DEF)) + N(COMMITTEE) → NP(N(COMMITTEE), DET(ART(DEF))), the testing of *interview* as noun (N) or verb (ZV), the inversion of the verb and its suffix *-ing* in order to

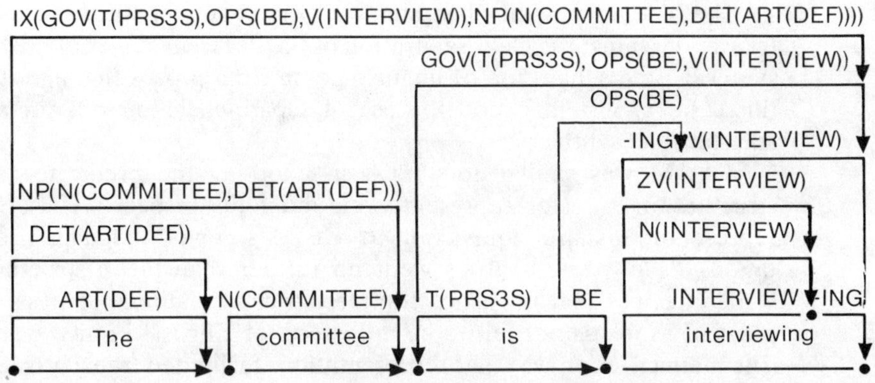

Fig. 23 — TAUM syntactic analysis.

identify the durative tense BE + -ING, and the placing of the verb information before the noun phrase (top line). During syntactic analysis some use was made of semantic features (derived from SL dictionary entries), e.g. checking for compatibilities of verbs and direct objects. This could also involve the incorporation of semantic features of dependent 'attributes' (adjectives or nouns) into the set of features of a 'governing' noun; e.g. in a *pound of cake* the properties of *cake* are subsumed in the features of *pound*, and in *defective pump* the selectional features relevant to *defect* are incorporated in the features for *pump*. Syntactic analysis was originally implemented by a Q-systems parser, but later in the AVIATION project the REZO parser was adopted.

Transfer had also two phases. First was Lexical transfer: the translation of English 'words' (base forms) with category labels into French equivalents via a bilingual dictionary, which could involve tree transduction, e.g. from *supply x with y* to *fournir y à x*. Although originally implemented in a Q-system formalism, for AVIATION the LEXTRA system was developed, which made it easier to specify the type of tree transducer required for particular lexical items. Unlike Q-systems (and similar formalisms), LEXTRA requires that input trees are stated explicitly. The constraint ensured correct formulation of lexical transfer rules. The second phase of Transfer was Structural transfer: the modification of certain parts of trees to simplify generation. Because of the close similarity of English and French 'deep' structures this phase was simpler than it might have been for other language pairs. Nevertheless, certain difficult problems were encountered, e.g. the handling of tenses and auxiliaries.

In Syntactic generation successive Q-systems broke down the complex tree output from Transfer into strings of trees. For example, the noun phrase:

SN(N(GENS), DET(LES), GP(P(DE), SN(N(VILLAGE), DET(LE))))
became: DET(LES) + N(GENS) + P(DE) + DET(LE) + N(VILLAGE)

Finally, Morphological generation converted trees and strings into single 'surface' forms, e.g. DET(LES) → *les*, P(DE) + DET(LE) → *du*.

The TAUM system illustrates well the characteristic features of MT transfer systems: the clear separation of the different stages of analysis and synthesis, the separation of linguistic data from processing algorithms (in this case, Q-systems), and the use of separate dictionaries for analysis, transfer, and synthesis.

TAUM was similar to CETA in adopting the predicate–argument structure for 'transfer' representation (and in this respect TAUM 'transfer' representations are equivalent to CETA's 'pivot language' representations). However, analysis went no further than 'deep structure'; and sometimes not that far, since complete transformational analysis was not pursued as it was not felt to be necessary for English–French translation. The main criterion was that representations facilitated transfer rules. As in CETA, semantic analysis in TAUM was confined to the use of semantic features (such as 'animate', 'mass', 'fluid') during tree conversion in Syntactic analysis and Transfer. No lexical decomposition was performed, and there was no pragmatic or discourse analysis.

The lack of a discourse component meant, in particular, that the achievement of coherent sequences of sentences during synthesis was virtually ruled out. TAUM translated sentence by sentence; the need for the retention of "global discourse information" during analysis was recognised, but could not be attempted (Isabelle 1984). Another aspect of text structure which TAUM could not tackle was anaphora. At an early stage of the project there had been a proposal to incorporate an intersentential routine, the so-called REF-Bug (Hofmann 1971), which moving left to right, across, into and out of sentences (or rather their 'deep structure' representations) would replace "each pronoun by the most recent noun of the same gender and number which it has met". It was, however, decided that too little was known at the time about the practicality of incorporating such text processing in large scale systems and so the routine was never implemented (Isabelle 1984).

13.1.2 The METEO project

In 1974 TAUM, under some pressure from its sponsor, was looking for some practical demonstration of its MT programs. It looked for an application within a limited domain. The Canadian government's bilingual policy (Ch. 9.1) led to a decision to broadcast weather forecasts in both English and French throughout Canada. As a result, TAUM was commissioned by the Canadian Bureau des Traductions to produce a system for translating meteorological reports from English into French. The development of TAUM-METEO (Chandioux 1976, Chevalier *et al.* 1978, Chandioux & Guérard 1981) took less than two years. Regional forecasts are written in a 'telegraphic' style with relatively limited vocabulary, i.e. a sublanguage 'dialect' of English. The research on METEO has in fact led to the development of a branch of linguistic analysis concerned with the 'sublanguage' concept (Kittredge & Lehrberger 1982), with potential application not only in MT but in many other areas of linguistic research.

The restricted vocabulary and stereotyped syntax of meteorological reports enabled the designers to greatly simplify the basic TAUM system. The most important departure from the TAUM prototype was the elimination of a Transfer component; most of the processing usually done during transfer was incorporated into the analysis component. In effect, the system was no longer a 'transfer' system since analysis was TL dependent, i.e. METEO is a version of a (simplified) 'direct' system, albeit with a more truly independent SL analysis than most such systems.

Another simplification was the dropping of morphological analysis before dictionary search, because there were so few variant forms of English words in this sublanguage. There was also a simplification of the arrangements for dictionaries. Instead of three separate dictionaries, only one was needed to give the French equivalents of English expressions and French morphological data; this was consulted only during stages of analysis. Changes in the usual TAUM parser were necessary because of the lack of tensed verbs in most meteorological reports. As a consequence METEO implemented a 'semantic grammar' (cf. Ch. 9.17 and 15), in which rules operated not on syntatic categories (N, Adj, etc.) but on semantic categories (TIME, CONDition, etc.). Many structures follow a general pattern, such as: atmospheric condition, modification of condition, place, time (Kittredge 1981). Such patterns are the basis for rules producing, for example, the tree in Fig. 24 for the sentence *Snow occasionally mixed with rain tomorrow* (Isabelle 1984).

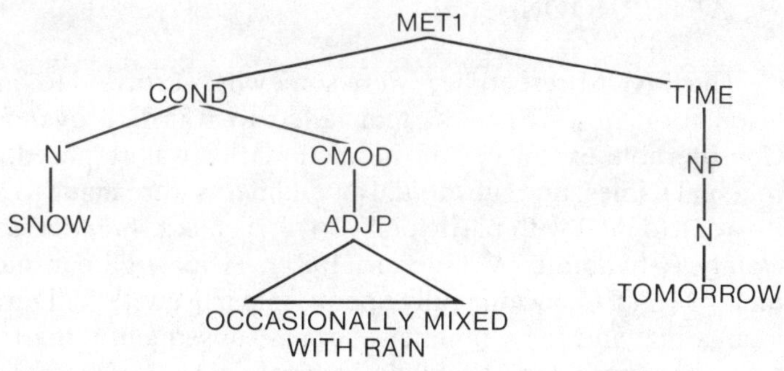

Fig. 24 — METEO analysis.

In this tree, MET1 is the label for the semantic pattern "atmospheric condition", and COND indicates a "basic condition" defined as a noun phrase whose head bears the feature "weather condition" (e.g. *rain, snow, cloudy, sunny*), and which may optionally have an "accompaying condition", CMOD.

The system was completed in 1976 and has been fully operational since May 1977, initially dealing with reports from Halifax and Toronto and extended to the whole country in June 1978 (Thouin 1982). The system runs on a CDC Cyber 176 (previously Cyber 7600), with a Cyber 720 (Cyber 71) as front-end for man–machine interaction), and it translates daily from 1500 to 2000 short reports for the Canadian Meteorological Center in Dorval (a suburb of Montreal), amounting currently to some 8.5 million words per year (Isabelle 1984, Isabelle & Bourbeau 1984). The output is not revised before public broadcasting. An example (from Chandioux 1976):

> VALLEE DU BAS ST JEAN HAUT ST JEAN FIN DE L'AVIS DE VENT POUR LES DEUX REGIONS. CETTE NUIT NEIGE ET POUDRERIE DEVENANT PASSAGERES VENDREDI A L'AUBE. VENDREDI NUAGEUX AVEC FAIBLES CHUTES DE NEIGE PASSAGERES. CETTE NUIT VENTS FORTS DU NORD EST SOUFFLANT EN RAFALES DEVENANT VENTS FORTS DU NORD OUEST VENDREDI APRES-MIDI.

(English original:

> LOWER ST JOHN VALLEY UPPER ST JOHN RIVER WIND WARNING ENDED BOTH REGIONS. SNOW AND BLOWING SNOW TONIGHT BECOMING INTERMITTENT NEAR DAWN FRIDAY. CLOUDY WITH PERIODS OF LIGHT SNOW FRIDAY. STRONG GUSTY NORTHEASTERLY WINDS TONIGHT BECOMING NORTHWESTERLY WINDS FRIDAY AFTERNOON.)

The TAUM researchers were somewhat surprised to find that on initial installation in 1976 the system failed to translate over 50% of reports. Considerable expansion of the dictionaries was required, particularly for regional names, and substantial amendments were made to analysis routines in order to deal with participial verb forms, e.g. *rain developing, becoming cloudy* (Chandioux & Guérard 1981). After eighteen months' improvements METEO became fully operational in May 1977. During the development stage and for a number of years subsequently the translators of the Meteorological Center made substantial contributions and suggested numerous refinements (Thouin 1982). It now fails to translate only 20% of reports, largely because input is unedited and contains errors of typing, spelling, and punctuation, all outside the control of the system itself. Failures from non-recognition of syntactic patterns are very rare (Kittredge 1981).

If the system is unable to parse it does not attempt a 'best guess' (by some 'fail-safe' strategy) but leaves the sentence to human translators. Translators are said to be pleased to be spared the boring aspects of their work; their intervention is limited to the more difficult and interesting cases. Productivity of translated bulletins has increased markedly: the average time spent on MT-aided versions is 3.8 minutes; previously, manual translations required 30 to 40 minutes. (Chandioux & Guérard 1981). Although limited in scope, TAUM-METEO is the first, and so far only, MT system regularly producing translations which are not edited before being made available for public consumption.

13.1.3 The AVIATION project

The TAUM-AVIATION project started in 1977 shortly after the installation of METEO at Dorval. The Translation Bureau of the Canadian Secretary of State commissioned TAUM to develop a system to translate the maintenance manuals of the CP-140 coastal patrol aircraft, amounting unofficially to an estimated 90 million words. TAUM was given a contract to develop a system to be ready for delivery of the aircraft three years later (Isabelle 1984, Macklovitch 1984). It was hoped that TAUM-Aviation would be the first advanced 'transfer' system to become operational.

Considerable organisational problems for such a large scale operation delayed serious detailed research for nearly two years. Nevertheless, there was a successful public demonstration in March 1979, and by the time of the deadline in May 1980, the operational prototype had been assembled (implemented on a Cyber 173), including dictionaries for a trial 70,000 word corpus from hydraulics manuals. The distinctive features of the sublanguage of the manuals have been described by Lehrberger (1982): typically such manuals have no interrogative and exclamatory sentences; commands omit articles, copulas, or anaphors (*Remove used filter and discard; Check reservoir full*); and they contain an abundance of complex noun phrases (*hydraulic ground test stand pressure and return line filters*). To deal with the latter it was suggested that AVIATION include semantic categorisation of constituent nouns, in order to produce for *left engine fuel pump suction line* the following analysis (Isabelle *et al.* 1978), which specifies functional (FUNCTION), locative (LOC), possessive (HAS), and object (OBJ) relations:

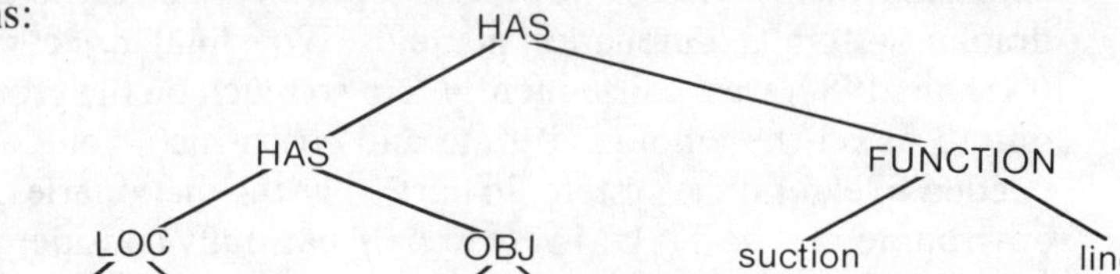

However, the idea could not be implemented within the time span of the project.

The basic structure of the AVIATION system followed the one outlined above, with new programs being compiled for certain stages. Non-inflectional morphological analysis was handled by SISIF, inflectional morphology in both analysis and synthesis by separate *ad hoc* Pascal programs, and dictionary lookup by a new program SYDICAN. Otherwise, the implementation was as described, including REZO for syntactic analysis and LEXTRA for lexical transfer.

Preliminary results seemed to be encouraging. For example (from Isabelle & Bourbeau 1984):

> Les clapets de décharge incorporés sont champignon, sont rappelés par ressort à la position fermée. Une pression de 3450 psi s'exercant sur le clapet-champignon est suffisante pour vaincre la force de rappel du ressort et le clapet-champignon se déplacera de son siège en couteau.
>
> (English original: The in-line relief of valves are poppet-type, spring-loaded to the closed position. A pressure of 3450 psi impingeing on the poppet is sufficient to overcome the opposing force, and the poppet will move from its knife-edge seat.)

The only manual revisions required were the replacement of *sont* by *du type* between *incorporés* and *champignon*, and the substitution of *s'écartera* for *se déplacera* in the last clause.

Although the quality of the material actually translated was quite good, the prototype system was failing to produce any output for between 20 to 40% of input sentences. The TAUM team took the view that it was better to produce nothing at all than to risk incomprehensible output. This was a reasonable strategy for a system under development, but not for one intended as an operational system. Evaluation in March 1980 (Gervais 1980, summarised in Macklovitch 1984 and in Isabelle & Bourbeau 1984) revealed that "raw machine output" had "a degree of intelligibility, fidelity and style which reaches 80% of unrevised human translations (HT)", but that "revision costs are twice as high for MT" and thus "revised MT turns out to be more expensive than revised HT." (18.3 cents per word compared to 14.5 cents per word). Costs could be reduced by suitable man–machine interfacing, but the system could not be cost-effective until a volume of processing had been reached (5 to 6 million words a year) which depended on the extension of the system beyond the prototype's restricted domain of hydraulic system maintenance manuals. The final rejection of the system (Gervais 1980) was, consequently, not so much on the grounds of quality of output as on the amount of time and cost which would obviously still be needed to extend the system, in particular the dictionaries, for a production environment. The TAUM researchers naturally considered that the evaluation had been premature, that the system was still in its early developmental stages and rapid progress would have followed shortly; internal technical evaluations had concluded that 70% of failures had known solutions which could be corrected within 12 person/months of work (Isabelle & Bourbeau 1984). In brief, TAUM-AVIATION had not had a chance to show its potential (Isabelle 1984) — it is a story which has been repeated on numerous occasions in the history of MT.

A further feasibility study was conducted in May 1981, which compared TAUM-AVIATION with the Systran English–French system developed for the Commission of the European Communities (Ch. 14.1) and with the interactive systems ALPS and Weidner (Ch. 17.11–12). Although both operating costs and costs of dictionary updating were lower in the three systems than those in TAUM, the quality of output was considered to be much inferior. Indeed, revisers refused to rank them in terms of technical accuracy, "saying that they were all . . . arduous to revise", often finding it easier to retranslate directly from originals. The authors of the feasibility study were, consequently, unable to recommend any of the systems for purchase and regular use by the Canadian Translation Bureau (Macklovitch 1984).

The most important and telling objection to TAUM was, therefore, the high costs of dictionary compilation. The sublanguage approach aiming for good quality translation within a restricted domain demands careful semantic classifications of vocabulary and time-consuming analysis of lexical items in semantic and syntactic contexts. Without such laborious analysis, the ambiguity of, e.g. *Remove fitting and drain plug* (is there an object called a *drain plug*?) could not be resolved. It can of course be argued that we should not expect any automatic system to be capable of resolving such ambiguities, but it was TAUM's aim to produce high quality MT output.

Between 1976 and 1980 the Translation Bureau had invested over 2.7 million dollars in a MT system which proved not to be cost effective. The Bureau has not lost interest in MT (it is still supporting MT-related research), but, as Macklovitch says (1984), TAUM had "made the unfortunate error of putting all its eggs in the same basket. When the AVIATION contract with the Bureau ended, it found itself with no other source of funding." In September 1981 TAUM was disbanded.

13.2 UNIVERSITY OF THE SAAR, SUSY (1967–)

Research on MT started in Saarbrücken in the mid-1960s with an experimental parser for German (Eggers *et al.* 1969) and an experimental Latin–German system (SALADIN) by Hubert Martin (Maas 1978). A more substantial project between 1967 and 1970 was set up to explore the possible development an early version of the Systran Russian–English system (Ch. 12.1) for translation from Russian into German (Janda *et al.* 1970). On the failure of this attempt, the Saarbrücken group decided to develop its own ideas for a protoype Russian–German system. In 1972 (stimulated in part by a change of computer at Saarbrücken), this project was combined with other activities on language data processing and mathematical linguistics to form the 'Sonderforschungsbereich 100 Elektronische Sprachforschung' subsidised primarily by the Deutsche Forschungsgemeinschaft. The Russian–German prototype MT system was the starting point for research on the multilingual MT system known as SUSY (Saarbrücker Uebersetzungssystem).

The SUSY system is an experimental 'transfer' system: programs for SL analysis and TL synthesis are independent, and there is the familiar separation of algorithmic procedures and linguistic data. It is designed as a multilingual system; programs have been written for a number of languages: Russian, German, French, English, and Esperanto (the latter being a 'private initiative' according to Maas 1977); at one point, Danish was also considered (Maas 1978). There have been various changes in SUSY operations over the years. All versions of the system have been written in FORTRAN, initially for a CD3300, later for a TR440 computer (Maas 1981). Development of the basic SUSY system was essentially brought to an end in 1980. Since 1981, under the direction of Heinz-Dieter Maas, research has been on two fronts. On the one hand there is the project to develop a new version, SUSY II, incorporating insights from earlier research, and on the other hand there are investigations into possible practical applications of the basic SUSY system (SUSY I).

A detailed description of the current situation has been given by Maas (1981) and by Luckhardt *et al.* (1984); details of the basic SUSY I system are given by Maas (1978), and a series of reports entitled *Linguistische Arbeiten*, particularly Luckhardt (1976), Luckhardt & Maas (1976), and Maas (1977a).

The system incorporates a number of dictionaries: SL morpho-syntactic dictionaries containing stems plus grammatical information; SL lexico-semantic dictionaries containing semantic markers, routines for disambiguation, for idioms, and for creating (interlingual) transfer representations; SL–TL bilingual dictionaries containing SL–TL lexical equivalences and routines for aiding syntactic transfer; TL lexico-semantic dictionaries containing routines for deriving TL lexical entries from transfer representations; and TL morpho-syntactic dictionaries containing TL syntactic and inflectional information. Dictionaries have been developed for the following as SLs: German, English, French, Russian, and Esperanto; and for German, French, and English as TLs. Bilingual (SL–TL transfer) dictionaries exist for English–German, French–German, Russian–German, Esperanto–German and for German–English, German–French, German–Esperanto; these pairs therefore represent the present SL–TL translation facilities of SUSY (Luckhardt *et al.* 1984) The largest dictionaries are those for German (140,000 entries in the SL morpho-syntactic dictionary, 75,600 in the lexico-semantic dictionaries, and 17,000 in the TL morpho-syntactic dictionary); the dictionaries for other languages are substantially smaller (the next largest is the Russian SL morpho-syntactic dictionary with just 15,000 entries), and only the English–German transfer dictionary has more than 10,000 entries. These sizes are indicative of the experimental nature of the system.

The basic SUSY I translation program has three main processes: Analysis, Transfer, and Synthesis, divided into a number of stages. The first stage of Analysis (LESEN) inputs text from the terminal or file, and identifies word and sentence boundaries. Morphological analysis (WOBUSU) consults the SL morpho-syntactic dictionary, identifying stems and inflections, and providing tentative information for any words not found. The next stage (DIHOM) attempts the resolution of homographs by: examination of the compatiblities of adjacent word classes (the LEMMAT routine); tests for irregularities and inconsistencies, e.g. a German preposition, as opposed to a separable prefix, cannot occur at the end of a sentence (the TABHOM routine); and statistical evaluation of probabilities, preferences, and weightings of word-class pairings (the GEWICHTE routine). The homograph resolution program is followed by SEGMENT, which divides the sentence into subclauses (on the basis of punctuation marks, conjunctions, etc.) and from such clues as relative pronouns provides a tentative dependency structure to indicate relations between the subclauses. The next two stages identify noun groups (NOMA) and verb groups (VERA), by using SL-specific information on possible combinations and structures. The following stage (KOMA, earlier: SYNAN) builds the phrase structures for transfer: noun groups are attached to governing verbs (using valency information), relative pronouns and reflexives are replaced by their antecedents, and uniform descriptions are provided for subordinate constructions (adjectival, participial clauses). The final stage of Analysis (SEDAM) operates with SL information from the lexico-semantic dictionary to resolve problems of lexical ambiguity; it also provides (interlingual) case markers for relevant prepositions or inflections, and identifies the valency relationships of verbal nouns functioning as nominalised governors, etc.; i.e. the result is a syntactic 'deep structure' representation with some (interlingual) semantic elements, akin to those found in GETA (13.3 below).

Transfer is a single stage process (TRANSFER) using the bilingual dictionary to replace SL lexical forms by TL lexical forms, and attempting to translate unknown words by reference to the morphological analysis (WOBUSU). Some entries may indicate changes in syntactic structures during transfer, e.g. in valency relationships; in the absence of explicit instructions, TRANSFER applies standard SL–TL syntactic transfer routines. The first stage of Synthesis (SEMSYN) is the counterpart of SEDAM, using the lexico-semantic dictionary to produce the TL forms for modal verb and idiomatic (fixed phrase) constructions, and TL lexical forms for (interlingual) case markers. Syntactic synthesis (SYNSYN) converts phrase structure trees into TL constructions using the TL morpho-syntactic dictionary. Then it produces sequences of strings (TL words) or stems with grammatical information, which can be handled by the final Synthesis stage (MORSYN) for the derivation of correct morphological forms and the production of the TL text.

A characteristic feature of SUSY I is its RESCUE mechanism. The main modules of analysis (SEGMENT, NOMA, VERA, KOMA) include checks for consistency of outputs. The identification of an inconsistency triggers RESCUE which sets less stringent checks and initiates a repeat analysis. In this way total failure of the program is prevented.

The basic framework of the SUSY programs was designed to handle inflected languages like German and Russian. The introduction of languages such as English, where information on syntactic relationships is carried mainly by word order, was an important test of the modularity and multilingual capabilities of SUSY (Freigang 1981). Integration of a new language entails both changes in existing programs to cope with new structures and adaptation of new linguistic data to existing practices. An example of the latter was the redefinition of the English gerund (normally considered a verbal form) as a substantive, in order that existing rules of phrase analysis did not need to be altered. An example of the former concerned the (German SL) rule that only one noun phrase may precede a finite verb. If applied to English, the sequence *commission measures* in the sentence *In the commission measures have been considered concerning aid for developing countries* would be analysed as a noun phrase. In order to ensure the correct segmentation, for English the rule had to state that finite verbs must be preceded by one independent noun phrase (i.e. not within a prepositional phrase). Since such rules are probably not unique to German and English, they are considered part of the 'interlingual body' of the SUSY multilingual system, i.e. procedures which can be called upon to augment the 'interlingual core' of absolutely language-independent routine. Each language specifies (through its 'linguistic characteristics') which of the procedures in the 'interlingual body' are to be employed. As a consequence, therefore, of the inclusion of English as a SL, algorithms were developed which could be directly applied in the analysis programs for other languages.

The new version SUSY II incorporates certain differences in stages of analysis and synthesis. In analysis, one of the main differences is that there is no longer a separate routine for homograph resolution; this is handled along with other disambiguation processes during syntactic analysis. After input (LESEN) and morphological analysis (WOBUSU), SUSY II has three analysis processes: the first deals with "linguistically simple cases", such as simple noun and verb groups which are unlikely to be ambiguous; the second deals with the construction of noun groups (including coordination, attribution, modification), computing 'scores' for semantic compatibilities, and passing on only those constructions with the highest scores (i.e. those judged most likely to be correct); the third stage of analysis deals mainly with clause structures and relationships. Transfer in SUSY II remains as in the basic SUSY system. The Synthesis programs in SUSY II are deterministic tree transducers deriving structured TL representations for handling by the same Morphological synthesis (MORSYN) program as in the basic system. An important feature of SUSY II is its ability to produce TL output even with incomplete analyses, primarily because it can linearise any sequence of trees, subtrees, or individual elements (cf. 9.14 above). There is thus no longer any need for the special RESCUE mechanism in SUSY II.

The SUSY II processes include, therefore, a heterogeneity of linguistic approaches and techniques. The system includes phrase structure rules (e.g. in SEGMENT) and transformational rules (in proceeding from surface structures to deep structures and vice versa). Operations may be rule-driven, lexicon-driven, or table-driven, and may refer to features, categories, or structures. The system includes valency frames, but not as obligatory conditions for acceptable parsings. In SUSY valencies represent preferred interpretations, thus allowing for incomplete or unusual grammatical relations in actual texts (cf. 15.1 below). Optional valencies permit both the parsing of almost any input sentence and the elimination of false parsings; obligatory valencies are, however, necessary for lexical disambiguation.

SUSY II includes other techniques to overcome problems of rigidity in analysis sequences, e.g. the lack of backtracking, irrecoverability of earlier structures (as encountered in SUSY I, CETA and the LRC system, Ch. 10 above). During the analysis of noun phrases, for example, parsing does not test for acceptability of input structures but applies all routines it can until there is a criterion which instructs it to stop. A number of stages include 'scored interpretations', preferential procedures and rule ordering; all methods for indicating that one procedure or analysis is better than others.

Much of this flexibiltiy has been made possible by the main innovation in SUSY II, the development of the chart data structure (as in Q-systems), for the representation of complex structural ambiguities (Ch. 9.15). Nodes of a chart representation can be individual elements (e.g. words) or subtrees (e.g. noun groups), and analyses can be made of any segments. Different types of analysis (subgrammars) can be attempted. Some will lead to 'dead ends', others will suggest alternative partitions of the string (sentence, clause). The analysis procedure, therefore, consists of repeated searches for the 'best' (most complete, least complex) combination of the partial analyses. The chart approach permits the easy incorporation of new analysis modules, it allows the definition of any sequence of subgrammars, it provides a uniform data structure, and it ensures that there is always a result of some kind even if some subgrammars fail. It is admitted, however, that SUSY II analysis procedures are likely to be much slower than those of SUSY I: where SUSY I fixes upon a single solution (which might turn out to be wrong), SUSY II pursues all the possibilities (Maas 1981).

Against these undoubted improvements in computational flexibility and multilingual capability must be set SUSY's sentence orientation. Analysis is explicity restricted to sentence structures, and it is predominantly syntax-based. Over the years more semantic processing has been incorporated, first by the insertion of some semantic analysis routines after syntactic analysis (in the basic SUSY I system since November 1976, when work began on the semantic disambiguation algorithm SEDAM), and later by the integration of some semantic procedures into syntactic analysis (in SUSY II). Nevertheless, semantic procedures remain relatively weak. But the principal consequence of SUSY's sentence orientation is the lack, both in SUSY I and (so far) in SUSY II, of procedures for discourse analysis and dealing with intersentential anaphoric reference; although admittedly, in this respect SUSY is little different from most other contemporary systems.

During the mid-1970s the SUSY group maintained close contacts with the GETA group. Between 1974 and 1978 much of the work on the French analysis program was carried out in Grenoble (Weissenborn 1977). There are a number of similarities in the techniques of SUSY and GETA (Ch. 13.3 below): tree transducer algorithms, semantic dependency structures, the use of valency information, and the development of chart representations. In 1975 the SUSY group joined with GETA in the Leibniz group which had been set up for international cooperation in MT research (Ch. 14.2); the formulation of a standard 'transfer' language appears to have owed as much to the Saarbrücken achievements as it did to GETA's influence. The later involvement of the Saarbrücken group in the Eurotra project (Ch. 14.2) has been highly influential, both in terms of overall MT philosophy and with respect to computational developments.

While the emphasis has continued to be on experimental and theoretical development, the Saarbrücken group has not neglected practical implementations of the SUSY system. Various possibilities are discussed by Thiel (1981) and Luckhardt (1982), such as the compilation of glossaries, translation of titles and abstracts, information retrieval, and question-answering systems. Some have already been tried. One of the first was SALEM (Saarbrücker Lemmatisierungssystem), which, using the SUSY analysis programs, automatically compiled concordances of German texts and provided a rich source of information on the syntactic and semantic contexts of German vocabulary (Eggers 1981). Shortly afterwards, there was the use of the SUSY-parser in an information retrieval system for the automatic indexing of legal documents (TRANSIT, under development by Harald Zimmermann since 1981). So far the system has analysed some 7 million words of patents texts and automatically compiled a "lexicon of 110,000 automatically decomposed German compounds" (Luckhardt *et al.* 1984).

Later, in 1981, came an investigation of the possible integration of SUSY I in the translation service of the Bundessprachenamt. The requirements for an operational SUSY translation system were outlined by Wilms (1981): sophisticated facilities for text processing before and after translation, access to specialised dictionaries (in this particular instance, integration with the service's own LEXIS databank (cf. 17.6), improved procedures for dictionary updating, and creation of text-specific *ad hoc* glossaries. According to the designers the project was terminated in 1983 after a test of SUSY output which revealed that the Bundessprachenamt was "not willing to accept any translation below the usual standard level of translations produced by its own translators" (Luckhardt *et al.* 1984). More pertinent perhaps was the lack of text-handling facilities in the SUSY configuration. A recent project SUSANNAH (SUSY ANwenderNAH, or 'SUSY user-oriented') plans to rectify this lack by developing a translator workstation which will support interfaces to term banks and glossaries, office communication systems, as well as access to SUSY itself (cf. Ch. 17 below).

The most recent application of SUSY is in the cooperative project since 1983 with Kyoto University (Ammon & Wessoly 1984–5). The goal is the automatic translation of German document titles into Japanese and of Japanese titles into German. The unusual feature of the project is the use of English as an intermediary (or 'switching') language: translation from German to English and vice versa will be done by SUSY, translation from English to Japanese and vice versa by the Kyoto system TITRAN (Ch. 18.13). Because translation is to be 'indirect' the differences in MT design between the 'deep analysis' approach of SUSY and the restricted 'surface analysis' approach of TITRAN are not considered to be as significant as they would obviously be if the two systems were to be directly coupled. For this project the two systems can be developed independently; all they need to have in common is an orientation to the same subject field (computer science). Nevertheless, both have their limitations. TITRAN is not able to insert English articles, it lacks routines for relative clauses, and it relies considerably on 'lexicographic' solutions to compound forms. On the other hand, the centrality of the verb in SUSY's methods of analysis (valency relations, clause structures) may inhibit satisfactory treatment of titles, which generally contain few finite verb forms. The project is strictly practical; the evaluation criteria are comprehensibility and readability by technical experts, and fidelity to information content, but not stylistic adequacy.

13.3 GROUPE D'ETUDES POUR LA TRADUCTION AUTOMATIQUES(GETA), UNIVERSITY OF GRENOBLE (1971—)

A change in computer facilities in 1971 encouraged the research team at Grenoble to rethink the design of their MT system. Now renamed Groupe d'Etudes pour la Traduction Automatique (GETA), the team decided on a transfer approach. Experience with the basically 'interlingual' CETA system (Ch. 10.1 above) had revealed disadvantages in reducing texts to semantic representations and destroying in the process a good deal of 'surface' information useful for TL synthesis. (There is no point, for example, in converting a SL passive form into an active representation if it has only to be reconverted into a similar TL passive.) The aim of the GETA team is to design a MT system which is highly flexible both in its programming and in its linguistic aspects, a system which will encourage cooperative activities with other MT research groups, a 'multilingual' system capable of translating from and into any European language, and which is as 'portable', i.e. machine independent, as possible. As in most contemporary advanced MT systems, GETA maintains strict separation of linguistic data and programming procedures (a feature also of CETA), thus enabling linguists to work with familiar linguistic concepts (grammatical categories, dictionaries, grammar rules, semantic features, etc.). The earlier stages in the development of GETA are described in Boitet (1978), Chauché (1975), Vauquois (1977). The most recent version of the GETA system, developed since 1978, has been named ARIANE-78; the most comprehensive descriptions are to be found in Boitet & Nedobejkine (1981) and Whitelock & Kilby (1983); and updating on the most recent versions is to be found in Boitet (1983), Boitet & Nedobejkine (1983), and Boitet *et al.* (1985).

GETA-ARIANE is basically a 'transfer' system with morphological and syntactic analysis, transfer, and syntactic and morphological synthesis. The results of the analysis programs are dependency-tree type 'deep structure' representations in essence rather like those in CETA, but including a certain amount of 'surface' information (to assist in TL synthesis). It is no longer the objective to establish 'universal' pivot languages, rather each SL has its own 'pivot' or 'transfer' interface. The Transfer program has two stages: the conversion of SL 'lexical' elements into equivalent TL 'lexical' elements (involving reformation of tree structures as necessary), and the conversion or transformation of SL 'pivot' structures into equivalent and appropriate TL 'pivot' structures.

GETA has three main algorithmic components, one for the conversion of string representations into tree structures, ATEF, one for the transformation of trees into trees, ROBRA, and one for the conversion of trees into strings, SYGMOR. In addition there is an algorithm for consultation of the transfer dictionary, TRANSF (recently modified as EXPANS, Boitet *et al.* 1985). Each algorithm is suited to particular stages of the translation process. There are basically six phases (Boitet & Nedobejkine 1981): 'Morphological analysis', using a battery of dictionaries to produce all possible category assignments and preliminary identification of some noun and verb groups, i.e. converting strings into partial tree structures by the ATEF algorithm; 'Multilevel analysis' (i.e. syntactic analysis), producing dependency-tree representations which combine both 'surface syntactic' information and the kind of 'deep syntactic' information found in the CETA trees (10.1 above) via the tree–tree conversion algorithm ROBRA; 'Lexical transfer', converting TL representations by SL–TL dictionary substitutions (via TRANSF); 'Structural transfer', transforming SL trees into TL 'pivot' trees (via ROBRA) — the two transfer phases working closely together; 'Syntactic generation', producing TL 'surface' trees; and 'Morphological generation', converting these trees into TL strings by the SYGMOR algorithm. The diagram illustrating the general system of ARIANE-78 (Fig. 25) is adapted from Boitet & Nedobejkine (1981).

A major premise of the GETA team has been that the algorithms employed at any particular stage should be no more complex and no more powerful than necessary for handling the linguistic data in question. On this argument it rejects the use of such powerful algorithms as the Q-systems (found in TAUM, cf. 13.1 above) and ATN parsers (Ch. 9.13) for the simple manipulation of strings in, for example, morphological analysis and synthesis. In GETA-ARIANE algorithms of various levels of generality are applied according to the relative simplicity of the processes; thus the algorithms for morphological analysis (ATEF), lexical transfer (TRANSF), and morphological generation (SYGMOR) are less general than the powerful ROBRA algorithm for syntactic analysis, structural transfer, and syntactic generation.

The ARIANE-78 system itself does not, in principle, define the 'depth' to which a text is analysed; the level for translation of particular structures may be determined by the linguist or analyst himself; and it could in theory range from surface syntax to an abstract interlingual representation (Whitelock & Kilby 1983). In practice, however, GETA researchers agree upon transfer structures combining both deep and surface syntactic information. It is indeed a major advantage of GETA's data representation that different levels of analysis can be incorporated simultaneously on a single labelled tree structure. It allows for interaction between levels and provides a fail-safe mechanism, i.e. if further analysis at one level is unsuccessful, analysis

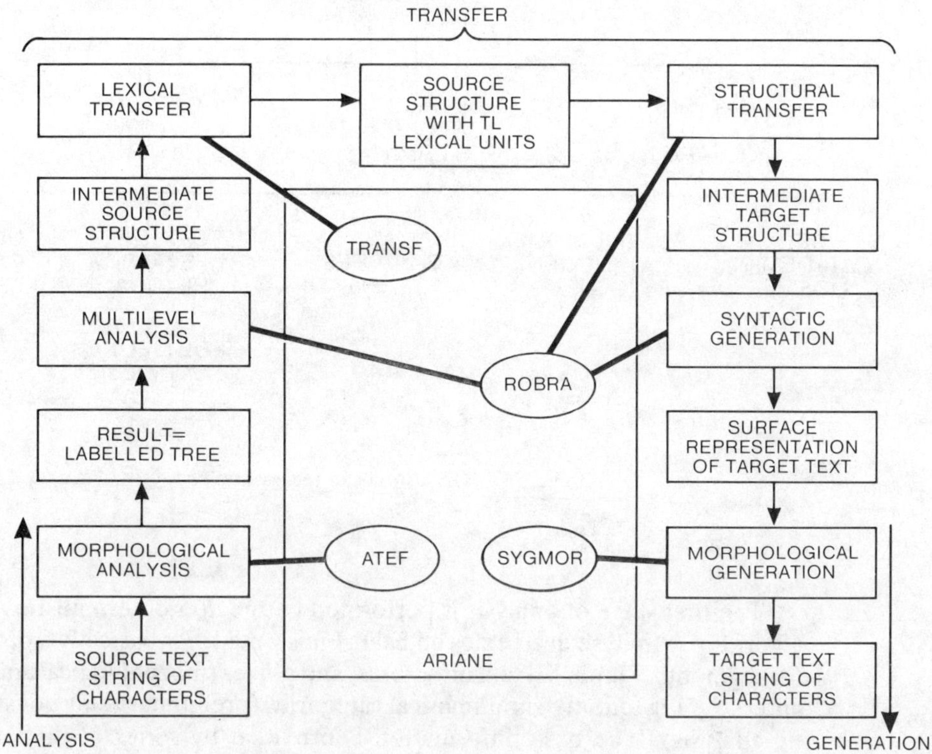

Fig. 25 — The GETA system.

at another level can be attempted — complete reanalysis of the whole text segment is not necessary. This is possible because representations may include information derived from a variety of levels of interpretation.

Experience with CETA had shown the value of including different levels of grammatical and semantic information in SL representations. In GETA 'deep structure' or SL transfer representations may include a mixture of: syntactic classes (adj, noun, NP, VP), grammatical functions (subject, object, etc.), and logico-semantic relations (predicates and arguments). In other words, they combine information about phrase structure relations, dependency relations and semantic or logical relations. For example, the sentence *Cette musique plaît aux jeunes gens* would have the tree shown in Fig. 26, where

(a) UL indicates lexical items (MUSIQUE), (GENS) etc.
(b) CAT indicates grammatical categories such as noun phrase (GN) and adjective (ADJ)
(c) FS indicates dependency relations such governing node (GOV), subject (SUJ) and attribute (ATR)
(d) RL indicates logico-semantic relations such as ARG1 and ARG2.

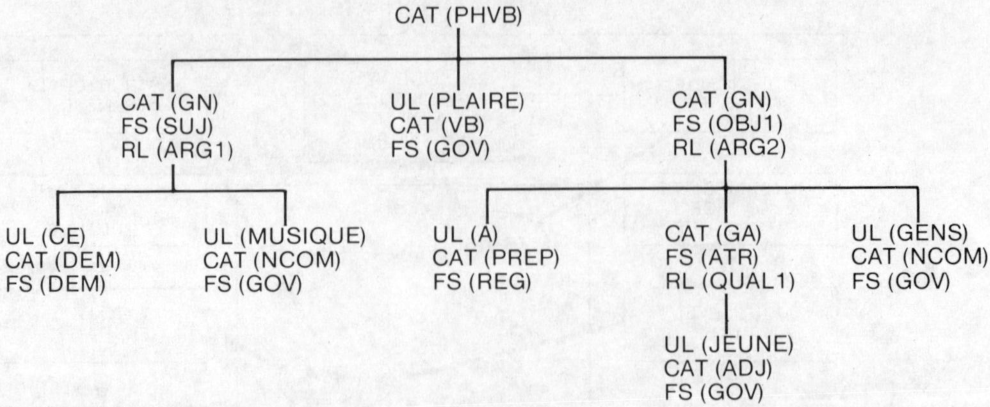

Fig. 26 — GETA transfer representation.

The first stage of analysis is performed by the non-deterministic ATEF algorithm (Analyse des Textes en Etats Finis). ATEF is basically a program for segmenting input SL text into stems, and affixes (morphological analysis) and assigning tentative grammatical categories (preliminary stage of syntactic analysis). The basic information is provided by series of dictionaries including dictionaries of idioms, lexical items (stems) and affixes. Essentially the procedure is as in TAUM (cf. 13.1 above) where all possible segmentations are tested against stem and endings dictionaries. However, in addition ATEF performs preliminary syntactic analysis by testing adjacent forms for morphological compatibilities, e.g. the endings of putative adjective and noun forms. In essence it is a finite state non-deterministic algorithm (but not as powerful as an ATN parser) transforming strings into sequences of labelled trees. (The argument for the adequacy of finite-state parsers for this purpose was made a number of years earlier by Vauquois *et al.* 1965, Vauquois 1971).

The basic ATEF procedure examines all the possible segmentations of a text form (i.e. usually a word). For example, German *AUTOMATEN* might be segmented as AUTOMAT+EN, AUTOMAT+E+N, AUTO +MATE+N; of these only the first will be retained by ATEF after consultation of a stem dictionary. Unless constrained, ATEF examines every possible segmentation of a word; the combinatorial implications can however be anticipated by linguists who may introduce conditions on application and intervene in procedures. The result is a highly complex algorithm; ATEF is undoubtedly highly flexible, allowing analysts to make use of whatever techniques seem most appropriate in each instance, but this flexibility would appear to be at the cost of a complexity of procedural structure which makes the linguistic bases of the algorithm less accessible to the researcher compiling and debugging programs.

For syntactic and semantic analysis the team has developed an algorithm for the transformation of one abstract tree or subtree into another. This is the extremely flexible ROBRA algorithm, deriving from translation formalisms of the CETA system (Ch. 10.1 above), cf. Veillon *et al.* (1967). ROBRA is a tree-transducing mechanism (Ch. 9.14) taking the output of ATEF to produce the kind of multi-level syntactico-semantic representation in Fig. 26. In effect, it operates by applying cycles of subgrammars (each consisting of ordered sets of 'transformational rules', i.e. tree transducing rules), where each subgrammar is concerned with a specific range of linguistic phenomena, e.g. relative clause structures, infinitive complementation, comparative structures, etc. A typical sequence (Boitet & Nedobejkine 1981) in Russian analysis might be: division into clauses (using punctuation, conjunctions, etc.), identification of noun phrases, searching for elements dependent on noun phrases, finding the nominal antecedents of relative clauses, looking for infinitives, identifying subjects, objects, etc., specifying case ('actant') relationships, and so forth.

In general transformational rules operate on subtrees and are constrained by the context in which they apply, i.e. the rest of the tree. Thus, as an abstract example, the subtree C(D,E) in the following (sub)tree:

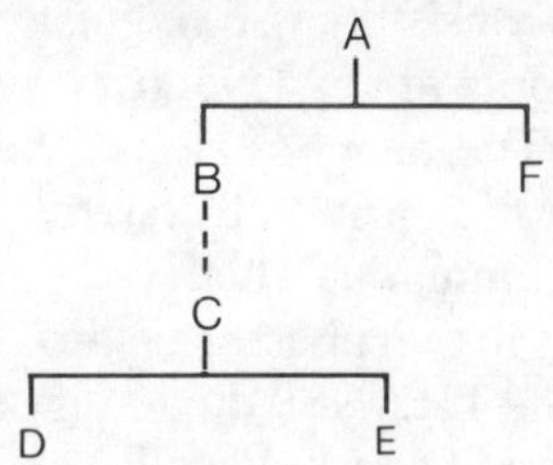

may be converted into C(E,D) only if B is to the immediate left of F in a subtree A(B,F). Other rules might permit B and F in any order; or might allow optional intervening elements or subtrees; or might allow intervening structures only of a specific type; and so forth. In addition, of course, conditions may specify information of any kind (e.g. grammatical category, constituency structure, dependency) already generated, whether by ATEF or by preceding phases of ROBRA.

The considerable variety of possible subtrees, the need to permit any number of optional structures within subtrees and the abstractness of the transduction procedures make ROBRA both a highly flexible and a highly complex algorithm. This abstractness and this flexibility allow the linguist to apply any methods of analysis which appear most appropriate. The linguist decides what transformations are to be used in particular instances and what conditions are to be attached to their use. The linguist can therefore construct subgrammars to be applied in any order and under any conditions he may specify. He might, for example, construct a set of different subgrammars for the treatment of noun groups, one for simple cases, another for complex cases. He might apply a strategy using dependency relations in one subgrammar and a strategy using phrase structures in another. Each subgrammar can function in a number of distinct execution modes (at the discretion of the linguist), e.g. (i) in mode 'U' (unitary) where rules are applied once only, or alternatively in mode 'E' (exhaustive) where rules may be applied to trees on which they have already operated, or (ii) in mode 'H' (high) where priority of application is given to subtrees at the highest level of the tree, or in mode 'B' (bottom) where rules are applied first to the lowest subtrees. The system provides the linguist with a vast choice of possible approaches to analysis and assures him that, whatever the strategy or 'grammar' used, there will always be a result at the end of a finite application of rules. This is because tree-transducing algorithms do not test for the *acceptability* of structures (i.e. they do not filter out ill-formed structures) but test for the *applicability* of transduction rules (Vauquois 1977). The subgrammars work on subtree specifications. If a rule does not apply the tree remains unchanged; if no rule of a subgrammar can be applied there will always be a tree as output on which other subgrammars may operate. However this very flexibility may perhaps have its disadvantages. The interactions of component procedures and the interrelationships of transduction rules reduce the modularity of the system as a whole. It is therefore difficult to maintain consistency in linguistic procedures, particularly when transfer rules may apply at any level (or any combination of levels) for any linguistic structure. The danger is an *ad hoc*-ness in grammatical analysis almost as great as in the early MT systems which worked virtually without any conception of grammatical theory.

Transfer operates in two phases: Lexical transfer and Structural transfer. The former utilises the TRANSF dictionary relating 'canonical' stems of two languages (Russian and French, usually) and specifying in transfer rules any necessary subtree constructions, e.g. in the case of idioms or where the equivalent for a SL word is a TL phrase (Russian *nuzhno*: French *il faut*; English *tend*: French *avoir tendence*) or a SL phrase is a single TL word (English *let . . . know*: French *informer*). In general, compound SL forms (e.g. English *carry out*) will have already been identified as units during an analysis phase. It is during Lexical transfer that most problems of multiple equivalence are resolved by taking into account SL structural relationships, e.g. English *look* becomes French *regarder*, if in SL transfer representation it is linked with *at*, or *chercher*,if linked with *for*, or *ressembler*, if linked with *like*, etc. Nevertheless, some problems remain unresolved and are left to post-editors for the final decision, e.g. English *process*: French *processus* or *procédé* (as in the example translation below).

Structural transfer is concerned with syntactic differences, e.g. where a Russian verb may govern the instrumental (*pol'zovat'sya*) the French equivalent may require a preposition (*utiliser de*). Other obvious changes are the transposition of nouns and adjectives and the treatment of negation. Again the ROBRA algorithm is utilised to transform subtrees. The stage is followed by Syntactic generation (of French), also using ROBRA. As in Syntactic analysis, it consists of cycles of subgrammars, handling such linguistic operations as the generation of TL articles, the specification of auxiliary verbs (in the determination of correct tenses and moods), the distribution of agreement information (e.g. adjectives modifying nouns), and the treatment of TL coordination.

The final stage is Morphological generation, converting labelled trees output by Syntactic synthesis into strings of characters. For this, the SYGMOR algorithm is applied; like ATEF, SYGMOR is a realisation of a finite-state mechanism, reflecting the lesser complexity of this process. There are two phases, tree–string conversion and string–character conversion, during each of which TL dictionaries are consulted (e.g. to establish correct morphological forms, such as: doubling of consonants, JET+E → JETTE; insertion of 'e', MANG+ONS → MANGEONS; contractions, DE+LE → DU, etc.). There would seem little doubt that SYGMOR is sufficiently flexible to deal with the linguistic operations appropriate at this level, e.g. contraction, elision, inflection (Whitelock & Kilby 1983).

In principle, the units of translation treated in GETA-ARIANE procedures are "not sentences but rather one or several paragraphs, so that the context usable, for instance to resolve anaphors" is more extensive than earlier systems (Boitet & Nedobejkine 1981). In practice, however, "the bulk of analysis and generation operates essentially at the sentence level" (Vauquois & Boitet 1984). During Structural analysis it is possible to use some inter-sentence context to resolve anaphors (if no suitable candidate can be found in the sentence being analysed), but in general ARIANE does not incorporate systematic discourse analysis; in particular no attempt has been made to derive 'hypersyntactic' representations of paragraph units.

The Russian–French version of ARIANE-78 has been developed on a corpus of scientific and technical texts in the fields of aeronautics, space science, thermodynamics, and nuclear physics. By June 1984 (Vauquois & Boitet 1984) the dictionaries contained 7000 Russian lexical units (about 17,000 words) and 5600 French lexical units (about 16,000 words). A number of example translations are to be found in Boitet & Nedobejlkine (1981); an example of a 'raw' translation is the following extract:

> LE SYMPOSIUM EST CONSACRE A LA SPECTROSCOPIE NUCLEAIRE ET A LA STRUCTURE DU NOYAU ATOMIQUE. DANS LE MOT D'ENTREE ON SOULIGNE LE ROLE IMPORTANT QUE LE SYMPOSIUM A JOUE DANS LE DEVELOPPEMENT DE LA PHYSIQUE NUCLEAIRE DES ENERGIES FAIBLES EN UNION SOVIETIQUE. PENDENT LE SYMPOSIUM ON A EXAMINE LA SERIE DES ETUDES IMPORTANTES REALISEES PAR LES SAVANTS SOVIETIQUES. EN PARTICULIER, ON A ETUDIE LA NON-CONSERVATION DE LA PARTIE DANS LES PROCESSUS?PROCEDES? NUCLEAIRES, CREATION DU MODELE DU NOYAU NON-AXIAL, DIVISION SPONTANEES DES ISOTOPES DES ELEMENTS SUPERLOURDS ET DECOUVERTE DE L'EFFET DES OMBRES POUR LA DISPERSION DES PARTICULES . . .

As the authors note, the only awkward rendition is that of *mot d'entree* instead of *introduction*, which could easily be solved by an addition to the idiom dictionary. The quality is impressive, but what must be kept in mind with ARIANE (as with most experimental systems) is that these are translations from prepared texts with a relatively limited range of vocabulary.

In many respects GETA is the most advanced of current MT systems, representing close to what is considered by most researchers at the present time to be the 'state-of-the-art'; nevertheless it has its shortcomings, as Whitelock & Kilby (1983) have pointed out. The GETA team are aware of these and are considering improvements: e.g. a unified formalism for the metalanguage of all components, a single data structure (the chart, cf. 9.15 above) to replace string and tree forms, and the improvement of system portability (by implementations in Pascal or LISP). The cost of 'portability' could be high, however, as Vauquois & Boitet (1984) have discovered. A comparison was made with Kyoto University's system, whose design is similar to that of ARIANE-78 (cf. 18.6 below) and whose GRADE tree-transducer is comparable to ROBRA, but which is implemented in a dialect of LISP rather than PL360 assembler. The results showed that "the LISP implementation is 40 times more voracious in computer time and space".

The strength of the GETA system is its linguistic and computational techniques, particularly in the areas of morphological and syntactic analysis and transformation. Its weakness remains, as Boitet (1982) readily admits, in its dictionaries; unlike other MT groups, such as TAUM, the Grenoble team has not been able to call upon terminological assistance.

Related to this weakness is what must be regarded as the main 'deficiency' of GETA from the viewpoint of current interest in the implementation of AI techniques (cf. 15 below): the lack of semantic processing beyond the traditional lexical approaches. Part of the reason for this is, of course, the experience with the 'pivot language' of CETA. However, researchers at GETA have outlined various ideas in this area. Boitet (1976) suggested the incorporation of a 'semantic parser' and the expansion of its semantic information to include 'preference' and 'inference' semantics on the lines indicated by Wilks (cf. 9.17 and 15.1). More recently in Boitet & Gerber (1984) and Gerber & Boitet (1985) plans have been outlined to incorporate 'real world' or 'metalinguistic' knowledge of the type found in AI expert systems. The basic idea is that two 'expert corrector systems' could be inserted between analysis and transfer and between transfer and generation. The first, for example, might resolve problems of adjective and noun coordination: in *The mixture gives off dangerous cyanide and chlorine fumes* the analysis required is not *(dangerous cyanide) and (chlorine fumes)* but *dangerous (cyanide and chlorine) fumes*. An expert 'knowledge base' for chemistry could help in such cases; but problems of practical implementation are yet to be tackled.

Development of the Russian–French system on ARIANE was the dominant activity at GETA from 1973 to 1980. By 1979 it became evident that GETA had to pay more attention to the construction of a practical working MT system. To this end, GETA has initiated an "experimental translation unit" using a "production-oriented subset of ARIANE-78, PROTRA" translating monthly about 50–60 abstracts from *Referativnyi Zhurnal* in the fields of space science and metallurgy (Boitet & Nedobejkine 1983, Vauquois & Boitet 1984). The dictionary contained 7000 Russian lexical units (about 20,000 words) in 1983 (Boitet 1983). With no OCR equipment and no access to magnetic tapes of abstracts, texts have to be entered manually. There is no expectation that 'raw' translations will be adequate; post-editing is envisaged as an essential component. In practice, revisers have available the original text, the 'raw' translation and access to dictionaries, from which they produce translations in an interactive environment. An example of output is from Boitet & Nedobejkine (1983):

> Ce satellite est destiné à l'étude des ressources naturelles de la terre à l'aide de l'appareillage télévisé et des radios mètres de micro onde élaborées et fabriquées par les spécialistes de l'Inde.

The main change on revision was to: *appareillage de télévision et de radiomètres à microondes*. Evidently, PROTRA would seem to have some potential as an interactive system (cf. 17.7ff.). In connection with this project, the Grenoble team has developed various software facilities: ATLAS for updating dictionaries, VISULEX for revising MT dictionaries, and THAM for interactive computer-aided translation (Bachut & Verastegui 1984, Boitet *et al.* 1985); the latter is constructed on similar lines to Melby's system described later (Ch. 17.10).

Although the Russian–French system has been the principal activity at GETA, the facilities provided at Grenoble by the ARIANE configuration have supported a number of other MT projects (Boitet 1982, Vauquois & Boitet 1984). From the creation of the 'Leibniz' group (Ch. 14.2 below) in 1974 until 1978, researchers of the Saarbrücken MT group (Ch. 13.2 above) made use of the GETA facilities in the French analysis projects of Stegentritt and Weissenborn. A somewhat similar arrangement was made between 1977 and 1980 with the Nancy MT group, which lacked sufficient computer facilities at the time. Using GETA-ARIANE programming facilities, members of the group were able to experiment on a English–French system, which in general conception apparently differed markedly from that of the GETA group — an illustration of the flexibility of the computational facilities at Grenoble.

Among the small-scale MT models developed on GETA facilities are the Portuguese–English MT project pursued intermittently since 1973 by P. Daun Fraga, a researcher from the University of Campinas (Brazil), a multilingual system from Chinese into Japanese, French, English, and German (Feng Zhi Wei), an English–Chinese transfer system (Yang Ping), an English–Thai system, an English–Japanese system in collaboration with the University of Kyoto (Tsujii Jun-Ichi 1982), a French–English system (J. P. Guilbaud and M. Dymetman), and a German–French system under development since 1979 using the same generation programs as in the Russian–French project (the analysis programs are being written by J. P.

Guilbaud and M. Stahl). More substantial is the English–Malay project, begun in 1979 in cooperation with Universiti Sains Malaysia, Penang, with the intention of producing teaching materials in technical fields. It is now approaching the stage of systematic testing of the prototype — although as yet the dictionaries are still small (1800 English and 1800 Malay lexical units). Most significant of all for the long-term future of the Grenoble MT group is the involvement since 1983 with a number of industrial companies in a French national project (ESOPE). The project's target is a system for the translation of aircraft manuals from French into English, and perhaps later for the translation of computer manuals from English into French.

Although, as remarked earlier, the quality of ARIANE translations appears to be quite high, a detailed evaluation of the system has not been undertaken, nor has any attempt been made yet to measure real costs (Vauquois & Boitet 1984). The team remain convinced of the overall validity of their 'transfer' approach; of the need for contrastive information about the languages concerned and its retention in 'multilevel' representations; of the use of mixtures of syntactic and semantic information during disambiguation; of the implementation of 'transducers' rather than 'analysers' given the non-specificity of linguistic 'knowledge' in MT systems (akin to the probabilistic nature of AI 'expert system' knowledge bases); of the use of heuristic techniques in programming grammatical analysis rather than complete searches of complex grammars; and of their insistance that the system produces some output, however full of errors, rather than stopping completely when ill-formed structures are encountered.

13.4 LINGUISTICS RESEARCH CENTER, UNIVERSITY OF TEXAS, METAL (1978–)

At the end of the German–English 'interlingua' MT project in 1975 (Ch. 10.3) there was a further hiatus in research at the Linguistics Research Center (LRC). The complexities of transformational parsing and the inadequacies of the syntactic interlingua led LRC to a redesign of their system on different principles. In 1978 the USAF Rome Air Development Center provided funds for researching an operational MT system, generally referred to as METAL. In 1979 this funding was augmented by support from Siemens AG, West Germany, who became sole sponsors of the project in 1980. The main objective has been the development of a German–English system for translating telecommunication and data processing texts, though there are reported to be other applications (e.g. English analysis) under investigation (Slocum 1984). The aim is not a fully automatic system, it is recognised that current techniques do not make such a goal realistic; therefore, post-editing facilities are built into the total configuration. The principal researcher for the LRC-Siemens project is Jonathan Slocum, while overall direction of the Linguistic Research Center remains in the hands of Winfred Lehmann.

Like the previous system, METAL is based on methods of theoretical and computational linguistics: context-free phrase-structure algorithms, transformational rules, and case-frame analyses. However, whereas previously 'deep structure' analyses were intended to be language-independent (interlingual), the METAL 'deep' analyses are representations specifically for bilingual transfer. The LRC group has concluded that a MT interlingua or 'pivot language' is "probably impossible" and have adopted the alternative, "a transfer component which maps 'shallow analyses of sentences' in the SL into 'shallow analyses of equivalent sentences' in the TL" (Slocum 1984).

In basic form then, METAL is a standard 'transfer' system with stages of Analysis, Transfer, and Synthesis. However, the stages of transfer and synthesis are not as clearly separated as in other 'purer' examples of the 'transfer' approach, since Transfer includes operations which might normally be considered part of syntactic synthesis. The programs are written in LISP, making this LRC system more accessible to other MT researchers than previous LRC systems which were written in lower-level codes. Since LISP functions may be driven by linguistic data, there is no longer in METAL a strict separation of algorithmic and linguistic data. Details of METAL are given by Slocum (1980, 1982, 1984), by White (1985), and by Whitelock & Kilby (1983).

METAL dictionaries are either monolingual (SL or TL) or bilingual (for SL–TL transfer). In 1984 there were about 10,000 lexical entries for each of the languages: German SL and English TL (Slocum 1984). Entries in both SL and TL monolingual dictionaries are formatted in the same way, namely a series of 'features': a 'canonical form' (i.e. base stem), a set of allomorphs or morphological variants (i.e. surface forms), grammatical information for each variant (adjective, noun, etc.), lexical collocation (e.g. indicating a discontinuous element associated with the stem, as in *look . . . up*), a concept number (used to relate semantically related forms, e.g. *compute, computer, computation, computational, computable*), and subject field (e.g. to assist in the disambiguation of polysemes). In addition, preferences (weightings) may be assigned to particular interpretations (e.g. a compound or fixed idiom may be investigated before simpler forms), thus enabling output to be ranked and highest-scoring interpretations to be selected. Lastly, there are sets of codes specific to particular grammatical categories. Nouns are given semantic markers (e.g. 'entity', 'material', 'temporal'); and the arguments of verbs are defined in terms of their semantic roles, i.e. case relations (e.g. 'agent', 'benefactive', 'instrument'), their grammatical types (e.g. noun phrase, prepositional phrase), and their syntactic roles (e.g. subject, object, complement).

The processes of Analysis and Transfer call at various stages upon a corpus of 'grammar rules' — about 550 in the case of German (Slocum 1984). Each grammar rule specifies a rule for phrase structure constituency, some tests for well-formedness, 'construction' rules, and transfer functions. In addition Analysis and Transfer may refer to a corpus of transformational rules which may apply to phrase structures.

Dictionary lookup locates surface forms in dictionary entries and retrieves the canonical forms with their grammatical and semantic data. The next stage refers to the grammar rules and identifies those whose phrase-structure components apply to the sentence in question. The result is a structure which can then be tested for well-formedness by the relevant part of the same grammar rule. If the tests are satisfied, the relevant 'construction' rules are then applied, giving a more abstract structure which may be converted to a 'deeper' (SL–TL intermediary) structure by transformation rules. This structure is then passed to the Transfer stage where the transfer rules indicated in the grammar rules are applied to derive a surface syntactic structure. The final Generate stage produces TL output.

An example of a simple grammar rule for building nouns is in Fig. 27 (from Slocum 1984).

```
NN          NST          N-FLEX
0           1            2
(LVL 0)     (REQ WI)     (REQ WF)

TEST        (INT 1 CL 2 CL)

CONSTR      (CPX 1 ALO CL)
            (CPY 2 NU CA)
            (CPY 1 WI)

ENGLISH     (XFR 1)
            (ADF 1 ON)
            (CPY 1 MC DR)
```

Fig. 27 — METAL noun building rule.

The first line indicates that a noun (NN) is to be formed from a noun stem (NST) and an inflected nominal ending (N-FLEX). The code (LVL 0) indicates this is a 'top-priority' rule. Each constituent (numbered 0 to 2) has individual conditions: the first element (NST) must be word-initial (WI) and the second (N-FLEX) must be word-final (WF). The TEST part of the rule states agreement restrictions: that when the values for the feature CL coded on NST are compared (INTersected) with those for CL on N-FLEX, there is at least one value in common. The appropriate tree can now be CONSTRucted:

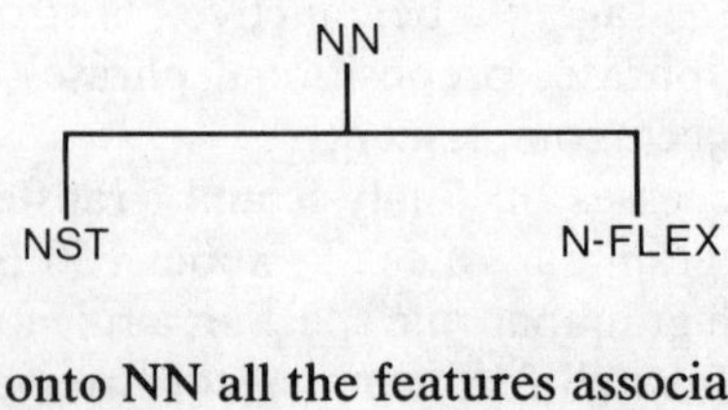

where CPX will copy onto NN all the features associated with NST except for the allomorph (ALO) and inflectional class (CL), the first CPY will copy the grammatical number (NU) and case (CA) features from N-FLEX, and the second CPY will copy the WI feature from NST (i.e. stem form). The final part of the rule is invoked during Transfer, deriving the equivalent English noun from top to bottom by copying and adding appropriate features.

Other examples of rule applications are given by Whitelock and Kilby (1983). Tests of structures may, for example, check for noun and adjective agreement or the presence of a past participle (*gegangen*) with a finite verb form (*ist*), or the occurrence of a preposition followed by a noun phrase. A 'construction' rule might, for example, derive a predicative representation from the conjunction of a passive auxiliary (i.e. WERDEN) and an infinitive (e.g. *gehen*), by attaching the indicators of tense, voice, and mood carried by the surface form of WERDEN (e.g. *wird*) to the 'abstract' verb form GEHEN. The conditions specified for the arguments of verbs may be referred to at any stage during tests or during 'constructions'; any structure which does not satisfy the specifications, whether in terms of grammatical roles or case relations, may therefore be rejected. For example, the analysis part of a 'grammatical rule' for verbs such as *gehen*, is formulated as in Fig. 28 (Whitelock and Kilby 1983).

```
(DEXPR I2AL (VC MD)
 (COND ((SYNTAX)
        (COND ((AND (ACTIVE)
                    (NON-COMMAND)
                    (FRAME N NP AGT)
                    (FRAME NIL NIL LOC)
               T)
              ((AND (ACTIVE) (COMMAND) (FRAME NIL NIL LOC))
               T)))
```

Fig. 28 — METAL verb analysis rule.

It may be interpreted as stating that if the verb is active and declarative (NON-COMMAND) then it has two arguments (AGT and LOC); the 'agent' must be a noun phrase (NP) in the nominative case, and the form of the locative depends on the particular verb. If, however, the verb is active and imperative (COMMAND) then there is just a 'locative' whose form is specific to a particular verb.

Transformational rules may be invoked in a grammar rule by a function XFM, which may be a combination of operations copying, adding, and deleting tree structures. For example, a 'construction' rule may include the following (Whitelock and Kilby 1983):

```
XFM (RCL:1 ((RCL:2 ((PRED:3 (—:4)) —:5)) PRF:6))
    (RCL:2 ((PRED:3 (—:4) (CPY 6 CAN) (ADD VC A)) —:5)
    (ADD CLF) (ADD SPX)))
```

This has the effect of transforming the subtree 29(a) into the subtree 29(b):

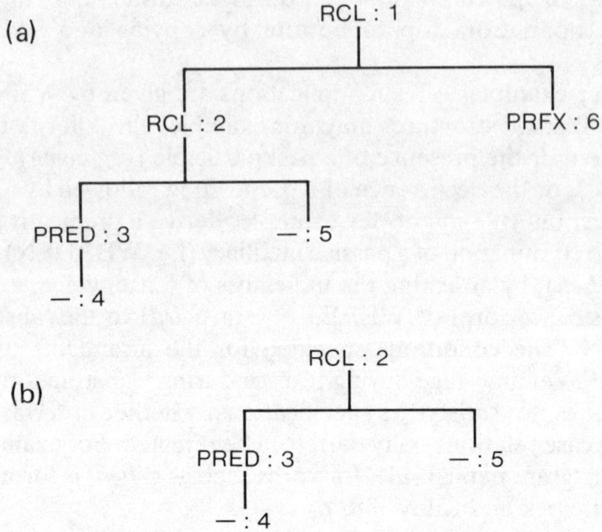

Fig. 29 — METAL transformation.

and, in addition, copying the feature CAN ('canonical form') from PRFX ('prefix') to PRED, and adding the feature VC ('voice') with value A ('active') to PRED, and adding the features CLF ('clause final') and SPX ('separable prefix') to RCL:2.

After the analysis of SL sentences into 'deep structure' representations, processing passes to the Transfer component. The purpose of this phase is to convert representations into TL surface syntactic tree structures. As such, Transfer assumes most of the operations of TL synthesis leaving relatively little for the final Generation phase. An example of a transfer rule is another part of the grammar rule cited already (Fig. 28) which dealt with verbs of the *gehen*-type. It continues as follows:

```
((AND (ACTIVE) (NON-COMMAND) (PRED AGT LOC)) (ROL-ORD-
ER (AGT) (PRED) (LOC))
((AND (ACTIVE) (COMMAND) (PRED LOC)) (ROL-ORDER (PRED)
(LOC))))
```

It has the effect of reordering the predicate–argument structure PRED AGT LOC into a form appropriate for TL (English) output, viz. AGT (subject) PRED (verb) LOC (location).

Lexical transfer involves access to the bilingual dictionary to identify the TL canonical form (e.g. *go*) corresponding to the SL canonical form (*gehen*). In cases where there is more than one TL form for a given SL form, the entry defines tests of local structure. For example the Transfer entries for German *in* would be:

(INTO (IN) PREP (GC A))
(IN (IN) PREP (GC D))

indicating that the German PREPosition '(IN)' may translate as the English PREPosition INTO if the G(rammatical) C(ase) of the German prepositional phrase is Accusative, and as IN if the GC is Dative. Finally, Lexical transfer accesses the TL monolingual dictionary in order to obtain the appropriate allomorph (morphological variant) for the English output, e.g. *went*. All that is left for the final stage, Generate, is to strip off the TL word string from the tree produced by Transfer.

There are clear advantages in employing the LISP formalism: ease of adding new rules, perspicuity of the grammar, and efficient parsing — it is estimated that a total of only 1000 rules may be adequate for sentences in technical texts. The METAL parser is described as "a variation on the Left-Corner parallel, bottom-up parsing algorithm", with resemblances to the Earley parser (for details see Slocum 1984). An important feature is the incorporation of the "some-paths" technique, in which the parser neither stops at the first 'successful' parse nor exhaustively explores all possible parses, but selectively pursues the 'most likely' ones. The parser is guided by linguists' judgments of preferred analyses, indicated by partial orderings of rules (i.e. LeVeLs, as in the example above). Nevertheless, on occasions, the parser will still fail to produce a complete analysis; METAL includes a "fail-soft" technique ("phrasal analysis") which looks for the longest constituent phrases recognised during analysis of a sentence and treats these as its parsing.

The efficiency of the parser is augmented by tying closely together phrase structure, construction, transformation and transfer rules in single 'grammar rules'. In this way, the METAL system seeks to ensure that a specific procedure is carried out at a later stage for a particular construct (e.g. tree representation). The objective is to avoid the difficulties of systems (like CETA and the earlier LRC system) which do not tightly control rule applications and which have to search a large corpus of grammatical routines for one which matches the structure under analysis. Tying rules of different stages together should eliminate the danger of inadvertently applying inappropriate or 'wrong' routines. On the other hand, the close linking of analysis rules and transfer rules would seem to reduce substantially the independence of the stages. Whitelock & Kilby (1983) argue that the inextricable coupling of lexical transfer and structural transfer reduces the modularity of individual stages of Transfer and increases the complications of writing and extending transfer grammars. Whatever the programming implications, these features do not seem to permit the characterisation of METAL as a pure 'transfer' system.

Since METAL is intended to be an operational system much attention has been paid to practical MT management (Slocum 1984). The system includes, therefore, facilities for validating input (correcting misspellings and syntax errors), updating dictionaries, text processing before translation (distinguishing what has to be translated from diagrams, acronyms, formulae, etc., which do not, identifying sentence boundaries, detecting unknown words for dictionary updating, etc.), and text processing after translation (post-editing facilities, reconstitution of original format).

The METAL prototype German–English system was tested between 1980 and 1984 on over 1000 pages of texts in the field of telecommunications and data processing. Quality control was measured in terms of the amount of text which, after revision by professional post-editors at Siemens, did not entail changes in morphological, syntactic, or semantic procedures. Figures for "correctness" varied between 45% and 85%. An evaluation in 1980 (Slocum 1980) revealed that 83% of sentences of a 50-page text were analysed and translated correctly, 7% were analysed but not correctly, 9% were not analysed but provided with tentative 'phrasal analyses', and only 1% could not be analysed at all. Improvements in computer speeds on Lisp machines and improvements in rates of post-editing (by 1984 around 29 pages a day) suggest that METAL may have reached the goal of cost-effectiveness for an operational MT system (Slocum 1984).

The METAL German–English system is to be marketed as LITRAS by Computer Gesellschaft, Konstanz (West Germany), in "an office work-station package" (White 1985). METAL will therefore be the first of the advanced 'linguistics-oriented' transfer systems to be brought into commercial production. In due course, it is anticipated that other language pairs will be added which are at present at various stages of development: German–Spanish, English–German, English–Spanish, and German–Chinese. Given the sophisticated nature of many features in METAL, its success in the market place will undoubtedly be watched with great interest.

13.5 CHARLES UNIVERSITY, PRAGUE (1976-)

After its earlier MT research in the 1960s (Ch. 6.10), the group at Charles University continued development of programs for automatic synthesis of Czech texts, largely within the framework of Petr Sgall's stratificational model. Particularly notable research was conducted in the area of text cohesion, topic-comment structures and anaphoric reference (cf. Sgall *et al.* 1973). MT research as such was revived in 1976 with a series of fairly modest experimental systems for English–Czech translation (Hajičova & Kirschner 1981, Kirschner 1984).

The linguistic group of the Department of Applied Mathematics at Charles University began its first experiment in close cooperation with the TAUM group in Montreal (Ch. 13.1). A relatively limited English parser was designed which resembled the TAUM analyser in its use of the Q-system formalism but which differed in that it produced a dependency structure analysis. Output from the parser was converted by a transfer program for input to the already developed system for random generation of Czech sentences. The system was tested on a small sample of journalistic texts on economics.

The second experiment introduced greater lexical and semantic complexity. Abstracts selected from the INSPEC database in the highly specialised field of microelectronics were taken for the corpus; the aim was to extend and refine the grammar, to provide more extensive morphological analysis, to tackle the complex problems of English noun compounds, and to develop a device for directly converting 'international' vocabulary into Czech forms without recourse to dictionaries, e.g. *application* into *aplikace*, *philosophy* into *filozofie*, etc. (Hajičova & Kirschner 1981). In addition it was hoped that the system might act as the front end of a natural language understanding system, TIBAQ (Text- and Inference-Based Answering of Questions), an AI project under the direction of Petr Sgall (Hajicova & Sgall 1981). In general, the experiment was seen as the first stage of an exercise in adapting the theoretical research of the Prague group to a practical application. Strict stratification of analysis and synthesis was compromised by orientation of procedures to particular source and target languages and to the specialised subject field.

The third experiment, beginning in 1982, represented a further step towards practicality (Kirschner 1984). Analysis does not go as far as in the TIBAQ system, remaining at a relatively 'surface structure' level; the 'random generation' program for Czech has now been abandoned in favour of a synthesis program linked more closely to the output, and the former single bilingual dictionary has been split into separate ones for analysis and synthesis. Finally the program for converting 'international' vocabulary has been moved from transfer to the stage of morphological synthesis. Starting from a fairly orthodox 'transfer' strategy, the system has gradually incorporated transfer components into analysis stages, which thereby have become more TL-specific; the Charles University group have concluded that "universal analysis . . . is not available at the present time". The group has also adopted an orthodox approach to semantic analysis: semantic features partially organised in verb 'frames', features specific to the subject domain and features specific to text structures of abstracts. Some ambiguities are left unresolved, e.g. English prepositional phrases where an equivalent Czech structure would be equally ambiguous. As in most other systems, problems of inter-sentence coherence and ambiguity have not been tackled yet.

The group has continued with the Q-language formalism, considering that the advantages of its simplicity and transparency outweigh its limitations. It has continued also with the TAUM system of English morphological analysis. The emphasis in the syntactic analysis program has been on dealing with the complexities of English nominal compounds, which are of course prominent in abstracts. Analysis results in a dependency tree representation (of the predicate and argument type found in TAUM). In synthesis this is restructured for Czech word order, Czech lexical items substituted for English, and Czech morphological rules are applied. The group recognises that the system is still at a very early stage and "much remains to be done". It is, however, a good example of the greater assurance and realism with which MT projects are now being undertaken.

13.6 LOGOS CORPORATION (1982-)

The earlier involvement of the Logos company in MT had been the development of systems for governmental and military applications (Ch.

12.2). In 1982 the Logos Corporation introduced their 'Logos Intelligent Translation System', a commercial product aimed at translation agencies. The first version demonstrated was the German–English system; an English–German version has also been announced (a prototype has been installed at Wang in the United States), and work has been reported on a French version (Lawson 1984). Logos are developing their systems on a mainframe and design programs to be machine-independent, running on small computers as well as large ones. However, at present, the German–English system is available only on the Wang OIS (Office Information System) word processor and the Wang VS minicomputer.

The system integrates machine translation into a word processing environment; translators are able to adapt the dictionaries to their special needs, run the Logos translation program, and revise the results, all at the same computer (or word processor) terminal (Hawes 1985). It is claimed that in the larger 256K Wang configuration the system is capable of translating more than 20,000 words in 24 hours, "enough to meet the needs of three translators engaged in post-editing" (Staples 1983). In 1984 the German–English system cost about £6500 ($10,000) to install, plus a charge of £200 a month for up to 10,000 words of 'usable output', and then £16 for every additional 1,000 words (Lawson 1984).

The German–English system comes with a basic dictionary of over 100,000 entries; to these can be added the terminology specific to translators' needs, using an interactive dictionary compilation system (ALEX), which asks questions concerning the syntactic and semantic properties of words being entered and ensures that their coding is compatible with entries already in the dictionary. In addition, users can specify subject fields for particular entries, thus ensuring that polysemes are translated appropriately (as far as possible) in accordance with the subject context.

In basic strategy the German–English system retains the characteristics of the earlier LOGOS, although now it is a true 'transfer' system, with language-independent programming and separation of SL and TL data files. Much is made by the manufacturers of the way in which "semantic information (is) integrated into the translation algorithm." During the 1970s Logos developed and refined a Semantic Abstraction Language (SAL), "a hierarchical tree-structure language into which the Logos system translates every natural language string before it begins its parse." As a result "semantic information is . . . present at every point of the analysis, available, as needed, for resolving ambiguity at whatever level — lexical, syntactic, or semantic." (Staples 1983). It is not clear whether this approach differs substantially from the practice in many MT systems of assigning semantic features to dictionary entries and using this information to resolve lexical ambiguity and syntactic ambiguities during analysis routines. It would appear, nevertheless, that Logos has paid greater attention to the establishment of semantic classifications than previous MT systems. It is possible, therefore, that SAL has elements of a genuine interlingual character (since the Logos Corporation has researched a wide variety of languages). Interlingual elements are to be expected in transfer systems, the line of demarcation between them is often blurred and for this reason there are grounds for Staples' (1983) claim that the "Logos algorithm entails an integration of both transfer grammar techniques and the interlingua approach".

Practical experience of Logos in a working environment has so far been relatively brief. One agency (Tschira 1985), which installed Logos in December 1982, estimated in 1983 that the quality of output was good enough "for preliminary information purposes, without post-editing, for about sixty to eighty per cent of the text". Tschira stressed however, that output can be deceptive; very often, considerable post-editing is still required to produce high-quality texts from MT output. Nevertheless, translation agencies in Germany report favourably about the capacity of the German–English system to increase their productivity (by up to 100% and at least by 30%), while also showing improvements in the quality and consistency of their translations (Lawson 1984). Logos was found to work best with highly specialised texts for which the agency had input its own terminology; it was least satisfactory for general correspondence and texts with comparatively few technical terms and for interdisciplinary texts.

An example of an unedited Logos translation from German is the following (extract from Tschira 1985):

> A field-by-field control of the occurrence of the different fields is luckily not necessary. There are groups of fields which occur always commonly, or occur not and which we sucked therefore too. Field-groups are able to combine. In fact, it suffices to relate the control mentioned above (depending on account and posting key) to field-groups instead of on fields what a considerable simplification means.

(German original:

> Eine feldweise Steuerung des Auftretens der verschiedenen Felder ist glücklicherweise nicht nötig. Es gibt Gruppen von Feldern, die stets gemeinsam auftreten oder nicht auftreten und die wir deshalb zu sog. "Feldgruppen" zusammenfassen können. Tatsächlich genügt es, die oben erwähnte Steuerung (in Abhängigkeit von Konto und Buchschlüssel) auf Feldgruppen anstatt auf Felder zu beziehen, was eine erhebliche Vereinfachung bedeutet.)

As this example shows there are obviously still problems with certain linguistic structures (the *was* construction in the last sentence), as well as familiar problems in distinguishing between abbreviations (e.g. *sog.* for *sogenannt(en)* in this passage) and the sentence marker, which can result in nonsense. Further such problems are: "the splitting of some phrases in parentheses, mixtures of letters and numerals" and some paragraph numbering interpreted as dates. These annoying errors are surprisingly difficult to circumvent. As for the strictly linguistic deficiencies, the Logos Corporation is itself aware of many of them (it admits, for example, that it has "only just begun to attack such problems as ellipsis and anaphora"), but Logos promises to continue research on improvements which it can pass on to its customers. As always, time will tell how successful the Logos system will be in the future.

14

Projects and sytems at the Commission of the European Communities (1976-)

With the accession of more countries to the European Communities, the multilingual policy of the Treaty of Rome was increasing the demands for translations at an alarming rate (Ch. 9.1). By 1975 the Commission had already started investigating the possibilities of MT. In that year it had the Systran system demonstrated in Luxembourg (Ch. 12.1). The next year a Plan of Action (CEC 1976) was approved which established a coordinated series of studies and projects to deal with the Communities' multilingual problems. Part of the plan was concerned with the development of Systran, part with the development of terminology databanks (with particular reference to EURODICAUTOM, Ch. 4.7 and 17.6), part with the development of MT for restricted languages (principally the TITUS system, Ch. 17.3), and part with long-term research on a full scale multilingual MT system (the Eurotra system, Ch. 14.2 below).

14.1 SYSTRAN

The translation service of the Commission of the European Communities began developmental work on Systran systems in February 1976 with the purchase of the English–French version. In early 1978 it acquired the French–English version, which had been under development by the World Translation Center (WTC) in La Jolla since mid-1977. The Commission's contract with WTC included an agreement for substantial development of the systems by staff of the Commission. Indeed most of the developmental work on these two systems took place within the Translation Department at Luxembourg. In 1979 an Italian synthesis program was coupled to the English analysis program, and the development of the English–Italian version was started, again most of it in Luxembourg by staff of the

Commission. By the end of 1979 there were thus three language pairs under development, and in March 1981 it was considered that each system was producing reasonable enough output to set up a pilot production service in Luxembourg. Since this date, the number of translations produced has grown steadily and develomental work on the three systems has continued. Encouraged by this achievement, the Commission began in 1982 to work on English–German and French–German systems (Pigott 1983, 1983a).

As we have seen (12.1) the basic software for the analysis and synthesis programs of Systran is in two parts: the language-independent programs for control and dictionary searching which are provided by the designers, and those specific to particular SL–TL pairs, the latter having been written partly by WTC and partly by programmers at the Commission (Van Slype 1979b). Initially all re-programming had to be done in La Jolla, but later the Commission sponsored Margaret Masterman at the Cambridge Language Research Unit (Ch. 5.2) to develop a program for the automatic annotation of the Systran macro-assembler code (Masterman 1980), and thereby facilitating emendation of programs by Commission staff.

Certain components of the computer programs show a high degree of reliability. According to Pigott (1984), morphological analysis and synthesis of French is "100 per cent successful", resolution of grammatical homographs (e.g. deciding whether *light* is a noun, adjective, or verb) is over 90% successful, and TL synthesis is unproblematic in general. Although "by far the most complicated part" is SL analysis, Systran has, in Pigott's opinion, "achieved a relatively high level of success".

Since so much of the success of the Systran translation process depends on the quality of the bilingual dictionaries, it has been the enhancement of dictionary entries which has received most attention from those involved with the develoment of Systran. However, such is the monolithic complexity of Systran's dictionaries that special care has to be taken to ensure that an 'improvement' introduced to deal with one particular problem does not degrade performance in another part of the system (as has been found in the USAF Russian–English system). This is of course always the danger when changes are introduced piecemeal, but there is little alternative with Systran. Lexical data are typically irregular, and changes have to be introduced by trial and error. Therefore, after Systran became fully operational in the spring of 1981, amendments to systems have been done on test versions and introduced into production versions only after extensive trials.

Probably the most significant innovation has been the considerable expansion of the use of semantic markers and semantic classification. At an early stage of the development work, Pigott (1979) had to find out how to use Systran's semantic markers. There were found to be available over 20 'process type' markers for different subject fields: AGPRO (agriculture), ANTEC (analysis), PRAVIA (aviation), PRIO (biology), PRCH (chemistry), PRCR (creative), PREL (electrical), etc. The assignment of these markers to dictionary entries depended largely on subjective judgements of the most appropriate subject field. If texts were restricted to specific fields this might work, but in the context of the Commission's work it was soon found that such subject limitations were impractical, and the use of 'topical glossaries' was dropped. Instead, a much reduced set of general semantic markers was developed which could be assigned more consistently, e.g. DEV (device, tool, instrument), CONTR (container), MATER (material or substance used for production or operation).

Other innovations introduced by the Commission's translator staff working on Systran include a routine for dealing with words not found in the dictionary (Wheeler 1984). In general such words are left untranslated (as in the Russian–English system), but it was felt that something could be done with those having regular endings. The routine enables not only the assignment of the probable semantic marker (e.g. a French word ending in *-meter* would be coded as a device, one ending in *-ologie* or *-isme* as a branch of science), but also the provision of standard TL endings, so that *-ogue*, as in French *radiologue*, would be rendered *-ogist (radiologist)*. Another innovation concerned the treatment of minutes of meetings (voluminous in the European Communities, and tedious to translate); in French and Italian these are conventionally recorded in the present tense, but in English the custom is to use the past. The routine involved the assignment of a 'typology category', which allowed for automatic tense conversion and the changing of words such as *demain* to *the day after*, and so forth (Wheeler 1984).

Although most innovations were concerned only with lexical problems, some involved syntax. For example, in order to prevent the erroneous translation of *The committe discussed faulty equipment and office management* as *Le comité a étudié l'équipement et l'administration de bureau défectueux*, semantic codes were incorporated which linked the adjective *faulty* and nouns categorised as 'devices' (Pigott 1984). As another example, the phrase *éviter que l'argent soit dépensé* should be translated by the English construction *prevent the money being spent*, and not *prevent that the money be spent*. Rather than introducing additional rules to the analysis routines, it was decided to include instructions in the dictionary entry for *éviter* (Wheeler 1984).

It is admitted that the pragmatic approach of the development team in Luxembourg renders the systems much more complicated. There are clearly dangers in confounding syntax and lexicon procedures (risks which are inherent in all Systran systems) and in devising rules which are so dependent on complex dictionary entries. To some extent, such problems have been eased by the development of tools such as the dictionary concordances, but it is still not known how far complexity can be increased before the limits of adaptation have been reached (Laurian 1984). As we have seen (Ch. 12.1) the Russian–English version seems to have now reached that limit.

When the Commission bought the English–French system in February 1976 its dictionary comprised just 6000 entries; by 1984 there were some 150,000 dictionary entries in each of the three language-pair versions, i.e. English–French, French–English, and English–Italian (Pigott 1984). At the same time the programming rules of analysis and synthesis have also expanded, from some 30,000 lines in the 1976 English–French system to some 100,000 lines in each of the 1984 versions. Obviously, a great deal of effort has been devoted to the development of Systran; in 1983, Pigott (1983a) estimated that "an average of about twelve professional staff (linguists and data processing experts) have worked full time on the project for the past eight years", with development costs reaching 4.5 million ECU (about four million dollars) in the same period. However, there are good grounds for believing that these costs can be amortised within a few years if the growth in usage continues. After a slow start (1250 pages in 1981, 3150 pages in 1982), "over 400,000 pages of MT were run in 1983 on the various production systems" (Pigott 1984) Most use is made of the French–English and English–Italian systems, "French translators have until now been less enthusiastic . . . and generally prefer to use more conventional methods" (Pigott 1983a). As an indication of the impact of MT at the Commission, Pigott (1983a) reports that "in January and February 1983, 50% of the English–Italian workload (293 pages) and 25% of the French–English workload (330 pages) were handled with the assistance of Systran". Since 1982 translation output has increased by the introduction of word processors linked directly to the IBM mainframe on which Systran runs (Pigott 1984).

Rather than fully revised translations, users have the option of a faster service providing lower-quality translations which have received minimal post-editing. The 'rapid post-editing' service is offered for French–English translations of informative texts (working documents, minutes of meetings, reports of activities). Editing is done on a word processor at a rate of up to 4 or 5 pages an hour. The option is popular with a number of users and, perhaps surprisingly, welcomed with some enthusiasm by CEC translators who find rapid post-editing an interesting challenge (Wagner 1985).

The English–French system at the Commission of the European Communities has been evaluated on two occasions; in October 1976, shortly after delivery (Chaumier *et al.* 1977), and in June 1978 (Van Slype 1979a, summarised in Van Slype 1979b). In both evaluations comparisons were made between Community documents in the form of human translation (HT) after revision, 'raw' unedited MT, revised MT, and the original English, each in terms of their intelligibility, their fidelity, and types of errors.

On scores of intelligibility (clarity and comprehensibility) unedited MT had improved from 44–47% to 78% (in both evaluations revised MT, at 92–97% in 1976 and 98% in 1978, equalled edited HT (98–99%), and the original texts at 94–99%). As for fidelity, the 1978 evaluation gave a figure of 73% for unedited MT, and a subjective assessment of style rated unedited MT at 76%. Correction rates may have slightly improved: in 1976, only 61–80% of "grammatical agreements (gender, number, elisions, contractions, person, voice, tense, mood) were correctly rendered.", while in 1978 the average proportion of words amended was 36% (over half involved the replacement of words). In both evaluations the main source of errors was the dictionary, and Van Slype rightly emphasised that improvements would come with the expansion and improvement of dictionary entries (in 1978 the English–French dictionary contained just 45,000 entries). Subsequent experience has demonstrated the truth of this judgement.

Van Slype (1983) considered that MT is acceptable to the user if intelligibility exceeds a threshold of 70–75%, and that post-edited MT becomes cheaper than revised HT if the revision rate is below a threshold of 30–40%. Both thresholds have now been reached by the English–French system.

The progressive improvement of the English–French system can be seen from example 'raw' unedited translations. In 1978, the following was produced:

> Pendant les dix premiers ans, la politique agricole commune principalement a été fondée sur l'organisation commune des marchés agricoles. Par la politique sur des marchés et des prix, on a éliminé la fragmentation des marchés agricoles dans la Communauté.
>
> (English original: During its first ten years, the common agricultural policy has been mainly based on the common organisation of the agricultural markets. Through the policy on markets and prices, the fragmentation of agricultural markets within the Community was eliminated.)

A translation from 1983 is the following extract from the minutes of a meeting (illustrating the tense conversion routine mentioned above):

> L'attention du groupe de travail est également attirée sur le fait qu'environ 50% de l'argent de traitement de données consacré à l'enquête doit être employé pour des contrôles et des corrections des bandes nationales de données, provoquant des contraintes financières ultérieures en analyses finales des données.
>
> (English original: The Working Group's attention was also drawn to the fact that about 50% of the data processing money devoted to the survey had to be used for controls and corrections of the national data tapes, causing subsequent financial restraints in the final analyses of the data.)

The achievements of the other versions can also be illustrated. Pigott (1983b) gives examples of unedited English–French, English–German and English–Italian versions of the same passage (on the introduction of MT in the Commission):

(English original:

> In addition to expansion of the dictionaries and programs for the three language pairs, increasing attention has been paid to the requirements of translators as users, system enhancement now being based largely on feedback from post-editors of machine-translated texts. In the interests of translator acceptance, text processing equipment was installed to eliminate transmission delays and provide appropriate means of post-editing on screen or paper.)

English–French:

> En plus de l'expansion des dictionnaires et des programmes pour les trois couples de langues, une attention croissante a été prêtée aux

besoins des traducteurs comme utilisateurs, amélioration de système maintenant étant basée en grande partie sur la rétroaction des post-éditeurs des textes traduits par ordinateur. Dans l'intérêt de l'acceptation de traducteur, l'équipement de traitement de textes a été installé pour éliminer des retards de transmission et pour fournir le moyen approprié de post-édition sur l'écran ou le papier.

English–Italian:

Oltre e espansione dei dizionari e dei programmi per le tre coppie linguistiche, l'attenzione crescente è prestata ai requisiti dei traduttori come utenti, potenziamento di sistema adesso che è basato in gran parte sul feed-back dai postredattori dei testi tradotti dall'ordinatore. Negli interessi dell'accettazione del traduttore, l'attrezzatura dell'elaborazione di testi è installata per eliminare i ritardi di transmissione e per fornire i mezzi appropriati di postredigere sullo schermo o sul documento.

English–German (still under development at this time and therefore of poorer quality than the others):

Zusätzlich zu Ausdehnung der Wörterbücher und der Programme für die drei Paare der Sprache ist erhöhende Aufmerksamkeit zu den Bedarf von Uebersetzern als Benutzer, Steigerung des Systems gezahlt worden jetzt, auf Rückkopplung von Revisoren maschinell übersetzter Texte grösstenteils stützend. In den Interessen von Annahme des Uebersetzers wurde processing Ausrüstung des Texts, um zu beseitigen Verzögerungen der Uebermittlung installiert und zu liefern geeignetes Mittel des Revidierens auf Schutzwand oder Papier.

Finally, two examples are given from the French–English system. The first is taken from the articles of an agreement:

The application of these methods to the definition of a management and possible valorisation policy of waste requires knowledge a variability of the behaviour of the co-products according to their origin (nature of the methods and manufactures) and to their time to production; indeed, if variability is low it will be possible to define general elimination rules and in the contrary case, it will be necessary to organise the catch counts some and the follow-up of waste on the level even the producing factories.

The second is from a technical report:

The detection of the gamma rays requires their interaction with a matter. It results from this interaction either an electron accompanied by the emission by a photon by lower energy (Compton effect), or a electron–positron pair, dominant phenomenon beyond some MeV. In both cases the produced charged particles take away certain information concerning the direction and the energy of the incidental gamma photon.

Clearly, Systran MT translations are a long way from being 'high quality' products, and there are instances of errors which would appear to be easily resolved, but in general the verdict must be that for those interested in what was intended (the information content) and not in how it was communicated such translations must be of considerable value. There should no longer be anyone who does not believe that MT is here to stay. The volume and quality of translated output in the Commission's translation service is ample proof.

14.2 EUROTRA

It was recognised from the outset that Systran's potential as a multilingual system was limited. It was true that new language pairs could be added within the general framework of Systran, but the fundamental structure of the system was not amenable to full multilinguality, nor open to advances in computational and linguistic techniques. In February 1978 discussions began under the auspices of the Commission among MT experts from European universities including Grenoble, Saarbrücken, Manchester (UMIST), and Pisa (Rolling 1978, King 1982). Development of the software systems and design of the linguistic framework began during 1979, and by 1982 the general structure of the proposed Eurotra system had been agreed among the participating groups (King 1982). The overall director of the project at Luxembourg is Serge Perschke, who had led research at EURATOM on a multilingual MT system (Ch. 11.1). The responsibility for coordination and secretarial services is in the hands of the Istituto per gli Studi Semantici e Cognitivi (ISSCO), Geneva, under the direction of Margaret King.

By 1981 it was estimated that there were some 80 researchers involved, mainly from universities, representing each of the eight member states. In November 1982 Eurotra became an independently funded project of the Commission, granted 16 million ECU (about 12 million dollars) by the Council of Ministers for a five and a half year programme of research and development, under the aegis of the Committee for Information and Documentation in Science and Technology, towards "the creation of a machine translation system of advanced design (Eurotra) capable of dealing with all the official languages of the Community. On completion of the programme an operational system prototype should be available in a limited field and for limited categories of text, which would provide the basis for development on an industrial scale in the period following the current programme" It was envisaged that work would be in three stages: two years of preparatory work, two years of "basic and applied linguistic research", and eighteen months of "stabilisation of the linguistic models and evaluation of results" (*Multiligua* 2 (1) 1983, p. 43). Initially the project is being wholly supported by the Commission; in later years, progressively larger proportions of the funding will devolve to national governments.

The specific requirements for Eurotra were, then, that it should be a multilingual system based on the most advanced linguistic and computational techniques, open to progressive improvements and to incorporation of new methods and techniques, that it should be a practical operational system for the use of translation services of the European Communities, and that it should involve all member countries in collaborative research. This ambitious project is still at an early stage, and details of the system are not publicly available (protection of the software from potential commercial exploitation has also played a role); however, brief accounts of the overall philosophy and general design features have been given by King (1981, 1982), King and Perschke (1982), Laurian (1984), Des Tombe *et al.* (1985).

Eurotra is probably unique in having been designed as a multilingual research system from its inception. Work on all languages is being pursued simultaneously: programs of analysis, of synthesis and of transfer for Danish, Dutch, English, French, German, Greek and Italian. Spanish and Portuguese will be added now that Spain and Portugal have become full Community members. To achieve multilingual output, the input to transfer and synthesis programs must be specified exactly; analysis programs must deal with all monolingual ambiguity; and, to reduce the potential complexities of bilingual dictionaries and grammars the transfer modules are to be kept as small as possible. As a consequence, transfer 'interface' structures have to be precisely specified in a highly abstract formalism of sufficient richness to carry information required in synthesis. Although approaching interlinguality, transfer elements will not be universals but be common to European languages, i.e. 'Euro-versals'. In many transfer systems, some steps towards TL-like structures are made during transfer; in Eurotra this will not be possible, and consequently, programs for TL synthesis have to be more powerful than envisaged in the past. For example, in translating English *must* (or its equivalent in another SL) the input to the French TL program has to specify *devoir* or *falloir*; but it should do no more. The different syntactic structures required for TL output are to be generated by the French synthesis program alone (finite verb + infinitive for *devoir* vs. impersonal + *que* + subjunctive for *falloir*). They are not to be produced by the syntactic transfer routines (as would be the case in GETA, SUSY and METAL). Likewise, the selection of the correct TL prepositional form is to be carried not by routines instigated by the bilingual SL–TL transfer dictionary, but by routines within TL synthesis which take into account only the relevant lexical and structural relationships of the TL.

The requirement that Eurotra should be a practical operational system as early as possible and that it should be as easily extensible as possible has important consequences. Practicality demands fail-safe mechanisms which can ensure that some reasonable translation is produced if analysis programs fail to derive the semantic representations required for transfer. To achieve this, it is desirable that SL structural features at all levels of analysis are retained: morphological information, lexical features, syntactic relations, semantic compatibilities, etc. Extensibility demands flexible incorporation of new grammars and dictionaries, easy amendment of dictionary entries and grammar rules without the risk of unforeseen side effects, and adaptability to new linguistic and computational methods.

Both aims are achieved by the Eurotra project's uniform data structure formalism, the 'chart' concept (Ch. 9.15). In the elaboration of the chart formalism the influence of GETA and the contributions of the Saarbrücken group have played major roles. Larger structures (e.g. trees) are built from smaller ones; if there can be more than one structure for a given SL text segment, the chart allows all possible analyses to be expressed. Different methods of analysis can be employed to build different parts of the analysis, e.g. non-deterministic strategies can operate alongside deterministic techniques. Charts can incorporate tree structures of considerable complexity: dependency tree structures on which all levels of linguistic categories and relationships can be represented (as in the GETA representations, Ch. 13.3 above). Tree structures are manipulated by production rules (tree transduction rules) which are externally controlled by series of (linked) 'subgrammars' (as in GETA). Grammar rules are formulated as specifications of input data structures (i.e. the expected partial analysis already achieved) and of the changes to be carried out. They may be as complex as required, specifying any combination of morphological, syntactic, and semantic information, any type of dependency subtree, etc. There are consequently no restrictions on the sequence of analysis; there is no requirement, for example, that morphological analysis must be completed before syntactic analysis, that semantic considerations can be introduced only at particular levels, etc. (King 1982). Methods which are appropriate for SL analysis of one language may not be appropriate for another.

A particular emphasis of Eurotra planning is that the design should allow the easy incorporation of new advances in linguistics and artificial intelligence. At present, the system does not include 'knowledge database' components or inference mechanisms (cf. Ch. 15 below). In certain respects, Eurotra is not an experimental project. It is not exploring new techniques as such, but it is attempting to unify the best of current systems — and this means adaptability and extensibility as well as robustness and reliability. There is no pretence that translations will be of high quality; it is hoped that 'raw' output will be usable unedited for many information gathering needs, but for other purposes revision will be necessary. Adequate text editing facilities are therefore essential for the final operational system.

Possibly the most inspiring aspect of Eurotra, but probably the most fraught with problems, is its multinationality: the ideal of harnessing the scattered expertise of European MT research in one grand project. It was thought to be impractical to gather together a team of experts in one place, and it was in any case politically desirable that all member states of the Community should participate in a project which was intended to benefit them all, and that they should all reap the side effects of research and development on advanced computer systems. Individual teams in each country are developing the analysis and synthesis programs for their own language, using the flexibility of the Eurotra framework to develop methods most appropriate to their language and applying any expertise they may have already in particular techniques. The only constraints are that they conform to the basic 'transfer' formulisms: dependency trees bearing at least information on surface structure functions (subjects, objects), case relations, valencies, etc.

Given the political logistics of European research it is perhaps not surprising that there have been difficulties in setting up the groups in individual countries. There was little problem with groups in Denmark, Belgium, the Netherlands, the United Kingdom, and the Federal Republic of Germany. In Denmark, the centre is at Copenhagen University; in Belgium it is at the Catholic University of Louvain; in the Netherlands it is at the Institute for Applied Linguistics in Utrecht; in the United Kingdom, research is centred at the University of Manchester Institute of Science and Technology (UMIST) and at the University of Essex; and in Germany the natural choice was the SUSY team at the University of the Saar. In Italy and Greece the establishment of expert teams has been difficult; there are willing individuals in Turin, Milan, Pisa, Bologna, Corfu, Thessalonika, and Athens, but the organisational framework is lacking.

Most 'political' problems, however, have arisen in France. Two MT groups have long been active, at Nancy and at Grenoble. Undoubtedly, the most substantial research has been done by GETA at Grenoble and it was natural that the GETA group in Grenoble should expect a leading role in the development of Eurotra. Furthermore, GETA had already established a cooperative project with international aspirations, the 'Leibniz' group.

In a number of respects, the Leibniz group was the forerunner of the Eurotra project. It had been founded in July 1974 by GETA on the initiative of Jean-Marie Zemb (Vauquois 1975, Boitet 1977, Chandioux 1976a). The aim was to promote collaboration between MT research teams in Europe and Canada. The participants included the research groups at Grenoble (GETA), Nancy, Saarbrücken (SUSY), and Montreal (TAUM), and some individual researchers, Yorick Wilks, Antonio Zampolli (Pisa), and Daun Fraga (Campinas, Brazil). Nearly all had at one time or another made use of the GETA facilities in Grenoble for research on their own systems (Ch. 13.3). At meetings in 1975 agreement was reached on the formalism of a 'pivot language' to function in transfer components: a labelled dependency tree incorporating certain 'interlingual' elements. The computational base was to be provided by the ATEF and CETA systems developed in Grenoble and the REZO parser developed in Montreal.

Having assumed the leading role in Eurpopean MT research for so many years it was perhaps not surprising, therefore, that GETA was unwilling to compromise by changing to the Eurotra approach. No other group could match its years of research experience; on the other hand, Grenoble had as yet produced no working system, and there were rumours that CNRS was withdrawing its support. It is a difficult dilemma: Eurotra owes much of its philosophy to the past research at Grenoble, but for political reasons, if for no others, it cannot permit one national group to dominate its progress.

If the Eurotra project fails, then it will be more likely to be for political and organisational reasons than for theoretical impracticality. In MT research there are no longer particular problems of finding systems or procedures or forms of representation which work; there are relatively few problems attached to particular constructions or linguistic phenomena; the problem is to determine the overall model of the system: the techniques exist, but the objectives are often unclear (for example, deciding when a system is producing 'good', 'usable', 'adequate' translations) — i.e. essentially the same questions which have concerned MT researchers from the beginning.

The particular contribution of Eurotra is that it has brought into sharper focus than before the real problems of designing multilingual systems. On the linguistic side may be mentioned in particular the definition of transfer components in the context of a system for languages of common historical origin, i.e. what are the 'Euro-versals' to be (case markers, tense markers), what should be the form of input SL 'transfer' structures and of output TL 'transfer' structures, and in what respects should they differ, if at all.

Some idea of the thinking on transfer rules has been given by Krauwer and Des Tombe (1984). The example given is the translation from the Dutch *het meisje zwemt graag* (equivalent to German *das Mädchen schwimmt gern*) into English *the girl likes to swim*. A fundamental principle is that transfer representations should be (internally) valid for the languages in question, i.e. they should not be distorted for the sake of supposed interlinguality. Therefore, assuming the interface representations are respectively:

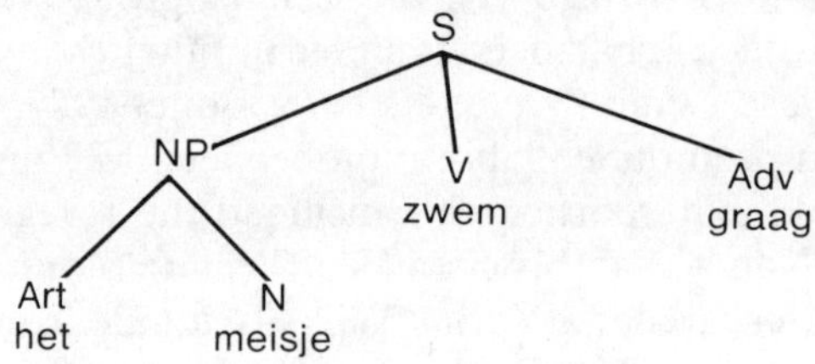

and

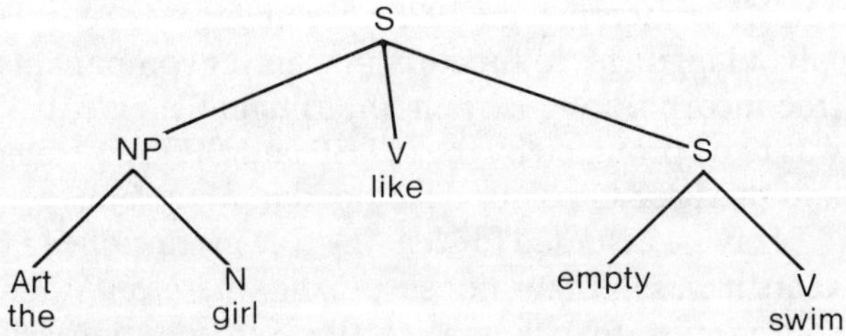

then it is clear that the structural changes must be triggered by a lexical transfer rule, i.e. informally (and grossly simplified):

⟨subject, adverb (graag), X⟩ → ⟨subject, verb (like), 'empty' (bound to subject), X⟩

The rule would operate in this way:

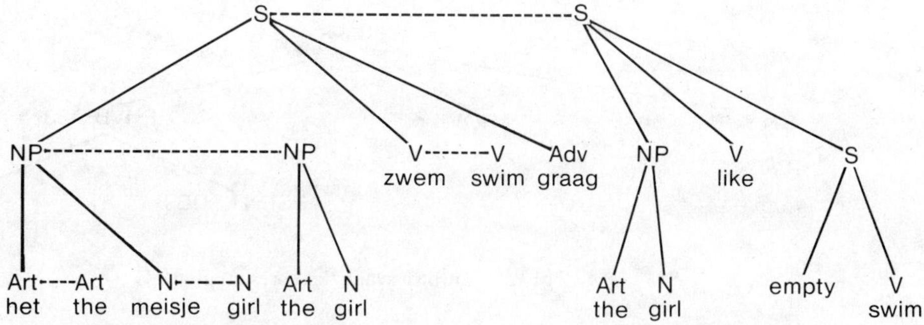

where the TL interface tree is built up a node at a time from SL nodes, starting at the bottom and working up to the topmost (NP and S) nodes; the dotted lines indicate the transfer of each node from SL tree to TL tree.

Much of the preliminary linguistic planning (e.g. Arnold *et al.* 1984, Des Tombe *et al.* 1985) has been concerned with the specification of 'transfer' and other intermediate structures (morphological and 'surface syntactic' representations) and with the provision of guidelines for individual (national) teams on the treatment of particular types of linguistic structure (e.g. coordination, modification, compound nouns). In general terms, representations are labelled dependency trees comparable to those of GETA. Facilities for lexical decomposition are included, e.g. *unanalysability* as the tree in Fig. 30.

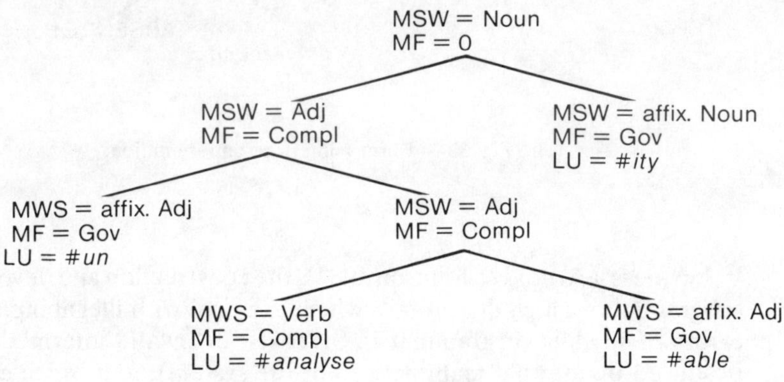

Fig. 30 — Eurotra lexical structure.

Surface syntax trees assume relatively familiar forms, e.g. *John must go*, as in Fig. 31. For transfer representations the trees can combine GETA-type mixed 'deep' and 'surface' labelling with lexical decomposition; e.g. for the sentence *He explained his position comprehensibly* the representation in Fig. 32.

A particular problem for a system as complex as Eurotra is that of

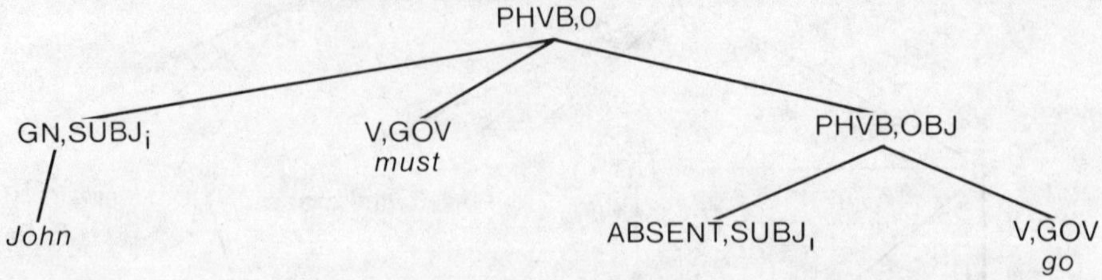

Fig. 31 — Eurotra syntactic representation.

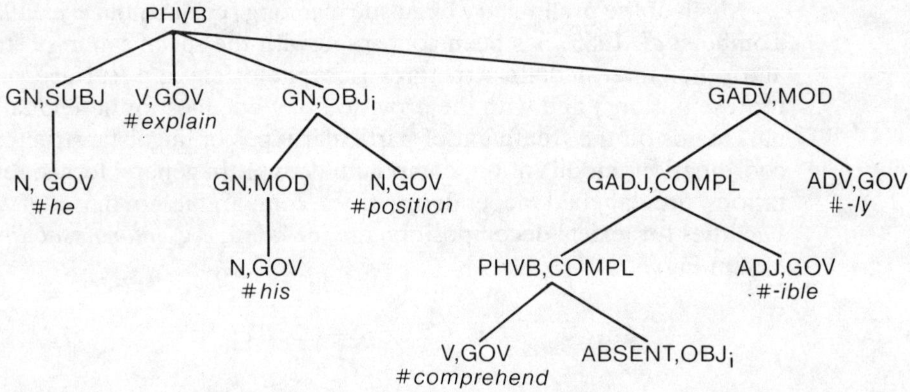

Fig. 32 — Eurotra interface representation.

'robustness' (Arnold & Johnson 1984), the construction and development of subgrammars which do not fail, which can deal with illegal input (whether errors of spelling or grammar in SL texts, or invalid intermediate results produced by internal malfunctions of the system), and which ensure 'correct' output, i.e. representations which are not just well formed but which are valid transformations ('translations') of the input representations. Such questions are linked to the development of software, which may well be the area in which the most substantial advances will have been achieved: the development of procedures for efficient handling of highly complex operations, and the development of higher-level software enabling linguists to specify structures and procedures without needing to know how the system or the programming languages would handle them. Even in other systems with a strict separation of linguistic data and algorithmic processes, linguists need to know how to program.

After five and a half years' research, sometime in 1988, the protoype

Eurotra system will be tested on texts, probably in the field of information technology. By that time, it is expected that linguistic and software development will have attained a high measure of completeness and that dictionaries of some 20,000 lexical items for each of the seven languages will have been compiled. At this point, the potential development of an operational system will be assessed.

Whatever the final outcome of the Eurotra project, there will probably be little doubt that it represents a milestone in MT research. There has been no previous project of such ambitions or of such complexity of organisation. No other project has had longer or more thorough preparations. No other project has brought together the linguistic and computational expertise of so many countries in a joint international research project on such an impressive scale. All expect that Eurotra will contribute immeasurably to the theoretical foundations of MT research for many years into the future.

15

Artificial intelligence systems (1970-)

Researchers in MT have taken an increasing interest in the possibilities of applying artificial intelligence techniques, particularly during the last 5 years or so. In 1960 Bar-Hillel believed he had demonstrated the impossibility of high-quality MT when he argued that many semantic problems could be resolved only if computers have access to large encyclopaedias of general knowledge (Ch. 8.3 above) However, it is precisely problems of text undertsanding involving knowledge structures which have been the subject of much research in artificial intelligence (Boden 1977). The relevance of AI research to MT systems has been obvious to many researchers, and AI techniques are applied increasingly in translation systems. Nevertheless there have been to date relatively few explicitly AI projects on MT as such, although in the future many more may be expected.

Language analysis in AI research has not been directly concerned with translation problems but rather with question-answering, summarizing, and general problems of language understanding. Characteristic of the AI approach is the abandonment of syntax-based models in favour of predominantly semantic models. Semantic analysis is not seen as just the next stage after syntactic analysis, in effect to tackle problems left over from syntactic analysis, but as the central component of systems. Problems of syntactic structure are left, if necessary, to subsidiary operations.

The main features of the AI approach are the application of semantic parsing (based on semantic categories, e.g. 'human', 'liquid', etc.), the building of semantic (or conceptual) representations of the meanings of texts, and the use of knowledge databases to assist in the interpretation of texts. Typically included in the latter are representations of conventional event-schemata (e.g. what happens when going to a restaurant), normal inference patterns, and common-sense expectations.

For AI researchers it is "obvious" that no good MT can be possible without 'understanding'. They point to such sentences as:

Israel seized large quantities of new weapons from the U.S.S.R.

and:

Israel seized territory from Syria.

and comment that in order to produce accurate Russian translations, "a translator needs to understand that:

(1) The weapons were seized *not* from the Soviet Union, but presumably from a neighboring Arab country.
(2) The weapons were manufactured in the Soviet Union.
(3) The territory was indeed seized from (*not* manufactured by) Syria." (Carbonell *et al.* 1981).

The distinctions would be reflected in Russian by the translation of *from* in the first sentence as *iz*, and in the second as *u*.

More pertinently, AI researchers emphasise the complexities of disambiguation and selection of TL equivalents. In syntax-based MT systems, disambiguation operates through the 'embellishment' of syntactic representations by attaching semantic features as 'selection restrictions'. The problem is that such refinements are static (Ch. 3.6). Such systems "do not have the capability to distinguish between all contexts in which an ambiguous word can take on its different meanings" For representations to be unambiguous the system needs to understand SL texts (Lytinen & Schank 1982).

Despite the evident interest of AI researchers in MT problems, there have in fact been very few translation projects undertaken within the AI community. Yet it can be argued that MT provides a useful "test of the rightness or wrongness of a proposed system for representing meaning, since the output in a second language can be assessed by people unfamiliar with the internal formalism and methods employed." (Wilks 1975a) Only in recent years have there been any substantial MT projects applying AI methods. These have been primarily Japanese investigations, stimulated in large part by the 'Fifth Generation' project. (They will be treated later in Ch. 18.).

15.1 STANFORD UNIVERSITY (1970-74)

One of the first to experiment with an AI semantics-based approach was Yorick A. Wilks in his prototype English-French MT system in the early 1970s (Wilks 1973a, 1973b, 1975a). Wilks had gone to Stanford University in 1970 after leaving the Cambridge Language Research Unit (Ch. 5.2) It was at Stanford between 1970 and 1974 that Wilks worked on his MT experimental system. Wilks saw his work on MT as essentially a 'testbed' for AI rather than as research on MT as such, and AI has been Wilks' principal interest in subsequent years, first at the University of Edinburgh (1975-76), then the University of Essex (1977-84) and now the New Mexico State University (Wilks 1985). Nevertheless, although Wilks did no MT research himself at Edinburgh and Essex he was heavily involved in the Leibniz group and in the overall design and semantic aspects of Eurotra (Ch. 14.2).

Wilks' experiment investigated an AI-based 'interlingual' MT system, using a semantic grammar and inference rules. The SL text is first partitioned at punctuation markers and 'function words' (prepositions and conjunctions) into fragments, e.g. *I advised him to go* becomes '(I advised him) (to go)'. Each fragment is then tested against an inventory of templates, semantic frames expressing the 'gists' of (parts of) sentences in the form of triples of semantic features. For example, the template MAN HAVE THING (paraphrased perhaps as "some human being possesses some object") would be matched on a sentence such as *John owns a car*. MAN, HAVE and THING are intended to be interlingual semantic primitives which would be found as the principal semantic features of the words *John*, *own* and *car* respectively. Semantic formulas or definitions of words are constructed from semantic primitives, e.g. the formula for *drink* is: ((*ANI SUBJ)(((FLOW STUFF)OBJE)((*ANI IN)(((THIS(*ANI (THRU PART)))TO)(BE CAUSE))))). This is to be read as "an action, preferably done by animate things (*ANI SUBJ) to liquids ((FLOW STUFF)OBJE), of causing the liquid to be in the animate thing (*ANI IN) and via (TO indicating the direction case) a particular aperture of the animate thing; the mouth of course" (Wilks 1973a) The semantic analysis of lexical items goes no further than necessary; in this context there is no need to distinguish *mouth* from other apertures. The notion of preference is a central feature of Wilks' method: SUBJ displays the preferred agents of actions and OBJE the preferred objects or patients, they do not stipulate obligatory features of agents and patients and thus allowance is made for abnormal usages, e.g. cars drinking petrol. In this way, Wilks' preference semantics can cope with many types of metaphorical expressions without adding to the complexities of dictionary entries (Wilks 1975b). The final stage of the analysis produces a dependency network of semantic relations on the basis of the case links specified. Thus, our example sentence *The watch was sold by the jeweller to a man with a red beard* might receive the analysis shown in Fig. 33.

At this point relationships between the networks of fragments are established; thus a temporal phrase (*during the war*) might be tied to the 'action' element of an earlier or later fragment. It should be noted that ties are made not only within sentences but also across sentence boundaries, since the basic unit is not the sentence but the phrase (fragment). Some ties involving pronominal reference make use of 'common sense inference' rules. For example, in the sentence *The soldiers fired at the women and we saw several of them fall* the linking of the pronoun *them* to the noun *women* rather than to the other noun *soldiers* is made on the basis of a common

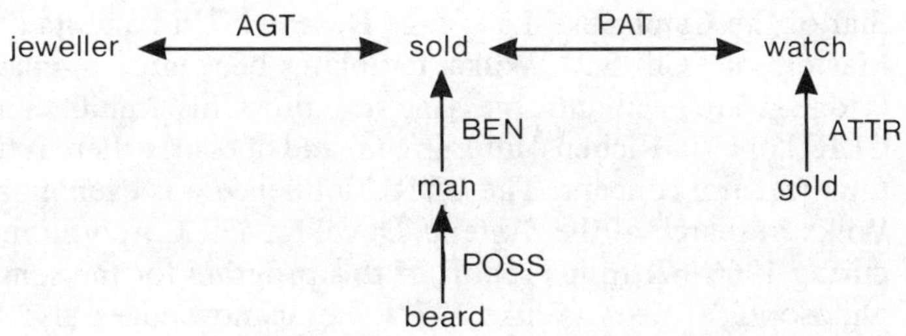

Fig. 33 — Wilks semantic representation.

sense rule stating that if an animate object is hit then it is likely to fall. In other words this rule establishes a causal relationship between the components of the templates of the fragments in question.

The distinctive feature of Wilks' analytical method are thus the use exclusively of semantic features in the 'parsing' of phrases, the use of preference semantics and common sense inference rules, and the analysis of discourse relationships. At no stage is there any reference to syntactic structures or indeed to the boundaries of sentences. Grammatical categories such as noun and verb have no role, not even in the resolution of homographs: to identify the verbal sense of *father* in a sentence such as *Small men sometimes father big sons* the program needs only to find that the semantic formula with CAUSE as its 'head' is the only one which will fit the other 'heads' in an acceptable template. In Wilks' system then semantic representations are reached without recourse to previous syntactic analysis.

After returning to the United Kingdom in 1975, Wilks suggested refinements to his preference semantics model. In *My car drinks gasoline* the system accepts *car* as filler in the template for *drink* because although expecting an animate entity there is no competitor. Rather than just accepting a preference-violating structure, the system might interpret the abnormal reading. The mechanism for this, Wilks (1978) suggested, is the incoporation of 'thesaurus information' as well as primitives in formulas (cf. the CLRU project, Ch. 5.2) and 'pseudo-texts' expressing knowledge about lexical items. Thus, the formula for *car* might include the thesaurus item 'engine': ((((engine PART) OBJE) (SELF USE)) WAY) ((SELF MOVE) GOAL) (MAN USE) (OBJE THING). The pseudo-text for *car* might include 'statements' (in formulas) to the effect that: (1) a human injects a liquid using a tube; (2) liquid is in the car; (3) the engine uses the liquid; (4) the car moves; (5) the human in the car moves; etc. Given *My car drinks gasoline*, this pseudo-text is used to make a projection on the basis of the similarity of *drink* and 'inject' (via the thesaurus entry for *inject*) that the sentence matches the third statement, i.e. 'engine uses liquid'. This projection supplies an interpretation of the sentence.

There are some similarities between Wilks' formula representations and Schank's conceptual dependency representations (Schank and Wilks were both at Stanford in the early 1970s.) But the main influence on Wilks was that of the Cambridge Language Research Unit and its director Margaret Masterman (Ch. 5.2). Wilks' templates bear much similarity to the Cambridge group's semantic message structures, his primitives match closely the CLRU ones in Richens' interlingua, and of course there is the application of the thesaural concept. The CLRU influence was even more transparent in Wilks' research at the Systems Development Corporation, Santa Monica, during 1966–67. In his report of this program for the semantic analysis of philosophical texts (Wilks 1972), he acknowledges also the influence of Wittgenstein on his conception of semantic relations (i.e. 'family resemblances') and semantic message forms. It was this work which formed the basis of his Stanford MT experiment.

15.2 YALE UNIVERSITY (1978-82)

There have been two projects at the Department of Computer Science in Yale University which have experimented with 'knowledge-based' MT. Both adopt interlingual representations based on the 'conceptual dependency' representations developed by Roger Schank (1975).

The essence of Schank's approach is that modelling human understanding of language requires the representation of meaning in terms of 'primitive' semantic relationships ('conceptual dependencies') which express not only what is explicit in the surface forms but what is also implied or can be inferred. Thus, a conceptual dependency representation of *John punched Mary* would be as shown in Fig. 34. (simplified from Schank 1973: 226).

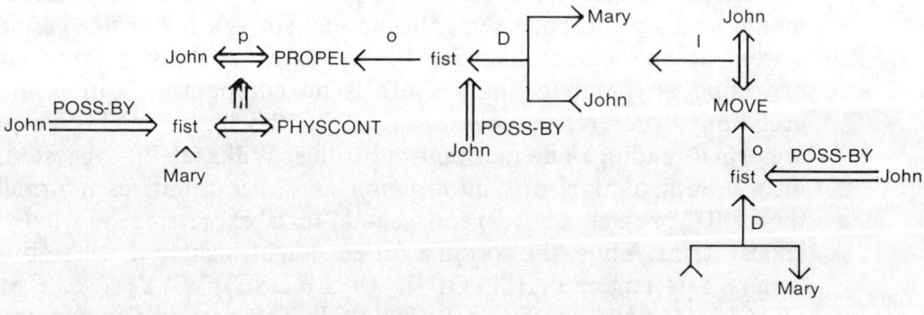

Fig. 34 — Schank conceptual dependency representation.

This representation can be 'paraphrased' as: At some time past, John applied a force to the object John's fist, in the direction from-John-to-Mary; he did this by moving his fist in the direction from-John-to-Mary; his action of applying force to the fist caused John's fist to be in contact with Mary.

Conceptual dependency analysis requires therefore databases of 'contextual knowledge'. Applied to a MT system, the approach can be schematised as in Fig. 35 (Carbonell *et al.* 1981).

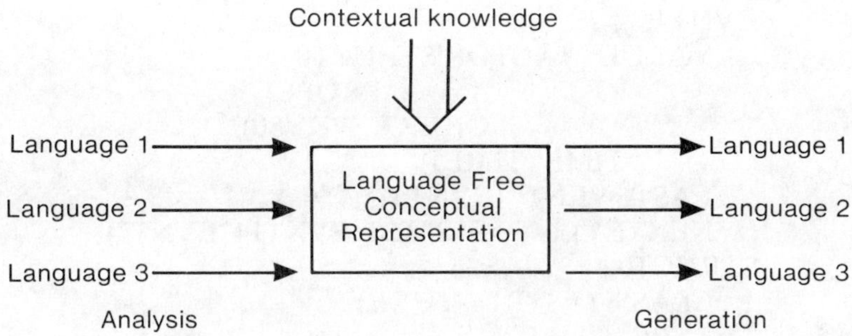

Fig. 35 — Yale 'machine translation paradigm'.

In the rudimentary interlingual MT system developed in 1978 by Carbonell, Cullingford and others (1981) a simple English text, the report of an accident, is analysed into a language independent conceptual representation by referring to 'scripts' about what happens in car accidents, ambulances, hospitals, etc. The resulting representation is the basis for generating Russian and Spanish versions of the original report.

The analysis stages of the system were as follows: the first module was the English Language Interpreter which analysed the SL input text into a meaning representation; then a second module identified and tagged referential objects (people, places, static things); then the 'script-applier' connects the text with an appropriate 'script' in its database of scripts (the knowledge database). The result at this point is the kind of representation shown below.

The basic task of text understanding is performed by the 'script applier': locating input to relevant parts of a script, linking new input to what has gone before, and making predictions about what is likely to follow. In each activity it uses 'world knowledge' to make explicit the connections which are only implicit in the text itself. Among the most important inferences it makes are those concerning the completion of causal chains of events, i.e. in this case the 'scripts' of accidents, ambulances and hospitals. For example, it makes the crucial connection (not stated in the SL text) that the person taken to hospital must have been injured in the crash. This is possible because it 'knows' what ambulances and hospitals are for. Other inferences establish pronominal references across sentences.

An illustrative extract of a semantic representation is given for the sentences:

Friday evening a car swerved off Route 69. The vehicle struck a tree. The passenger . . . was killed . . .

```
SCLAB3:
    SCRIPTNAME  $VEACCIDENT
    MAINCON  EVNT4
    SCENECONS  (EVNT4  EVNT17  EVNT33)
    INFERENCE  ((EVNT20  EVNT26)  (EVNT14))
    SCORECARD  (EVNT33)
```

```
EVNT4:
    VALUE  ((ACTOR STRUCT0
                      <=> (*PROPEL*)
                      OBJECT  PHYS0)
            TIME (TIME))
    LASTEVENT  (EVNT3)
    NEXTEVENT  (EVNT20  EVNT14  EVNT7)
STRUCT0
    CLASS  (#STRUCTURE)
    TYPE  (*CAR*)
    SUPERSET  (*VEHICLE*)
    ELEX  (AUTOMOBILE)
    SLEX  (AUTO)
    SROLES
        (($VEHACCIDENT . &VEHICLE)
        ($DRIVE . &VEHICLE1))
PHYS0
    CLASS  (#PHYSOBJ)
    TYPE  (*TREE*)
    ELEX  (TREE)
    SLEX  (ARBOL)
    SROLES
        (($VEHACCIDENT . &OBSTRUCTION))
EVNT14:
    VALUE  ((ACTOR HUM0
                      FROM  (*HEALTH*  VAL  (*NORM*)))
                      TOWARD  (*HEALTH*  VAL  (-10)))
                      TIME  (TIME17))
```

The main structure (SCLAB3) indicates the type of script ($VEHACCIDENT), the main story in EVNT4, episodes of the story (SCENECONS) and the inferred events or actions (INFERENCE). The representation EVNT4 expresses the crash itself: a 'structured physical object' (STRUCT0) hitting (*PROPEL*) an 'unstructured physical object' (PHYS0). The representations of STRUCT0 and PHYS0 indicate that these are respectively a *VEHICLE*, specifically an AUTOMOBILE, and a *TREE*. Connected to EVNT4 are other events, including the result (EVNT14) that someone (HUM0) died, i.e. went from state of normal health to state of non-health.

From such a representation the system generates TL sentences. These are not, therefore, translations of SL sentences, but expressions of the text as interpreted, i.e. paraphrases. The generator would, for example, take the part representation EVNT4 and 'expand' it as (*A car hit a tree Friday evening*):

```
((ACTOR (#STRUCTURE TYPE       (*CAR*)
                    SUPERSET (*VEHICLE*)
                    TOKEN      (STRUCT0))
   ←——→ (*PROPEL*)
  OBJECT (#PHYSOBJ TYPE (*TREE*)))
  TIME ((WEEKDAY FRIDAY) (DAYPART EVENING)))
```

producing the Spanish version:

EL VIERNES AL ANOCHECER UN AUTO CHOCO CONTRA UN ARBOL.

There are three possible Spanish translations of *hit* (i.e. PROPEL): *pegar, golpear, chocar*. The representation is claimed to provide sufficient information for the correct choice to be made (via a 'discrimination-net', i.e. decision tree).

The Yale researchers admitted that what they produced were 'retellings' of the SL text in another language and not 'translations'. However, they insisted that they were "not trying to simulate a professional translator", but rather "to simulate an average nonprofessional person with a working knowledge of two languages who is asked to read a text and then to reproduce its content at a desirable level of detail." (Carbonell et al. 1981). It was considered more important to convey the sense unambiguously than to preserve the structure and style of the original.

A little later at Yale, Lytinen & Schank (1982) experimented with a MT model based on a more abstract type of knowledge base. Instead of scripts relating to specific stereotypical event-schemata, the Yale group now proposed MOPs (Memory Organization Packets). These are representations of knowledge common to many different situations. For example, whereas a 'script' for visiting a doctor would specify a sequence: having a medical problem, making an appointment, going to surgery, sitting in waiting room, having treatment, etc., a MOP would cover all 'professional visits' to lawyers, dentists, doctors, etc.

The Yale experiment, called MOPTRANS (MOP-based TRANSlator), has been designed to read newspaper stories about terrorism in Spanish and French, and to translate these stories into English. The MOPTRANS system uses two types of knowledge: packaging knowledge (the abstract event sequences referred to) and abstraction knowledge. The latter represents conceptual relations, e.g. that to arrest someone is to GET-CONTROL of them, and that police searches are types of FIND.

The system is illustrated by Lytinen & Schank (1982) on the Spanish sentence:

La policia realiza intensas diligencias para capturar a un presunto maniatico sexual . . .

This is to be translated (roughly) as:

Police are searching for a presumed sex maniac . . .

Given the multiple senses (i.e. vagueness) of *diligencias* ('search', 'determine', 'shop', 'go' according to context), it can initially be assigned only a very general structure *DO*. However, the goal or purpose of this action (indicated by the FOLLOWS-FROM relation expressed by *para*) is to GET-CONTROL of someone (the general unspecific sense of *capturar*). This instantiates a MOP (called M-GET) specifying the sequence KNOW + FIND + GET-CONTROL (i.e. that when one wants to get control of an object, one first has to know where it is, and then one has to find it). Consequently it can be inferred that *diligencias* actually refers to the structure FIND. Since the police are the agents of this FIND, it is now possible to replace FIND by the more specific POLICE-SEARCH. As a consequence, a new more specific MOP can be set up, viz. M-POLICE-CAPTURE, with the sequence POLICE-INVESTIGATION + POLICE-SEARCH + ARREST. In this MOP, ARREST corresponds to the GET-CONTROL of the M-GET, permitting the final recognition of the sense of *captuarar* as 'arrest'.

It is stressed by the Yale researchers that this system does not require rules which look for specific lexical items in order to disambiguate *diligencias* (as in most syntax-based MT systems). The recognition of its sense as FIND follows from the occurrence of GET-CONTROL, and this procedure could apply to any item represented as *DO*. The rules which use abstraction knowledge and packaging knowledge (MOPs) are independent of any particular language and its lexical relationships.

It should be noted that the MOPTRANS approach does not ignore syntactic information completely. As Lytinen (1985) illustrates with the simple sentence *John gave Mary a book*, the parser would build a conceptual dependency representation for *give* in which the 'person' (*John*) already identified could be either the ACTOR or the RECIPIENT of the transaction. Syntactic rules would identify *John* as a subject and thus confirm this 'person' as ACTOR. As a consequence MOPTRANS integrates semantic and syntacic analyses, with semantic parsing playing the dominant role.

15.3 OTHER AI APPROACHES

In a sense, almost any AI project which involves 'conceptual' representations in the analysis and generation of natural language text may be regarded as an embryonic interlingual MT system. Tucker and Nirenburg (1984), for example, describe the work of Wilensky and Arens in the Berkeley AI group as providing such a potential. The group has developed analysers and generators of English for natural language interfaces for the UNIX computer operating system (Wilensky et al. 1984). Both the parser PHRAN (phrasal analyser) and the generator PHRED (phrasal English diction) are claimed to be easily extendable to languages other than English, and such extensions of PHRAN have been implemented in Spanish and Chinese. Apparently a small English-Spanish translation system has been attempted.

With the exception of Wilks' system, all the groups mentioned above adopt basically Schank's conceptual dependency approach to 'interlingual' representations. Other AI projects have taken different lines.

15.4 MASSACHUSETTS INSTITUTE OF TECHNOLOGY (1971-74)

At roughly the same time as Wilks was experimenting at Stanford there was also a small-scale project at the Massachusetts Institute of Technology which attempted to integrate AI methods into a MT system. Sponsored by the Office of Naval Research, the research was done as part of the thesis of Gretchen Purkhiser Brown (1974). Brown's objective was a German–English system which implemented Winograd's PROGRAMMAR (Winograd 1972) in an interlingual MT design.

SL analysis involved initial morphological and syntactic analysis and then transformation into representations in terms of semantic primitives. The English TL forms were to be generated from semantic representations. For the dismbiguation of SL analysis structures (i.e. those ambiguities which could not be resolved by syntactic means), the system was to include an 'understanding' component. Representations were to be checked for consistency and comprehensibility against a knowledge base, containing definitions of lexical items in terms of semantic primitives and information about the 'real world'. One of its tasks would be, for instance, the determination of the antecedents of pronouns on the basis of semantic information about relationships within the text and of conceptual hierarchical relationships, e.g that octopuses are sea creatures. The 'understanding' component was also to deal with thematic information, given and new information, problems of metaphoric usage. Unfortunately none of the 'understanding' was implemented. At a result, the actual system (which was based on a very small text corpus) comprised little more than a conventional analysis and synthesis program.

15.5 UNIVERSITY OF ESSEX AND NEW MEXICO STATE UNIVERSITY (1983–)

The research by Xiaming Huang of the Institute of Linguistics, Chinese Academy of Social Sciences, Beijing, China, has been conducted since 1983 first at the University of Essex (Colchester, UK) and later at New Mexico State University (Las Cruces, USA). It is an implementation in Prolog of 'definite clause grammar' (a version of context-free phrase structure grammar), case grammar and Wilks' preference semantics. Huang (1984, 1985) describes a small-scale English-Chinese 'interlingual' system XTRA designed principally to test problems of ambiguity in coordinate structures, in relative clauses, in participle clauses, and in prepositional phrase combinations. Parsing incorporates both syntactic and semantic analysis, and interlingual representations are basically dependency trees with case frame slots and conjoined semantic features.

15.6 GEORGIA INSTITUTE OF TECHNOLOGY (1982–)

Richard Cullingford, who had collaborated with Carbonell at Yale, has continued to investigate the AI approach at the Georgia Institute of Technology (Cullingford & Onyshkevych (1985). As before, the basic component is an interlingual representation based on the conceptual dependency approach. However, rather than drawing inferences from 'scripts' (or MOPs) in order to predict and build representations, the main sources of predictions are lexical entries. The entry of, for example, *punch* would be:

```
(propel actor (person)
        obj (bpart btype (hand))
        to (physcont val (bpart partof (person))))
```

The 'slots' for actor, obj(ect) and recipient (to) would be filled by appropriate items in the sentence analysed. The method has been tested on a small Ukrainian-English system. Ukrainian lexical entries contain information on case (nominative, accusative, etc.), gender and number in addition to semantic information. Cullingford's method of "lexicon-driven analysis" might be regarded as a refinement of the 'case frame' parsers (without the syntactic information), and as closely related to the 'word expert' parser of Small (1983), see Ch. 19.3 below.

15.7 COLGATE UNIVERSITY (1983–)

The MT system being developed at Colgate University by Allen Tucker, Sergei Nirenburg and others (Tucker & Nirenburg 1984; Nirenburg *et al.* 1985) adopts an AI approach in that it has an interlingua and a knowledge base. There is, however, one important addition: the TRANSLATOR system is also intended to include representations of the expertise of human translators. In this sense, the project is an experiment in modelling human translation. The aim is a multilingual MT system for the four languages English, Japanese, Russian and Spanish.

In overall design TRANSLATOR is a 'conventional' interlingual system: morpho-syntactic and semantic analysis converts SL text into IL representations (producing normally sets of alternative interpretations), and a generation module converts IL representations into TL text. It differs in the insertion of an 'Inspector' module, the embodiment of an expert translator, which examines the alternative interlingual parsings of SL texts and decides which is the most plausible in the context by reference to a knowledge base. The Inspector is thus envisaged as a simulation of the human consultant in an interactive MT system, cf. below the early Brigham Young system (Ch. 17.10) and the DLT system under development (Ch. 16.3); or as the designers put it: "The challenge . . . is to simulate the behavior of the post-editor and thus arrive at a high-quality translation *before* the target text is synthesized rather than after." (Tucker & Nirenburg 1984).

The knowledge base of TRANSLATOR has the following components

(Nirenburg *et al.* 1985): IL dictionary, SL-IL dictionary, IL-TL dictionary, SL grammar, SL-IL translator program (set of parsers), IL grammar, IL inspector, Inspector knowledge base, TL grammar, IL-TL translator program. The AI features of TRANSLATOR are the embodiment of 'language-independent' world knowledge in the IL dictionary, and the inclusion of an 'expert system' in the IL inspector.

The interlingua (IL) is envisaged as a 'full' language with its own lexicon and grammar. As in the case of the majority of interlingual systems (cf. Ch. 10), the designers of TRANSLATOR do not attempt componential analyses of meaning (e.g. decomposition into semantic primitives); the IL dictionary is thus essentially a set of SL and TL mappings. Entries in the IL dictionary include hierarchical relations ('is-a', 'consists-of', etc.), specification of 'sublanguage' context, and valency information, i.e. 'frames' specifying what types of items may be related to them in texts (or rather, in IL representations of texts). For the latter, the familiar 'case relations' are suggested: agent, patient, source, goal, instrument, etc. Finally, the IL grammar specifies the types of relationships and constituency structures in which IL dictionary items may occur in IL representations. Particular attention has been paid to the representation of time relations, space relations, and inter-clausal relations (Nirenburg et al. 1985).

Entries in SL and TL dictioaries are to be constructed on the same design. For example, the English word *we* might appear as:

(*speaker* ;'we'
(isa human)
(subworlds everyday-world)
(agent-of process)
(object-of process)
(patient-of state)

and the entry for *computer* as:

(*computer* ;'computer'
(isa device)
(subworlds computer-world business-world college-world)
(object-of use)
(instrument-of solve analyze)
(source-of information)
(consists-of CPU *memory* peripherals)

These examples illustrate the amount of 'world' knowledge incorporated in the IL dictionary.

As yet there are no details of the most innovative feature of TRANSLATOR, the Inspector expert systems. It is envisaged, however, that its knowledge base would include a'short term memory' for information about the subject matter of the text being analysed (used for disambiguation), and a 'long term memory' of information relating to sets of texts on similar subject matters (e.g. sublanguage information).

15.8 UNIVERSITY OF MASSACHUSETTS AT AMHERST (1985-)

The project by McDonald (1985) aims to develop a SL parser which establishes the discourse decisions made by the writer in composing the original text, for use by the TL generator in synthesis. The parser is intended to identify the 'realisation class' for a given analysis, i.e. the set of rules which determined the particular surface form, such as selection of subject noun, selection of *there*-sentence form, selection of passive verb, etc. These realisation rules are then to be converted into equivalent generative rules of the TL. Except that the parser itself is AI-based, the basic idea is akin to the 'analysis by synthesis' approach at MIT in the 1960s (Ch. 4.7).

15.9 THE FUTURE RELEVANCE OF AI APPROACHES IN MT

These examples of the AI approach to MT give some flavour of the complexity demanded in semantics-based methods. Their feasibility in full-scale MT must, however, remain doubtful. The problems of expanding AI techniques for a large-scale MT system are clear enough. The earlier research at Cambridge (Ch. 5.2) showed the difficulties of defining semantic 'primitives' and applying them in the creation of large dictionaries. Even more problematic would appear to be the elaboration of all the scripts (or templates, or MOPs), the 'knowledge databases' and the inference rules to cope with a much wider range of possible texts than in the restricted domains of AI systems. In particular it should be noted that no AI project has yet tackled scientific and technical sublanguages, and that most research has concentrated on narrative texts (stories and newspaper reports) rather than expository or argument texts.

Naturally, AI workers are confident that their approaches are expandable. Thus, Carbonell *et al.* (1981): "Our experience . . . suggests that the increase in . . . understanding abilities does not lead to any serious decrease in its speed. The combinatorial 'explosion' feared by Boitet has not come to pass". The MT experience has been frequently that the expansion of small-scale experimental prototypes into large-scale systems intended for operational implementation has often resulted in disheartening degradations in quality. Perhaps AI approaches will be more successful.

It needs to be stressed, however, that none of the AI workers are expecting their work to result in the near future in 'operational' MT systems. What they are engaged in is the fundamental research which is the necessary preliminary for more advanced MT systems. In a number of respects therefore, AI projects on MT are the successors of the 'perfectionist' projects of the 1960s (cf. Ch. 3.10 and Ch. 8.2 above).

16

Other interlingual projects since 1975

In recent years the interlingual approach is most often associated with semantics-based projects, and these have usually been inspired by AI methods of analysis, particularly semantic parsing. Interlingual approaches based on older traditions have, however, continued. The concept of intermediary representations formulated in terms of logical formulae (present for example in the CETA and LRC concepts, Ch. 10 above) is to be found in the SALAT project at the University of Heidelberg and in the Philips project at Eindhoven in the Netherlands. The argument for Esperanto as a MT interlingua has been revived in the ambitious multilingual project in Utrecht under the direction of Toon Witkam. And there are other conceptions of 'intermediary' representations to be found in a number of interactive systems (Ch. 17 below).

16.1 UNIVERSITY OF HEIDELBERG (1973–)

The SALAT (System for Automatic Language Analysis and Translation) project began in 1973 in the Institut für Angewandte Sprachwissenschaft of the University of Heidelberg. The project is supported by the Deutsche Forschungsgemeinschaft (Sonderforschungsbereich 99 'Linguistik'). The SALAT design is an interlingual MT system with recourse to a knowledge database and inference rules. The system does not, however, have an interlingual lexicon. As in CETA (Ch. 10.1), its interlingual features are restricted to syntactic and structural relations. Lexical conversion is through a SL–TL dictionary of equivalences. SALAT is similar to CETA also in that its interlingual syntax is based on logico-semantic foundations.

The system has the following stages (Hauenschild *et al.* 1979, Maier 1978): a two-step surface structure analysis of SL input (i.e. morphological analysis and syntactic analysis); transformational analysis into SL deep structure representations; disambiguation of SL structures (by reference to the knowledge data base); creation of TL deep structures (by reference to

SL–TL dictionary and to 'deduction rules' for SL–TL structural transfer); and transformational synthesis into TL surface structures. The transformation of structures is implemented by tree transduction rules (Ch. 9.14).

Though having logico-semantic representations, SALAT has also AI features. These are located in the application of 'knowledge-base' disambiguation and in the use of 'deduction rules' for SL–TL transfer. Interlingual representations are formulated as logical formulae , e.g. for *Das alpine Gebiet ist klein* (The Alpine region is small) the SL (German) representation is as shown in Fig. 36.

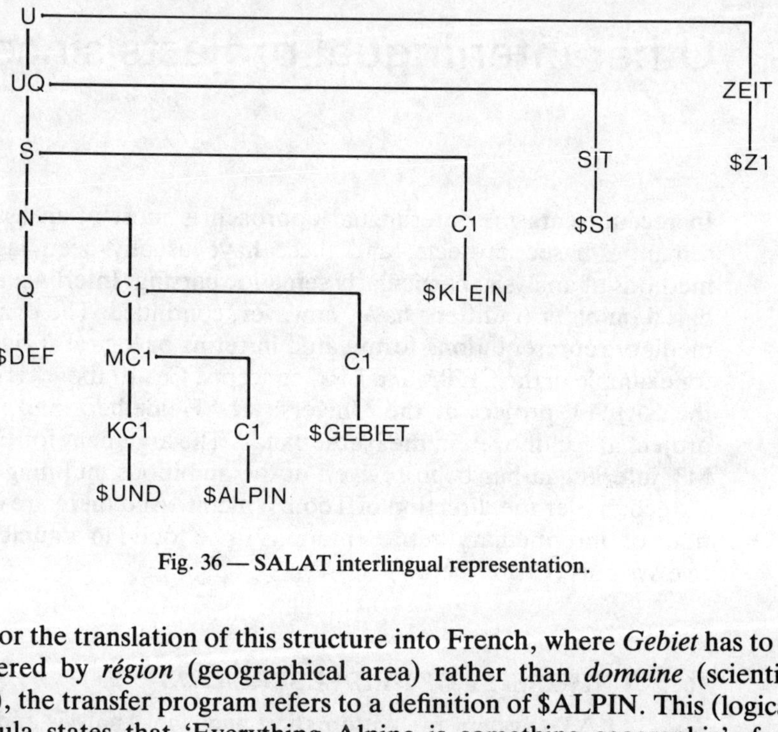

Fig. 36 — SALAT interlingual representation.

For the translation of this structure into French, where *Gebiet* has to be rendered by *région* (geographical area) rather than *domaine* (scientific field), the transfer program refers to a definition of $ALPIN. This (logical) formula states that 'Everything Alpine is something geographic', from which it deduces that $GEBIET is also geographic and the TL substitute must be $REGION.

In SALAT the clear objective is to devise logical formulae both for 'deep structure' interlingual representations and for 'knowledge base' representations, on which can operate logical deduction rules for disambiguation and for SL–TL transfer. The logical foundations are the work of Suppes, Montague, and Cresswell (Maier 1978).

16.2 PHILIPS RESEARCH LABORATORIES, EINDHOVEN (1980-)

The semantic theory of the philosopher Richard Montague (1974) forms the foundation of the experimental MT system 'Rosetta' under development by Landsbergen (1981, 1982) and his colleagues at the Philips Research

Laboratory. A 'Montague grammar' defines a language by specifying a set of expressions and their grammatical categories, and a set of syntactic rules prescribing how these expressions may combine to form new expressions and what the grammatical category of the new expression will be. Thus, an expression x of category N may combine with an expression y of category ADJ to form xy of category NP. The way in which expressions are derived are represented by derivation trees (D-trees). For each syntactic rule a Montague grammar provides a corresponding logical composition rule which shows how the meaning of the expression constructed is derived from the meanings of its constituent expressions.

The assumption may be made that equivalencies can be established between the derivation trees (and the corresponding logical composition trees) of different languages, e.g. between the simple English derivation above and one in French for combining nouns and adjectives (in this sequence) into NPs. These equivalencies may in turn be represented by 'logical derivation trees' which may serve as 'intermediary' representations. Fig. 37 gives an example from Dutch and English (Appelo & Schenk 1985).

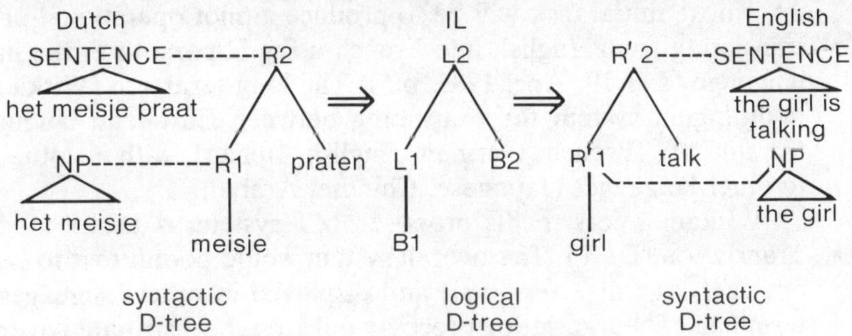

Fig. 37 — Rosetta representations.

The aim of the Rosetta MT project is to explore this possibility in the construction of a multilingual system. Whereas in SALAT the logical formulae themselves are interlingual, in Rosetta it is their derivation trees which mediate between languages. The reversibility of the Montague grammar formalism means that grammars can be used both for analysis and for synthesis. As in SALAT, the scheme is highly speculative and as yet far from even experimental implementation. Initially the system will be designed for English and Dutch, with Spanish as the next language. Appelo and Schenk (1985) have begun by looking at the problems of idioms and tenses.

16.3 BURO VOOR SYSTEEMONTWIKKELING, UTRECHT (1979–)

The idea of using an international artificial language as an intermediary language in an 'interlingual' MT system has been put forward on a number of occasions during the history of MT research. The most common choice has been Esperanto, not surprisingly in view of its widespread acceptance (Large 1985). Its supporters claim that Esperanto combines the regularity, consistency and 'universality' required of an MT interlingua with the flexibility towards new technical and scientific vocabulary which is the attribute of a 'living' language.

Despite its obvious attractions, Esperanto has rarely been studied in MT projects. The Saarbrücken team investigated the problems of translating into Esperanto as a TL (Ch. 13.2), but only one MT project has so far studied the possibilities of using Esperanto as a MT interlingua. This is the recent project of A. P. M. (Toon) Witkam, a senior consultant at the Buro voor Systeemontwikkeling in Utrecht, the Netherlands. Preliminary investigations began in 1979. Witkam has presented his ideas at a number of conferences (Witkam 1981, 1984) and at greatest length in the report of a feasibility study (Witkam 1983), supported during 1982–1983 by a grant from the Commission of the European Communities. The favourable reception of this report influenced the Dutch Ministry of Economic Affairs in granting a six-year contract (1984–1990) for the continuation of the project. A team of ten under the leadership of Toon Witkam has been set up, whose initial task will be to produce a pilot operational prototype for translating from English into French using Esperanto as the intermediary language (*LM* 19, Apr. 1985, p.5). The long-term aim (Witkam 1984) is a multilingual system for translating between European languages of the Community (French, German, English, Italian), with eventual extensions to other languages (Japanese, Chinese, Arabic).

Witkam refers to his proposed MT system as Distributed Language Translation (DLT). The overall system would permit text to be entered in one language at a terminal, and displayed in other languages at remote terminals. The translation process would thus be distributed over a network: conversion of SL text into the interlingua (Esperanto) would take place in one location, and conversion into the TL text would take place in another part of the network. Like other current projects, DLT is intended as a practical economically viable system for translating 'informative' literature (abstracts, manuals, reports, regulations) with little attention to stylistic subtleties. It is also envisaged as a system necessarily involving on-line clarification of ambiguities, etc., through computer-initiated interaction at terminals with persons sending SL texts. DLT is not designed as a tool for translators; it requires only that those entering SL texts have sufficient knowledge to resolve ambiguities in the text; it does not expect them to suggest TL equivalents. The system is conceived within the framework of an international videotex information network. Witkam emphasises the importance of a good communication environment, with word processing facilities and personal desk-top computers. Only in such an environment will DLT be a realistic proposition.

Most MT interlinguas and 'interface representations' are characteristically tree representations with complex labels and abstract formatives, e.g. the SUSY, GETA, and Eurotra representations (Ch. 13.2, 13.3, 14.2). By contrast, Witkam's DLT interlingua will be more like a natural language, "a linear string of lexical formatives". It will also be a true interlingua; whereas the 'pivot language' of CETA (Ch. 10.1) and the intermediary representations of LRC (Ch. 10.3) were interlingual only in syntactic structures and for lexical transfer the systems relied on bilingual dictionaries, the use of Esperanto makes the DLT system fully interlingual in both syntax and vocabulary. The advantages of adopting as MT interlingua an "existing universal auxiliary language" are claimed to be twofold: as a (semi) 'natural' language (used as an instrument of human communication since 1887), Esperanto has a richness and flexibility surpassing constructed logical interlinguas (cf. Andreev's remarks on interlinguas in Ch. 8.11 above), and it provides a ready-made standardised vocabulary based on common Indo-European roots. It is conceded, however, that Esperanto cannot function as a MT interlingua without some modification. Although an artificial (constructed) language, Esperanto exhibits such 'natural' features as homonymy, lexical ambiguity, and structural imprecision. An important component of the feasibility study was therefore an examination of the modifications which were necessary to enhance Esperanto's suitability as a MT interlingua.

Remedies for some of Esperanto's known deficiencies are already available. For example the homonymy of *marko* (brand or stamp) can be avoided by using *fabrik'marko* (brand) and *post'marko* (stamp). The syntactic ambiguity arising from the multiple uses of *de*, which (like its French correspondent) may indicate commencement, possession, or agency, can be circumvented by the use of more precise prepositions: *disde, al, far*. These would also in part reduce the familiar problems of analysing prepositional phrases. With the aim of greater regularity and unambiguousness Witkam proposes further modifications. These include the strict prescription of word order (basically: subject verb object); the introduction of a limited number of new function words (e.g. for *whereas* and *besides*); the consistent use of punctuation; and the inclusion of special markers to indicate the antecedents of pronouns and the scope of coordinators.

A more serious defect of Esperanto, however, which cannot be so easily overcome is its lack of technical vocabulary. Esperanto permits national speakers to coin their own specialised terms; there is no standardisation. The DLT project is to take a "pragmatic" approach, adopting the form common to at least two of the languages English, French, and German. In effect, the project will be building an interlingual dictionary for international technical terms from scratch, with all the dangers of pragmatic *ad hoc*-ness. The difficulties of terminological standardisation would appear to have been minimised in the interests of initiating the DLT prototype project.

Since the DLT system is intended to be fully interlingual (in lexicon as well as syntax) and the interlingua, 'modified Esperanto', is not an abstract representation but a regularised language, SL analysis and TL synthesis represent in effect two 'translation systems': from the SL to Esperanto and from Esperanto to the TL. Although described as an 'interlingual' MT system, DLT is (as Witkam (1983) readily acknowledges) in fact a network of bilingual MT systems with 'modified Esperanto' at the centre. Only the economies of a full multilingual system can justify the added complexity.

Each bilingual MT system comprises a separate set of analysis and synthesis programs. Witkam envisages the systems for conversion of SL texts into Esperanto texts as versions of 'direct' MT systems, while the systems converting Esperanto texts into TL texts would be basically designed on the 'transfer' principle. Only the SL–Esperanto 'direct' systems have been described in any detail (Witkam 1983: III. 50–97). This part of DLT is semi-automatic, operating via computer-initiated interactions. It is intended to implement a single-pass SL-parser; words will be sought in SL dictionaries during text input, syntactic analysis will operate word by word (an ATN parser, with a 'moderate' degree of parallel parsing), input errors (e.g. misspellings) will be corrected automatically as far as possible, semantic disambiguation will occur at ends of sentences first by reference to lexical and valency information and then by interactive consultation with the person entering the text (in a manner similar to that of the MIND system, Ch. 17.8) and eventually, it is hoped, by reference also to a 'world knowledge' database. The 'direct translation' strategy is evident from the explicit orientation of SL analysis to the lexical and structural features of the Esperanto interlingua (e.g. an English *-ing* clause is analysed as a pronoun and finite verb; English words are treated as homonyms only if there is more than one possible Esperanto output, etc.). It is evident also in the preservation of SL sentence styles in the Esperanto interlingual string, and therefore subsequently in TL sentence output, e.g. French *Ils traversèrent la rivière à la nage* will appear in English as *They crossed the river swimming*. In the long term, it is hoped that DLT will incorporate conversion modules within the interlingual stages to reflect TL stylistic preferences, and produce the more idiomatic English *They swam across the river*.

The Esperanto–TL 'transfer' system (intended to be fully automatic) is sketched in less detail. Most attention is paid to the details of the more regular syntax and morphology of the 'modified Esperanto' interlingua and its ATN formalisation (Witkam 1983: IV. 28–111). Three stages are envisaged: conversion of Esperanto strings into tree representations; bilingual transfer (tree transduction and lexical substitution); and TL synthesis from tree representations.

A striking feature of the DLT process is the amount of tree–string and string–tree conversion: SL strings to IL-oriented trees; IL trees to Esperanto strings; Esperanto strings to IL (Esperanto) trees; IL trees to TL trees; and TL trees to TL strings. The inclusion of an Esperanto string representation may appear to sceptics to introduce unnecessary complexity: why cannot the IL-oriented trees from SL analysis be directly converted into TL trees without going through the intermediary stages of IL strings and IL trees? In other words, why not a 'transfer' system with Esperanto-inspired 'interface' representations? The fact that the DLT interlingua Esperanto, being a language in its own right, is much more accessible (to system developers as well as users) than the abstract interlingual representations of other MT systems, would seem not to be in itself sufficient justification for the greater complexity of processing.

A key feature of DLT is the emphasis on the application of computational techniques which are well tested; hence the selection of ATN parsers and an orthodox approach to design features. Slightly more innovative is the choice of Prolog as the programming language (still relatively new in natural language processing). In general, DLT is not intended to be an experimental system as regards its MT techniques and strategies; it is experimental principally in the exploration of an interlingual system based on a refined Esperanto. Future developments will indicate whether Witkam's confidence in the flexibility and regularity of Esperanto is justified or whether the sceptical predictions of DLT's excessive complexity are fulfilled. Whatever the ultimate success of DLT, it represents so far the only MT project incorporating a full-fledged interlingua; previous efforts have either been semi-interlingual, primarily syntactic (e.g. CETA and LRC), or primarily lexical (e.g. the CLRU thesaurus), or have not been implemented (e.g. the 'meaning-text' model). In this respect the DLT multilingual project is as ambitious and innovative as the Eurotra project.

17

Interactive and human-aided systems

The experience of the last decades has revealed the strengths and weaknesses of computers in handling natural languages and in translating from one language into another. Dictionary lookup and morphological analysis are now largely unproblematic; but certain types of syntactic ambiguity and wide areas of semantic analysis continue to cause problems. Many of these problems appear to be intractable, or at least to be still far from satisfactory solution or adequate treatment. However, there is now a sufficient body of well-tested techniques for the construction of economically viable practical systems by combining reliable computational methods and human expertise. The systems remain within the presently known limitations of the computer. There are two basic approaches: either input is deliberately restricted, or the expertise of human translators is called upon during translation processes. In the first case, texts are simplified for the system or the system itself is simplified; in the second case, translations are produced interactively by exploiting the on-line text-editing facilities of modern computer equipment.

17.1 PRE-EDITED INPUT

Proposals for simplifying or doctoring MT input texts were made in the earliest days of MT activity. Reifler suggested that a 'pre-editor' (Ch. 2.4.1) could mark up SL texts so that analysis could be made easier. Dodd proposed that texts for MT could be written in a simplified regularised

English (Ch. 2.4.3). More recently the idea has appeared again in organisations which, while using a MT system otherwise capable of accepting unedited input, limit the vocabulary and grammar of texts for translation in order to reduce problems of post-editing.

A number of companies which have installed operational systems have established standards for SL text input. The Xerox Company (Elliston 1979, Ruffino 1982) installed the Systran system (Ch. 12.1) for translating technical and servicing manuals. An initial experiment with uncontrolled input resulted in texts requiring an unacceptable amount of post-editing. It was decided to experiment with control of the input. The company had previously had experience with "Caterpilla English", a highly limited version of English similar to Ogden's Basic English (1968). This had proved unacceptable to personnel already used to documentation of a high standard. For its own controlled English, the Xerox Company has developed 'Multinational Customised English' (MCE) based on a general and technical vocabulary of 3000 words and rules for writing unambiguous English. For example, *replace* may express two different actions, as in: *Remove part A and replace it with part B*. This is clearer as: *Remove part A, adjust part B and then replace part A*. It was found that such steps not only improved Systran performance but also improved the English of the authors of technical manuals. Fears that MCE would be a kind of pidgin English were unfounded. Systran translations with MCE input are being produced from English into French, Spanish, and Italian.

17.2 RESTRICTED LANGUAGE SYSTEMS

Proposals for simplifying the MT system itself are based on the recognition that in certain circumstances the grammar and vocabulary of input texts constitute an identifiable and definable sublanguage. The MT system can then be designed specifically for such 'restricted language' texts. One example has already been described, the successful METEO system for translating meteorological reports into French (13.1.2). This system was devised by the TAUM team which pioneered the study of sublanguages, particularly Kittredge and Lehrberger (1982).

17.3 INSTITUT TEXTILE DE FRANCE: TITUS SYSTEM (1970–)

TITUS is a system devised specifically for input which is highly restricted in both vocabulary and syntax. TITUS was introduced by the Institut Textile de France in 1970 for the translation of abstracts from and into four languages: French, English, German, and Spanish (Ducrot 1973). Abstracts for TITUS are formulated as sequences of clauses consisting of only permitted keywords (index terms) and a fixed set of 'function words' (prepositions, conjunctions, negatives, auxiliary verbs, and modals). Nouns may be compound, verbs may be inflected, and adjectives may be simple, compound, or verbal derivatives. Abstracts are input and checked on-line, with interactive prompting of abstractors for reformulations if the TITUS vocabulary or syntax are violated. Abstracts are stored in a 'swivel language' (i.e. interlingua) from which they are translated into one or more of the four languages. The TITUS syntax permits a sequence of up to four clauses: main clause followed by subordinate or relative clauses. Each clause consists of the sequence: subject, prepositional phrase, verbal group, complement of verb, and prepositional phrase. In order to avoid the confusion of subordinating and prepositional uses of *before, after, since*, etc., diacritical marks are added to indicate the beginnings of subordinate clauses. The latest version TITUS 4 was implemented in 1980, and is claimed to permit abstracts to be written in "sentences or phrases which closely resemble free-language sentences or phrases" (Streiff 1985).

17.4 SMART AI, INC. (1977–)

In the belief that linguistic approaches to MT were misguided, John M. Smart based a computer-aided system on the premise that MT was possible only if the vocabulary was well defined. The foundation was provided by Caterpilla Fundamental English (which had attracted Xerox); the system was developed by Smart Communications Inc. (now Smart AI Inc.) into a computer-aided translation system, programmed in Burroughs Algol, and marketed first in 1978 (Smart 1985).

The Smart system was adopted by the Canadian Department of Employment and Immigration for translating job descriptions from English into French. These are limited in syntax (basically sequences of noun phrases) and with standardised vocabularies. The initial trials began in February 1982, and the full system has been operative in the Toronto region since early 1983. The dictionaries have now reached about 10,000 entries. Smart claims that the system can deal with more complex input: technical manuals, telex messages, engineering specifications. Evidently, there are some considerable constraints in input vocabulary. Details of the linguistic processes of the system are not available; it is claimed to be an "expert system for translation" (Smart 1985), but to what extent AI techniques are employed is not known.

17.5 OTHER 'RESTRICTED' SYSTEMS

The most obvious application of restricted language MT is in the translation of titles. The TITRAN system developed at Kyoto University (18.13 below) has been devised to translate English titles of articles in the field of metallurgy into Japanese. Another system recently reported (Valle Bracero & Fernández García 1982) translates the titles of Russian journal articles into Spanish. The titles are taken from the metallurgy sections of the *Referativnyi Zhurnal*. The system has been developed at the Instituto de Informacion y Documentacion en Ciencia y Tecnologia in Madrid.

Finally, there has been a proposal to use a version of Basic English in SL texts by Straub and Rogers (1979). The experimental BEAST system (Basic

English Analyser System), written in COBOL, was designed to demonstrate the feasibility of a SL analysis program. The intention was that analysis would be interactive (as in the Brigham Young system, Ch. 17.10) and output would be in Basic versions of other languages. Of a similar nature also was the proposal by Goshawke (1977) for a numerical interlingua, SLUNT (Spoken Languages Universal Numeric Translation), which was to operate on simplified SL (English) input.

17.6 AUTOMATED DICTIONARIES AND TERM BANKS

Advances in computer technology since the early 1970s have made possible other conceptions of how man and machine may collaborate in translation processes. The crucial developments are time-sharing systems, on-line access, text editing facilities, and remote access over telecommunications networks.

One of the earliest implementations was the project by Erhard Lippmann at the IBM Research Center, Yorktown Heights, NY. He investigated an experimental computer-aided translation system, designed as an 'extension' of the translator's capabilities (Lippmann 1971). Seated at a terminal, the translator would be able to "(1) enter and/or edit a text, e.g. a translation or a dictionary; (2) look up words or phrases in a dictionary; (3) update dictionaries or other text files; (4) print his text volumes completely or selectively . . ." etc. In other words, Lippmann was describing what is now known as a 'word processor' used in combination with automatic dictionaries or terminology databanks.

Machine aids for translators are now commonplace in many translation offices and service bureaux. Many translators and translation offices create their own in-house dictionaries, not only because published dictionaries in scientific and technical fields are inevitably out of date but in order to ensure consistent usage. Larger translation services, such as the European Communities in Brussels, have made their databanks available for other users. There are now numerous multilingual and monolingual terminology databanks for specialised scientific, technical, administrative, economic, political, agricultural, medical, etc., vocabulary, e.g. EURODICAUTOM at Brussels, LEXIS at the German Bundessprachenamt in Bonn, TERMIUM at Montreal, and TEAM at Siemens, to mention only the best known.

It should be noted that the information contained in computer-based dictionaries does not coincide with that contained in automatic dictionaries for MT systems. The needs of translators are quite different. Translators rarely need to know about grammatical functions, syntactic and semantic categories, inflected forms, etc. — all data essential for automatic analysis processes. Translators can consult under 'base forms'; they do not need access from all variants. Nor do translators often need to consult dictionaries for items of general vocabulary. The primary need is to find the appropriate equivalents of specialist and technical terms. What is needed is reliable information about precise meanings, connotations, ranges of application, authoritative definitions and, if possible, examples of actual usage.

In the earlier days of MT these differences were not appreciated, and a number of researchers suggested that the MT dictionaries they were compiling could be used as machine aids for translators. Now it is recognised that the aims and methodology of automatic dictionaries and term banks has to be quite separate from MT research. This has been the reason why they have not been treated in this account of MT development (for references on term banks and similar machine aids see Bruderer 1978, Hutchins 1978, Snell 1979, Aslib 1981, Lawson 1982, Lawson 1985).

17.7 INTERACTIVE SYSTEMS

Automatic dictionaries and computer-based terminology databanks represent the lowest level of man–machine collaboration in translation; the human translator still undertakes the essence of the translation process, the conversion of a SL text into a TL text. At the next level of man–machine collaboration, the computer provides versions of input sentences which the translator can improve.

The dividing line between human-aided (interactive) MT and machine-aided translation is ill-defined; in broad terms, we may agree that the crucial question is whether the computer translates individual lexical entries, which may include complex phrases as well as single words, or attempts to translate whole sentences. In the first case, human assistance involves the combination of lexical elements into coherent texts; in the second, human assistance involves the correction, improvement, or editing of a computer-generated text. In the first case, the human translator is aided by a computer-based dictionary, i.e. it is 'machine-aided translation'. In the second case, the basic (even if rudimentary) translation process is undertaken by the computer, it is human-aided MT.

Interactive (human-aided) MT has been made possible by the development of on-line and text-editing facilities. There are now a number of systems on the commercial market, and no doubt there will be many more in the future. The range of collaboration is considerable; some systems demand intervention at many stages of the translation process, others only to help solve problems of ambiguity. The basic features of interactive MT, however, are that the system provides more than dictionary equivalents and that there is some interrogation initiated by the computer system itself.

17.8 RAND CORPORATION, THE MIND SYSTEM

In the late 1960s and early 1970s an important project in computational linguistics was the MIND (Management of Information through Natural Discourse) system at Rand Corporation. Its chief designers were Martin Kay, who had been a member of the Cambridge Language Research Unit (Ch. 5.2), and Ronald Kaplan. MIND was intended as a general-purpose language data processing system comprising "an extensible set of fundamental linguistic processors that can be combined on command to carry out a great variety of tasks from grammar testing to question-answering and language translation." (Kay 1973a). Its components were: a morphological analyser, a syntactic processor, a disambiguator, a semantic processor, and an output component. The syntactic processor was an early and influential implementation of the 'chart' technique, devised by Kay (1973a) and Kaplan (1973) for parsing natural language (Ch. 9.15). The semantic processor was intended as a means of representing semantic relationships (logical and thesaural) and of deriving semantic representations of input sentences.

The disambiguator was a system for dealing with problems of ambiguity not resolved by the morphological and syntactic components. It was envisaged as an interactive system, the computer asking users to assist in solving problems. For example, acting as a MT system (English–French) and encountering a sentence such as *They filled the tank with gas* the system might ask a human consultant:

DOES THE WORD 'TANK' REFER TO
1. A MILITARY VEHICLE?
2. A VESSEL FOR FLUIDS?

If the user types "1" the system would translate *tank* into French as *char d'assaut*, otherwise it would translate it as *tanque*. The system might then ask further questions:

DOES 'GAS' REFER TO
1. GASOLINE?
2. VAPOR?

(If the answer is "1" the translation would be *essence*, if "2" *gaz*.)

DOES 'THEY' REFER TO
1. THE SOLDIERS?
2. THE TANKS?
3. THE SHELLS?
4. THE ENEMY? (or any other recently used noun)

As well as such problems of homonymy and pronominal reference, the user might be asked to resolve syntactic ambiguities, e.g. in the case of *He saw the girl with the telescope*:

DOES THIS MEAN:
1.'SAW WITH THE TELESCOPE'?
2. 'GIRL WITH THE TELESCOPE'?

The disambiguator itself decided what the problems were and what set of questions would resolve them in the most efficient way.

In general approach there were similarities with the earlier interactive CLRU experiment (Ch. 5.2). Although the MIND project remained strictly a 'laboratory' experiment, its approach has been adopted by many later interactive systems.

17.9 CHINESE UNIVERSITY OF HONG KONG (1972–)

Research on Chinese–English MT was begun by Shiu-Chang Loh at the Chinese University of Hong Kong in late 1969. A prototype system for translating Chinese mathematics texts into English was programmed on an ICL 1904A in October 1972. In the following years it developed into the CULT system (Chinese University Language Translator), which, in January 1975, with the sponsorship of the Asia Foundation (and later the Rockefeller Brothers Fund), began to be used regularly for the production of a cover-to-cover translation of the mathematical journal *Acta Mathematica Sinica* published in Peking. (For a brief period CULT was also used to translate physics articles from *Acta Physica Sinica*.)

CULT is an interactive on-line MT system, based on the 'direct translation' strategy (Loh & Kong 1977). Sentences are analysed and translated one at a time in a series of passes, and the parser identifies little more than 'surface' groupings of grammatical categories (noun and verb groups, modifiers). After each pass a portion of the sentence is translated into English, the human 'editor' intervening for the insertion of articles, the determination of voice and tense of verbs, and the resolution of semantic and syntactic ambiguities. If the parser fails, the 'editor' adds entries to the dictionary and may translate the whole sentence. Although analysis and synthesis are integrated there are, however, identifiable stages of the translation process (Loh & Kong 1979, Loh *et al.* 1979): source text preparation; input (via Chinese keyboard); lexical analysis (i.e. SL dictionary lookup, including on-line updating of dictionary); syntactic and semantic analysis (determination of grammatical categories, identification of noun groups, verb groups, modifier groups, and auxiliaries); relative order analysis (recognition of relationships among nouns groups, verb groups, and modifiers); target equivalence analysis (resolution of multiple meanings); output (TL dictionary lookup); output refinement (reformatting, insertion of mathematical formulae).

CULT was originally implemented in batch mode, where a major problem was that of inputting Chinese characters. They had to be manually encoded into four-bit standard telegraph code and punched onto cards. The process was both laborious and prone to considerable error. For this reason, Loh devoted considerable effort to the development of a Chinese keyboard, which enabled on-line input and a genuine interactive system. CULT is now implemented on a PDP11/34.

Development in subsequent years has apparently concentrated mainly on dictionaries, initially from the need to compile up-to-date glossaries of Chinese mathematical terms. Later, there has been some experimental work on an extension of CULT to English–Chinese translation, and this has involved the reorganisation of dictionary structures to facilitate bi-directional translation (Loh & Kong 1979, Loh *et al.* 1984).

As an interactive MT system CULT was a pioneer, conceived long before on-line systems were common. It was also designed to translate specific types of texts and not as a general purpose system. In consequence

CULT appears somewhat crude in comparison with later interactive MT systems such as ALPS and Weidner (below). The designers of CULT had no pretensions about achieving high-quality MT; they were interested simply in producing 'translations' for a specific practical purpose. In this respect CULT is successful: the system works, translations are produced, and the publication is sold. An example from *Acta Mathematica Sinica* vol. 18, 1975:

> IT IS GENERALLY KNOWN THAT, THE MAXIMAL CONDITION AND THE MINIMAL CONDITION FOR RINGS ARE MUTUALLY INDEPENDENT, BUT IN MANY PROPERTIES OF RINGS THERE ARE OFTEN CASES IN WHICH THEY ARE MUTUALLY RELATED. FOR EXAMPLE ASSOCIATIVE RINGS SATISFYING THE MAXIMAL CONDITION OR THE MINIMAL CONDITION, THEIR NIL RADICALS ARE NILPOTENT. PARTICULARLY IN 1939 C. HOPKING POINTS OUT, SO LONG AS AN ASSOCIATIVE RING CONTAINS A LEFT UNIT ELEMENT, THEN THE MINIMAL CONDITION FOR ITS LEFT IDEALS MUST IMPLY THE MAXIMAL CONDITION FOR LEFT IDEALS. UP TO NOW THIS IS THE MOST GENERAL RESULT, IN A COMMUTATIVE ASSOCIATIVE RING CONTAINING A UNIT ELEMENT COHEN HAS SIMILAR RESULTS. THESE RESULTS SUFFICIENTLY ILLUSTRATE THAT BETWEEN THE MINIMAL CONDITION AND THE MAXIMAL CONDITION THERE IS AN ESSENTIAL ASSOCIATION AND THEIR MUTUAL EXCHANGE RELATION. DIALECTICAL MATERIALISM IS IN CONTRAST TO METAPHYSICS. IT REGARDS THAT ALL MATTERS ARE IN MUTUAL ASSOCIATION AND MUTUAL CONSTRAINT. CONTRADICTION AND OPPOSITION CAN ALL MUTUALLY BE EXCHANGED UNDER DEFINITE CONDITIONS. THE PROBLEM IS HOW TO GRASP DIALECTICALLY THE CONDITION WHICH MAKES OPPOSITION EXCHANGE MUTUALLY . . .

17.10 BRIGHAM YOUNG UNIVERSITY (1970–79)

The Translation Sciences Institute was established in 1970 under the leadership of Eldon G. Lytle at Brigham Young University (BYU), Provo, Utah, funded by the University and the Church of Jesus Christ of Latter-day Saints (the Mormons). The project was the development of an interactive MT system for translating English texts into a number of languages (initially French, Spanish, Portuguese, German, and Chinese), to be called the Interactive Translation System (ITS). The system was based on Lytle's theory of 'junction grammar', a modification (in parts radical) of transformational grammar, which was to provide the formalism for 'transfer' representations of SL sentences (Lytle 1974, Lytle *et al.* 1975, Lytle 1980, Melby 1980a, 1980b). English analysis was to be performed interactively at a terminal, linked to an IBM mainframe computer; multilingual TL synthesis was to be fully automatic. It was argued that accurate unambiguous 'transfer' representations could be produced only by making use of the linguistic knowledge of human operators, and that the amount of interaction involved could be justified only if multiple TL texts were output.

The BYU system ITS had the usual stages of a 'transfer' system. Analysis had three phases: dictionary lookup; division of sentences into 'phrases' by making cuts after each noun, e.g. *(The boy) (in the car) (ate a very good hamburger) (while driving down the street)* — cf. Wilks' similar procedure (15.1 above); and syntactic analysis to produce junction grammar tree-representations, during which both lexical ambiguities (e.g. homographs) and structural ambiguities (e.g. of prepositional phrases) were resolved in interaction with human operators. Thus, given *The boy threw the ball on the table*, the operator would be asked, as in the MIND system, 'What does the prepositional object modify?'.

The Transfer algorithm converted SL junction trees into TL junction trees, adjusting as necessary by reference to TL dictionary information. For example English V$(P+N), as for *to stare at X*, became French (V+N)$(A+E), *regarder X fixement*. Finally, Synthesis included lexical reordering rules and morphological formation.

Most research activity was devoted to the development of junction grammar and the interactive analysis routines. The distinctive feature of Lytle's theory was the treatment of relative clauses (Lytle *et al.* 1975). In transformational grammar (cf. 3.5 above) they are regarded as subordinate constituents of noun phrases whatever the semantic relationship, e.g. both *The book that John read* . . . and *The fact that John came* . . . would be represented as:

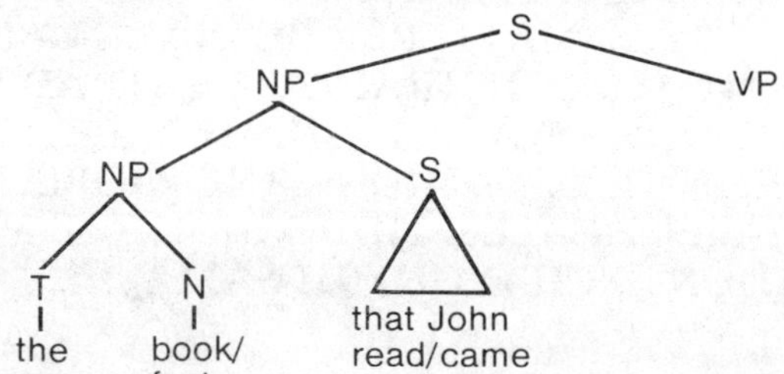

Junction grammar distinguishes between 'subjunction' (indicated by ★) as in *the fact that John came*:

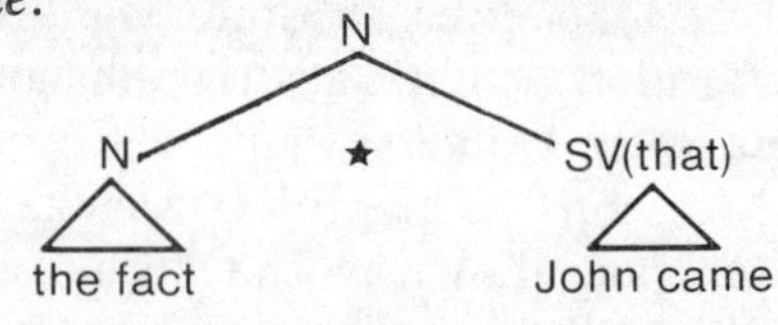

and 'interjunction' (indicated by +) as in *the book that John read*:

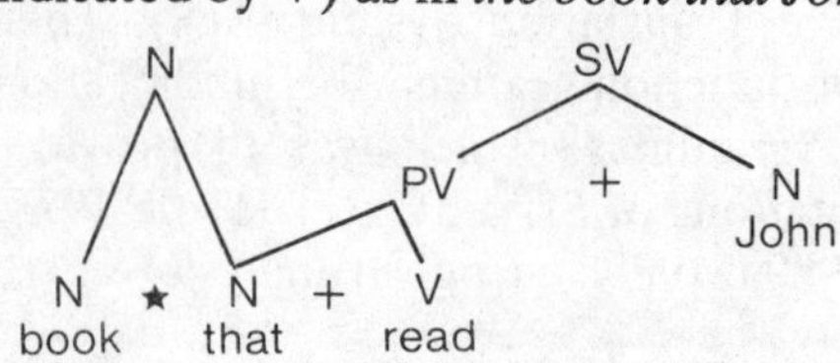

In this way, the two interpretations of *The fact that he learned surprised us* can be distinguished. Interjunctions were also identified within noun phrases, e.g. *the obviously rich boy* (Lytle 1980):

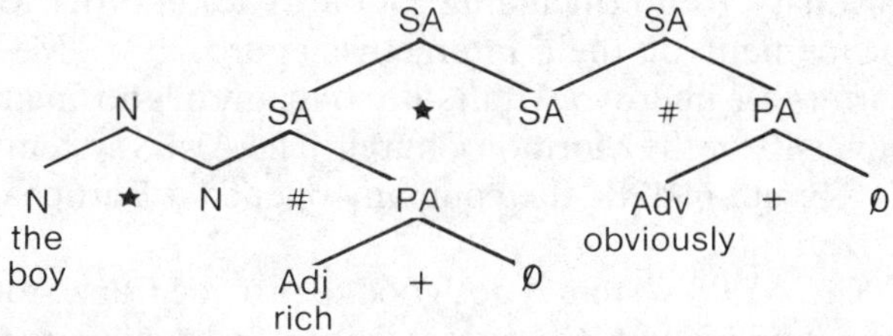

In interactive analysis, the operator would be asked to specify what type of relationship pertains to a given structure — i.e. knowledge of junction grammar was a prerequisite for ITS analysts. Given the complexity of the interaction it was obviously essential, on cost grounds if for no other, to work towards multilingual synthesis.

An evaluation of ITS in 1979 by its sponsors concluded that the system had little commercial possibilities. The system had become too elaborate, it was decided, and it was more practical to develop translator aids. With other members of the project Lytle left BYU for the private sector and established ALPS (below). The company which had been set up to market the BYU system, Computer Translation Inc. (CTI), found it had no product and turned successfully to selling microcomputers (Beesley 1982).

After the formation of ALPS, Alan K. Melby continued working at Brigham Young on the development of a new version of ITS (Melby 1982, 1983, 1984). Translators were feeling as if they were working for the machine; ITS forced them to answer "many uninteresting questions and to revise many sentences they thought should be retranslated"; in the new version, the translators are to be in control, making the machine work for them. Melby proposes a three-level approach: at the first level translators operate a word processor with optional access to an automatic bilingual dictionary or (multilingual) terminology databank; level two adds dynamic processing of SL texts, the automatic searching of term files and display of possible TL equivalents, and the automatic amendment and on-line editing of TL texts; level three integrates a full MT system to give translations which may be accepted, revised, or rejected as appropriate (in some cases the MT system may fail completely, in others it may have only partial success). The aim is to please both users "because they are in control and choose the level of aid" and designers of MT systems "because they are not pressured to make compromises just to get automatic translation on every sentence". The system integrates a MT system and a terminology aid system, representing a shift of direction which was also followed by those BYU members who went to ALPS and by the rival group in Provo, Weidner Communications (below). Melby himself has not researched the MT system but has concentrated on the design of the workstation.

17.11 AUTOMATED LANGUAGE PROCESSING SYSTEM, ALPS (1980–)

ALPS was formed in January 1980 by members of the Brigham Young University group (including Eldon Lytle) in order to continue commercial development of their interactive approach to MT. Although its headquarters are in Provo, Utah, the company has no financial ties with either the University or the Mormon Church. The ALPS system came on to the market in 1983 and in 1984 the company opened a European office in Neuchâtel, Switzerland.

The ALPS system is designed to provide translators with a wide range of computer aids with a good text editing and dictionary facilities (Danik 1984), Kingscott 1984). Developed for Data General equipment, it is intended in time to be 'hardware independent'. The basic component is a multilingual word processor (i.e. one capable of handling all Roman scripts), linked to a printer. The user can choose to augment this facility by

(i) Selective Dictionary Lookup, which when required accesses the users' own dictionaries, which may be monolingual, bilingual, or multilingual according to preference, and displays the entries.
(ii) Automatic Dictionary Lookup, in which the computer searches dictionaries for SL words and displays TL equivalents (in 1984 available for English, French, German, Spanish, and Italian). Words found are listed with contexts, words not found are listed for dictionary updating. No syntactic processing takes place, but there is automatic morphological analysis to determine stem forms.
(iii) Computer Translation System (CTS), which creates a working dictionary of SL text words, asks translators about ambiguities of spelling, lexical choices, and syntactic problems (as in ITS, above). For example, it would display the possible TL equivalents for a SL word and ask translators to select one, or if the word is not in the dictionary to provide one. (In 1984 the CTS was available for the pairs English–French, English–German, English–Spanish, English–Italian, and vice versa.)

The emphasis is on close involvement of translators, a user-friendly, interactive system, which users can adapt to specific needs (from simple dictionary lookup to unedited translation) and to organisational requirements, e.g. by developing personal programs (particularly through the word processing software) and interfacing with other computer equipment, such as OCR readers (Danik 1984).

In an effort to simplify the translators' tasks and to retain their confidence that they are "not merely . . . proof reading the computer's work, but . . . actively participating in the production" (that "the translator is in control"), the ALPS system has reduced the complexity of dictionary information to a minimum. The argument is that technical linguistic knowledge cannot be assumed, that dictionary compilation should not be onerous, and that any information given by translators should be seen to be actually used. There is no need to incorporate sophisticated semantics and AI-type knowledge representations in the dictionaries; the translators themselves are the best sources of this kind of information (Lonsdale 1984). As a consequence, the dictionary information appears to be minimal, little more than data on morphological variants, grammatical categories, and potential TL equivalents. The system comes with a starter dictionary of 10,000 base forms, representing (it is claimed) over 90% of the running words of most general texts (Wood & Wright 1985).

It is not only dictionary information which has been kept simple. It would appear that syntactic processing has also been simplified. It is argued that questions during SL analysis should be as succinct and unambiguous as possible, and that translators should not be asked 'trivial' questions of syntax (Lonsdale 1984). By reducing the complexity of analysis programs, the ALPS system has less need for powerful processing algorithms. Although details of ALPS syntactic processing are not available (for good commercial reasons), it certainly includes "inflection, conjugation, agreement, and word ordering" of some unspecified kind (Danik 1984). However, it would appear that the BYU junction grammar no longer plays a significant role (Beesley 1982).

With its emphasis on interaction, simplified grammatical data in dictionaries, and rudimentary syntactic analysis, ALPS would appear to be not a great deal more than a sophisticated text processor with immediate access to bilingual dictionaries. No doubt good results can be achieved, and translators' time can be saved, but it is almost impossible to assess the relative contributions of the system itself and of the translators to the actual translation processes and to the final products.

17.12 WEIDNER COMMUNICATIONS CORPORATION (1977–)

The Weidner Communications Corporation (WCC) was established in Provo, Utah, and for some time was in competition with the Translation Sciences Institute of Brigham Young University. The rivalry, occasionally bitter it seems, has continued to exist between Weidner and the ALPS group (Beesley 1982). Although founded by members of the Mormon Church, Weidner is a private company with no financial links with either Brigham Young University or the Church. In 1982 WCC moved its headquarters to Northbrook, Illinois, near Chicago, while retaining its Research and Development Center in Provo. In 1984 Weidner was acquired by Bravis International, one of Japan's largest translation companies.

From the beginning the aim was a system for computer aided translation (CAT), a text processing system linked to an interactive MT system, with dictionary updating by translators. In brief, the translator (or typist) enters the SL text at a terminal, words are checked in the dictionary , a translation appears sentence by sentence on the screen, corrections are made to the text using the word processing software, and the corrected TL text is printed out.

The WCC translation system itself operates in the following steps (*LM*

10, July 1984, p.12–13; WCC handout 1984. Exact details are not available for obvious commercial reasons, and the precise sequence of some stages is uncertain.) The 'Input Handler' controls SL text input and breaks up text into words and sentences; 'Dictionary lookup' performs morphological analysis (removing endings) and searches the dictionary; and the 'Idiom Converter' recognises idiomatic expressions entered by translators in the dictionary. Then follow stages of 'Homograph resolution' (consulting contexts as indicated in the dictionary), and 'Syntactic analysis' for the identification of noun and verb phrases and recognition of interrelationships in order to form some kind of phrase structure analysis. The final stages of transfer and synthesis includes routines for reordering text according to TL structures, 'Verb conjugation' and 'Agreement' (i.e. morphological synthesis of TL verb and noun forms), 'Cosmetic routines' for inserting TL articles and prepositions as necessary (according to dictionary information). Finally, an 'Output Handler' reorganises the text into a format corresponding to the SL original.

The TL text is then passed to the 'Text Amender', a word processor system for editing. To assist revision the translator has access to a 'Synonym dictionary', alternative TL expressions which have been entered during dictionary compilation. Any items of vocabulary not found during the translation process can be displayed for the translator either alphabetically, by frequency in the text, in text order or by context. To save translators' time, dictionary searching can be done as a separate operation, e.g. overnight.

As in all MT systems, dictionary quality is vital for good results. The WCC dictionary compilation program ensures consistency of dictionary information by asking translators for specific data about the vocabulary being entered. Hundt (1982) gives some details. The information required for nouns includes a semantic category (e.g. Human Group, Body Part, Animal, Inanimate, Concrete, Abstract) as well as gender and number, whether it is a proper noun or a noun indicating time or place, and its inflection (the compiler is asked to select the relevant paradigm). For verbs the information includes data on its conjugation (selected from paradigms, 42 in the case of German), valency, transitivity, reflexivity, type of direct object, whether it takes an indirect object, whether its prefix is separable, whether its present and past participle forms can be adjectives. In addition, dictionary entries include information on TL word order, e.g. in the case of an adjective whether it follows nouns in TL. In the case of idiomatic expressions (which of course may include specialised terminology as well as true idioms), entries have to be made under each of the component items and indicate which of them are invariant in SL and in TL. Where a particular SL word or expression can have more than one TL equivalent in different contexts, the possible alternatives (up to six) are entered in the Synonym dictionary which is accessed during the TL text editing processes.

Weidner market the system on a 'turnkey' basis at a fixed price for a language pair. There are now two versions: MacroCAT running on a DEC PDP11 or DEC Vax computer, and MicroCAT running on an IBM PC microcomputer. Both packages include computers, terminals, the translation software, the text processing software, a printer, and a dictionary of current vocabulary containing 8000 stems and 3000 expressions. MacroCAT translates at a rate of 14,000 words per hour, and MicroCAT at 1600 an hour. In 1985 the language pairs available were English–Spanish, Spanish–English, English–French, English–Arabic (not MicroCAT), English–German, English–Portuguese, English–Italian, with versions under development for French–English, German–English, German–French, and French–Spanish, and (since the acquisition by Bravis) for Japanese–English. For both versions there is available a maintenance agreement which provides for the delivery of improved versions of the software every six months.

The WCC system is not claimed to be more than a 'computer-aided translation' system and there is no expectation of good quality output without editing. Nevertheless, 'raw' translations do not appear to present particular difficulties to translators when revising. In a 1980 evaluation Pigott considered that the "quality of the Weidner Spanish–English system was comparable to that of Systran French–English" but the quality of the English–French and English–Spanish versions was "markedly poorer than that of the Systran English–French and English–Italian" (Van Slype 1983).Nevertheless, postediting time was a third of the time required for full human translation of the same text, and so there were considerable benefits. WCC claim that revisers can work at a rate of 600 to 1000 words an hour, which users such as the Mitel Corporation in Canada can corroborate (Hundt 1982).

Some example unedited translations into English are the following (from ITTE Technical Translations & Linguistics Centre, Feb. 1984):

French–English:

> This function assigns ports to the exchanges and to the workstations by the parameters introduction. She allows also to put these circuits into service or out of service and authorises the ports of the workstations to carry out some functions or all functions. At last she allows to assign periodically recording equipment for the output of the message.

Spanish–English:

> Because of it these functions were considered as of prime importance during the development of the digital exchange ITT 1240. Taking advantage of to the maximum the inherent advantages of the digital technology and of the distributed control, the majority of the facilities of operation and maintenance has been incorporated directly to the equipment.

German–English:

> The automatic switching on of the operating voltage takes place after connection the supply voltage of the exchange after short voltage failures, after voltage fades and after the failure of a supply voltage branch. The manual switching on of a supply voltage branch is caused by pressing of the key "voltage converter" at the signal field (MAP).

17.13 OTHER INTERACTIVE SYSTEMS

A number of projects in Japan are developing interactive MT systems (Ch. 18.2ff below). It is interesting to note that three recently established projects outside Japan are investigating English–Japanese interactive systems.

One project was established in 1985 at the Centre for Computational Linguistics in the University of Manchester Institute of Science and Technology (a centre already involved in the Eurotra project, Ch. 14.2 above), with the sponsorship of the British Information Technology Programme (Alvey) and International Computers Ltd. The system design envisages a 'transfer' model where the human expert assists during the analysis and transfer stages by providing information derived from his SL knowledge and his knowledge of the subject matter (Johnson & Whitelock 1985). In this way, it is believed that a writer knowing only English should be able to produce high quality Japanese text.

The project is related to the proposed implementation of a Japanese–English analyser at the Department of Japanese Studies of Sheffield University (Jelinek and Hawgood 1984). The analyser was developed and programmed by Jiri Jelinek at Prague University before 1968. At Sheffield it has been successfully adapted in a printed form (the Integrated Japanese–English Grammar Dictionary) for teaching English businessmen and scientists to read Japanese. It is expected that the experience with learners and in particular with their ability to cope with multiple choices (in grammar and vocabulary) will be of assistance in the design of an interactive system based on the same principles.

At the Carnegie-Mellon University, Pittsburgh, Jaime Carbonell has recently revived his knowledge-based MT project (Ch. 15.2 above) which he investigated at Yale, although now as the foundation for operation in an interactive mode. It is planned to integrate the approach with the interactive system of Masuru Tomita which was developed with Nishida and Doshita at Kyoto University (Ch. 18.6 below). The aim is an English–Japanese system for composing and simultaneously translating short personal texts in interactive mode (Carbonell & Tomita 1985; Tomita 1985).

18

Projects and systems in the Soviet Union and Japan (1974–   )

18.1 THE SOVIET RESEARCH (1974–   )

In the mid-1970s Soviet MT activity saw changes in both approach and personnel. The theoretical and experimental work at Moscow by Mel'chuk, Kulagina, and their colleagues, and at Leningrad by Andreev, Fitialov, and others (Ch. 10.2 and 11.6) has been largely replaced by the more practical pragmatic activities of Piotrovskii in Leningrad and Marchuk at the Centre for Translation in Moscow.

18.2 LENINGRAD, GROUP FOR SPEECH STATISTICS

Since the mid-1970s the main centre for MT research in Leningrad has been at the Group for Speech Statistics (Statistika rechi), under Raimund Piotrovskii of the A. I. Herzen State Pedagogical Institute. The emphasis of Piotrovskii's research has been on stochastic modelling of languages, on the argument that natural languages are "open, dynamic and fuzzy" systems and that "MT problems cannot be treated exclusively on the basis of set theory and generative grammar" (Piotrovskii 1980). The system is being designed to be modular and "extendable without reprogramming the whole system" and capable of development "on the basis of step increments". At the centre of the system is the "automatic dictionary which is included into a linguistic data bank where information about the relationships between various linguistic and encyclopaedic objects is stored in the form of a semantic network". So far only the dictionary has been developed, and it is being used for word-for-word translations of English and Japanese patents. Later research is to develop modules for resolving lexical and syntactic ambiguity "based on an analysis of their contextual environment and the thesaurus reading" and for syntactic and semantic analysis based on dependency models and case frame grammars. In basic strategy, the system recalls the earliest suggestions of Kaplan and Harper (Ch. 2.4.1 and Ch. 4.4); only the mention of case frames and encyclopaedic knowledge reveals the influence of more recent developments in natural language processing.

18.3 MOSCOW CENTRE FOR TRANSLATION

In Moscow the main centre for MT activity has since 1974 been the All-Union Centre for Translation of Scientific and Technical Literature and Documentation (Vsesoyuznyi tsentr perevodov nauchno-tekhnicheskoi literatury i dokumentatsii), Moscow, under the direction of Yurii N. Marchuk. Systems have been developed for translating from English, French, and German into Russian.

Initially there were two English–Russian projects. The first, "based on cyclic methods of analysis" and using disambiguation routines on the basis of a "contextological dictionary" (Marchuk 1977), had apparently been developed originally for translating political texts (Kulagina 1976). This system is now known as AMPAR (Avtomatizirovannyi Mashinnyi Perevod s Angliiskogo yazyka na Russkii), and it came into operational use in 1979 (Kotov *et al.* 1983). The other English–Russian system, using a "continuous analysis method based on tree-representation of English syntax" (Marchuk 1977), would appear to have been a product of Martem'yanov's research under Rozentsveig at the Moscow Institute for Foreign Languages (Martem'yanov 1977); however it seems that it must have been abandoned shortly afterwards. The German–English system followed the AMPAR model of "cyclic-type analysis" (Marchuk 1977); this system (NERPA) became operational in 1981 (Kotov *et al.* 1983). The system for French–Russian translation (FRAP), described by Marchuk (1977) as employing a "continuous filter-type analysis", has been developed under Leont'eva. This system also became operational in 1981 (Kotov *et al.* 1983).

18.4 THE AMPAR SYSTEM

The AMPAR system is explicitly characterised as a one-directional bilingual 'direct translation' system. Marchuk *et al.* (1975) point out the integration of linguistic data and algorithmic processing and stress, in particular, the interlocking of analysis and synthesis procedures. Further indications of its 'direct translation' character (Ch. 3.9) is the lack of specific stages of syntactic analysis and synthesis: the syntactic rearrangement of SL text sequences into appropriate TL sequences is determined by local lexical and grammatical rules.

The AMPAR program has 17 stages distributed in the following phases (Marchuk *et al.* 1975, Marchuk 1984):

(1) search of the basic dictionary, and morphological analysis,
(2) identification of segments (by punctuation marks), and assignment of tentative grammatical categories to words not found in the dictionary,
(3) search of the idiom dictionary,

(4) treatment of English *-ing* forms (some being left to later phases),
(5) homograph resolution on basis of grammatical categories,
(6) 'gramatical analysis' determining the information needed for synthesis (e.g. regarding Russian aspect), establishing the syntactic functions of words on the basis of morphological, syntactic and semantic context, rearranging English negative constructions to conform to Russian negative forms and analysing residual *-ing* forms,
(7) translation of 'unambiguous' words (i.e. those English words which have only one Russian equivalent),
(8) translation of polysemic words via the 'contextological dictionary', on basis of morphological and syntactic information and of semantic classes of SL words,
(9) translation of any residual polysemes by 'best-match' equivalence table,
(10) generation of TL morpho-syntactic information (case, number, congruence, etc.) on basis of TL grammatical information introduced at stage 6; sometimes involving further analysis of SL text (e.g. search for relative pronouns and identification of their gender, number and case congruence),
(11) morphological synthesis of TL word forms.

It is evident that syntactic analysis is limited to the identification of grammatical categories (i.e. traditional parts of speech) necessary for Russian synthesis,; there appears to be some check for syntactic compatibility but there is clearly no phrase structure analysis. There is also no distinction between levels of analysis: stages use mixtures of morphological, syntactic, and semantic information as appropriate. Routines for analysis and synthesis are introduced whenever it seems best, e.g. synthesis of negation occurs in stage 6 before lexical translation (stages 7 to 9) and before relative clauses have been analysed in stage 10. In particular, the system is basically dictionary driven; the system uses a number of dictionaries (totalling 25,000 English words and 35,000 Russian entries): a 'common vocabulary dictionary', a 'general technical' dictionary, a specialised dictionary for 'computer science and programming' (the field in which AMPAR is operational), a dictionary of idioms, also divided by subject field, and a dictionary for Russian synthesis; but the crux of the system is the 'contextological dictionary' for dealing with English words which have more than one possible Russian equivalent.

The English–Russian contextological dictionary was compiled on the basis of distributional and statistical analyses of English newspaper texts on political, economic, and scientific topics amounting to some 700,000 words. The dictionary, compiled by students at the Moscow State Pedagogical Institute for Foreign Languages, was created to support English language teaching as well as the MT system (Marchuk 1979). Dictionary entries consist of algorithms which search to the left and right for particular words or grammatical categories or semantic classes. On the basis of such contexts the Russian output is determined. For example, the algorithm for English *issue*:

1	lft	1	list 1	3
2	tr		*nomer*	
3	rgt	1	periodical	5
4	tr		*nomer*	
5	rgt	1	list 2	7
6	tr		*vypusk*	
7	rgt	1	order (n)	9
8	tr		*otdacha*	
9	rgt	1	statement	11
10	tr		*opublikovanie*	
11	tr		*vopros*	

where the numbers on the right refer to the rule to be followed next if the condition does not apply; and where 'list 1' includes *today* and *yesterday*, and 'list 2' *note (n), currency,* and *bond*. As in the remarkably similar algorithms of Panov for the first Russian MT experiment (Ch. 6.1), output can sometimes be empty (e.g. for English prepositions). Although it is admitted that verbs and prepositions cause difficulties it is claimed (Marchuk *et al.* 1975) that cases of multiple meaning that can only be resolved by contextual analysis and require extra-linguistic information are relatively rare. Nevertheless, a statistical analysis of errors revealed that 10% of homographs were incorrectly resolved, mainly of the 'verb–noun' type (Kiselev 1984). The MT philosophy rejects syntactic analysis in favour of lexical context: "As is widely known, automatic recognition of syntactic structures is a task more complicated than resolving lexical ambiguity. Besides, the syntax depends largely upon the semantics of words in combinations and as such upon the lexical level" (Marchuk 1979). While many researchers may agree that semantics should play a much greater role in MT analysis than in some previous systems, not all would advocate a return to the statistical and contextual approaches of the earliest MT research.

Output from AMPAR is postedited, although the quality is considered good enough for unedited texts to be understood by specialists for "preliminary pilot information." There is work both on qualitative improvements of the system "based on a wider use of semantic and word combination properties", and on extension to other subject fields. It is claimed that for any new sublanguage "it is sufficient to supplement the system dictionary with 4–5 thousand Russian and English lexical units, and the word combination dictionary with 5–6 thousand dictionary entries" and that this can be completed by eight researchers in 3–4 months (Marchuk 1984).

18.5 THE NERPA SYSTEM

The German–Russian system NERPA is based on the same linguistic and programming principles as AMPAR. The only major difference is the considerable role played by morphological analysis: German compounds not located in the dictionary are segmented and each part translated and synthesised into Russian phrases, e.g *Informationsverarbeitung* becomes the noun phrase *obrabotka informatsii*. NERPA came into experimental operation in 1981 covering the fields of computer science and programming (Marchuk 1984).

Both AMPAR and NERPA are designed as practical operational systems ('industrial' is the term used by the Russians), translating within relatively limited subject fields. Tikhomirov (1984) describes them as "multifunctional" systems, i.e. designed to translate polythematic documents, to be adjustable to any form of input, to provide interactive editing, to facilitate lexicographic research, and to permit prompt correction and upgrading. A unified software for AMPAR and NERPA has been designed to facilitate modification of programs by linguists; a 'special process control language' permits the easy insertion, correction, deletion, and reordering of program modules, the alteration of dictionary information, the maintenance of files, and the monitoring of the system. There are two translation modes running concurrently: the operational mode, and an upgrading mode for revision of the system and dictionaries and for evaluation of the effects of any changes before implementation in the operational system (Marchuk 1984, Tikhomirov 1984).

18.6 THE FRAP SYSTEM

The other MT project at the Centre for Translation is the French–Russian system FRAP, designed on different principles. This is apparently an operational development of the FR-II system of Kulagina at the Institute of Applied Mathematics (Kulagina 1976). The system is based on the 'transfer' approach, with the following familiar stages: morphological analysis, identification of verb phrases, dependency structure syntactic analysis, filtering out of semantically anomalous dependency analyses (some filters applied iteratively), syntactic transfer of all acceptable SL trees, substitution of SL lexical items by TL ones, syntactic synthesis, and morphological synthesis. In essence, the system as described by Kulagina (1976) employed the 'filter' analysis approach seen in CETA (Ch. 10.1 above) and the 'interlingual' LRC system (Ch. 10.3).

Evidently, this basic design has been retained in FRAP. Marchuk (1984) describes it as having a "modular structure" divided into dictionaries and algorithms, and operating in several modes. The first is an "auxiliary word-for-word translation" enabling checks of the SL and TL dictionaries. The second mode, the 'syntactical mode' translates via syntactic representations and refers also to "the semantic component to verify the meaning of links and translated equivalents". The third mode is described as the "textual-and-semantic" mode, translating via a semantic representation "which may be accompanied by conciseness and semantic editing of the text content". The fourth mode, an "informational" mode, produces translated abstracts for a system of selective dissemination of information. Evidently FRAP is conceived, like AMPAR and NERPA, as a multifunctional system, integrating MT, lexicographical work and an abstracting service. The interface between syntactic and semantic representations has been designed but apparently not yet implemented. The nature of the semantic representation is not clear, but the main function of semantic analysis is to filter out "doubtful links found in the syntactical representation" (Marchuk 1984). The basic configuration of FRAP would appear to be on the standard 'transfer' model (Ch. 3.9) and most similar to the TAUM approach, although details of the current system are meagre.

The recent version FRAP has been developed for three subject areas: electronics, computer science, and aviation and aircraft construction (Marchuk 1984). There are no indications of the quality of its output as yet. The earlier version FR-II (Ch. 11.6) had been designed for translating French mathematics texts and had produced output which was evaluated on the same basis of CETA output (Vauquois 1975); a comparable quality of translation on a similar quantity of text was achieved: comprehensibility was judged to be "very good" by 61–63%, grammatical correctness "very good" by 49–54% and adequacy "very good" by 60–68% (Kulagina 1976).

18.7 OTHER SOVIET SYSTEMS

It is clear that FRAP is now the most advanced MT system under development in the Soviet Union. Since 1976 the emphasis has been on practical systems of admitted low quality output. An example given by Marchuk (1984) is the system developed at the Chimkent Pedagogical Institute for the Kazakh Academy of Sciences which translates "British and American texts on chemistry and polymers". It is evidently no more than a 'dictionary translation' word-for-word system, but claiming to have "completely satisfied customers' needs for several years now".

There is evidence that Russians are beginning to exploit the potential of the computer for machine-aided translation. Marchuk (1984) mentions the work at the Minsk Institute of Foreign Languages on a databank of Russian–English phrases, "frequently encountered colloquial clichés used in stereotypical city conversational situations", with the intention of developing a microcomputer based translation system. As in Western Europe, there is considerable activity on large-scale term banks. The Centre for Translation in Moscow is creating term banks for English, French, German, and Hungarian in the fields of computer science and aviation. It is also collaborating with Moscow State University on the MULTILEX computer dictionary (Russian, English, German, French), which provides on-line interrogation and output on screen or hard copy (Oubine & Tikhomirov 1982); in content and structure it is rather similar to EURODICAUTOM.

Interest in the 'sublanguage' concept derives naturally from the strong lexicographic tendencies of Soviet linguistic research. Marchuk (1984) traces the Soviet interest in the question to Andreev, and mentions a recent (1983) book by L. L. Nelubin on the topic which describes sublanguages in terms of four 'models' (functional-communicative, statistical, informational, and linguo-statistical) and an English–Russian system, presumably experimental, based on these models for translating "organisational and management documents". Another example of the work being done is the research of Zubov (1984) at the Minsk State Pedagogical Institute of Foreign Languages, proposing to base MT systems on statistically derived characterisations of sublanguages.

While it is quite clear that theoretical studies are not neglected — there is evidently still interest in the 'combinatorial' dictionary (Ch. 10.2), Marchuk (1984) — it would seem that the current emphasis in Soviet MT work is on practical bilingual systems for relatively restricted domains. In this respect it is in accord with the views of many Western groups, as Marchuk (1984a) is aware when he admits that "MT in the USSR is perhaps developing rather slowly but in an undeviating manner because other ways to overcome increasing language barriers in the USSR, as well as all over the world, are available".

18.8 RESEARCH IN JAPAN (1975–)

After a period during the late 1960s and early 1970s when little original MT research was done in Japan, there has been a considerable revival in recent years. Some of this revitalisation can be attributed to the ambitious Fifth Generation Computer project of the Japanese government, which has included MT as one of its main objectives. However, probably more important has been the Japanese 'language barrier': Japanese is an isolated language with no similarities to any other language, and despite popular impressions, the Japanese learn other languages with great difficulty; the need for good translation services is crucial to Japan's commercial and economic growth. The greatest demand is for translation to and from English, but French, Spanish, German, and Chinese are also important. The Japanese realise that MT is only a partial answer; as in Europe, more immediately attractive are high quality text processing facilities and terminology databanks. In the latter respect, Japanese researchers admit that they lag a long way behind Western Europe and Canada, and the Kyoto University MT project (below) includes the creation of a large term bank for science and technology eventually to reach one million entries (Nagao 1984).

There has been and continues to be considerable research activity in Japan in the fields of computational linguistics and natural language processing. Much of the research has taken place within industrial and commercial companies or in joint university and government/industry projects, and for this reason it has not been widely disseminated. In addition, of course, most of the documentation is available only in Japanese and for this reason inaccessible to most Western researchers. Some idea of the extent of Japanese involvement in research on natural language processing, text analysis, linguistic databanks, and Japanese character processors can be found in the survey by Nagao and Tsujii (1980a). While the West may know little of Japanese research, the Japanese have followed developments in Western linguistics and computer science closely. An article written in 1979 by Tsujii (1980) reveals detailed familiarity with current research on artificial intelligence and linguistics in the United States and Europe. Nearly all of the most recent MT projects aim to explore various AI techniques, as we shall see, and many of the Japanese MT projects are part of larger research efforts within the fields of artificial intelligence, robotics, and control systems; the Hitachi group is typical (Ishihara *et al.* 1985).

One of the major influences in MT system design has been the case grammar model of Fillmore (Ch. 9.16), primarily because Japanese, as a language with 'surface' case indicators, relatively free word order and verb-final sentence structure, lends itself more readily to the fluid parsing of the case grammar approach than to the more rigid 'static' parsing of the phrase structure approach. However, the Japanese have not, on the whole, assumed that 'deep' cases (i.e. roles such as 'agent', 'instrument', 'location') are interlingual universals; indeed Tsujii of Kyoto University, who spent some time at GETA (Ch. 13.3), has argued strongly against such an assumption. The general view seems to be that in view of the substantial syntactic and semantic differences between Japanese and, for example, English, the most practical MT strategy is the 'transfer' approach.

18.9 UNIVERSITY OF OSAKA PREFECTURE

An example of a 'transfer' system using the case frame approach is the MT research project at the University of Osaka Prefecture (Nishida and Takamatsu 1982). Experimental systems have been developed for both English–Japanese and Japanese–English translation. In both, SL and TL 'transfer' representations are basically (semi-structured) lists of predicates and arguments with semantic case markers. For example, the Japanese sentence (with English lexical items in place of Japanese characters):

cars -(no) number -(ga) rapidly increase
(i.e. in English: *The number of cars is rapidly increasing*)
The SL interface representation is: (PRED-ATTR.TRANS: increase, TENSE: present, ASPECT: progressive, OBJ-NUMber: number (NUM: *, OBJ-PHYS.OBJ: cars), MANNer: rapidly).

The Osaka system produces multiple parsings of SL input, checking all potential case frames for verbs in parallel. (The verb patterns were based on those given in Hornby's *Advanced Learner's Dictionary*(1963).) Rules for SL–TL structural transfer specify equivalent SL and TL sentence patterns, e.g. between a Japanese 'be' possessive and an English 'have' possessive:

(PRED-EXIST: is, OBJ-HUM: a daughter, LOC-HUM: with him)
i.e. *he -(ni wa) a -(no) daughter -(ga) is*

becomes:

(PRED-POSS: have, POSSESSOR-HUM: he, OBJ-HUM: a daughter)
i.e. *he has a daughter*

The English–Japanese system is claimed to have given "good results in the analysis of wide variety of English sentences." The Japanese–English system has given output such as the following:

Comparing two signals gives a measure of force exerted by fluid, and then an electronic circuit converts this measured value to a scale of a flow rate.

18.10 HITACHI

The research on the English–Japanese system at the Systems Development Laboratory of Hitachi exemplifies an empirical approach (Nitta *et al.* 1982, 1984). The Hitachi group argue against the rigid, detailed parsing of other MT systems (claiming that after all, few practical MT systems have resulted) and prefer looser heuristic parsing, akin to that of language learners who cope with "elementary grammatical knowledge". Their Heuristic Parsing Model is based on a "non-standard" grammar.

English sentences are segmented into Phrasal elements and Clausal elements (on the basis of punctuation, prepositions, and conjunctions, rather like Wilks' method, Ch. 15.1 above); then restructured as trees in which inclusive relations are distinguished from modifying relations (e.g. nouns in apposition, and noun phrase plus dependent prepositional phrase). The resultant structure is permuted, basically by pattern matching, and the appropriate Japanese equivalents are inserted with any necessary case suffixes and postpositions. The ATHENE system (Automatic Translation of Hitachi from English into Nihongo with Editing Support) is a deliberate attempt to explore low-level techniques of syntax-directed parsing, keeping to 'surface structures' and simple pattern matching and using a minimum of semantic information (mainly case frame valencies) for disambiguating dependency relations (Nitta *et al.* 1984). A large burden is thus placed on dictionary information, and the project has taken care to design lexicon structures and procedures which can be easily understood and applied by linguists unfamiliar with computer operations (Okajima *et al.* 1983). The primary emphasis of the ATHENE project has been on the syntactic analysis of English; the Japanese output is stylistically awkward word-for-word translation, although some refinement has been introduced by heuristic rules for the selection of Japanese postpositions. The limitations of the present system are indicated by the fact that problems of multiple meaning can be handled only during post-editing, and that the parser cannot deal with a number of ambiguous English constructions, such as the *ing*-form plus noun (either adjective plus noun or gerundive plus object) and the scope of coordination. Editing of output is clearly essential. A dictionary of some 70,000 entries has been compiled and the system has been tested on American economics articles from the *Wall Street Journal* and *Business Week*.

The group is exploring also Japanese-English translation. In this case a semantics-based approach has been adopted for analysing Japanese, essentially a case-frame parser producing a 'conceptual dependency' representation (Nitta *et al.* 1984, Ishihara *et al.* 1985). The Hitachi approach is characterised by practical realism: while syntax-directed parsers may be best for English, semantics-based approaches are better for Japanese. Whereas the English–Japanese system is essentially based on the 'syntactic transfer' strategy (Ch. 3.9), the Japanese–English system adopts a purer orthodox 'transfer' strategy. Both systems are written in PL/1.

18.11 FUJITSU

Research on the ATLAS projects at Fujitsu combines work on a practical MT system using well-tried techniques and long-term work on a system using advanced AI methods (Sawai *et al.* 1982). The advanced ATLAS/U system is designed as a high-quality multilingual transfer MT system applying knowledge representations and inference mechanisms. There are plans to collaborate with the University of Stuttgart on a Japanese–German model (Ammon & Wessoly 1984).

The ATLAS/I is designed as a practical system translating a limited range of materials from Japanese into English. Essentially it is still experimental, but an operational version has been handling translations of software reports for the company. The translation process goes through the following stages. 'Preprocessing' segments the Japanese text on the basis of punctuation marks; next comes consultation of the SL–TL dictionaries: 'Phrase dictionary reference' (for idioms and compounds), 'Word dictionary reference', 'Adjunct analysis' (which identifies Japanese postpositions and assigns codes), and 'Proper noun processing' (which gives the semantic marker for names to any word not found in the dictionary). Then follows 'Syntactic analysis' (identifying noun phrases and their relations), 'Surface case analysis' (involving nouns and their postpositions), 'Deep case analysis' (on the basis of patterns of verb case frames and 'surface' cases), 'Structural translation into English' (via a Japanese–English pattern translation table), 'Synthesis of English sentence' (invoked by the selected pattern, and including the insertion of prepositions, articles, and plural endings), and finally 'Morphological synthesis'.

A distinctive feature of the system is the use of a uniform representation of case frames, syntactic conditions, and English synthesis rules. This 'frame knowledge representation' (based on AI ideas, cf. the similar concept in METAL, Ch. 13.4) facilitates the expansibility of the system. The number of sentence patterns it can handle in the structural transfer program is being gradually increased by additional rules. In 1982 the dictionary of the operational system (translating software reports) contained 5000 words and there were 400 grammar rules. The system evidently depended to some extent on interactive assistance at various stages of analysis in order to handle structures and vocabulary not yet included.

18.12 NIPPON TELEGRAPH AND TELEPHONE CORPORATION

More ambitious in conception is the project at the Musashino Research Laboratories of the Nippon Telegraph and Telephone Corporation (Nomura 1983, Iida *et al.* 1984, Naito *et al.* 1985). The LUTE project (Language Understander, Translator & Editor) is a good example of an AI-based MT experimental system. The goal is high-quality Japanese–English and English–Japanese translation. The prototype LUTE system was developed in May 1982. Basically, it is a bi-directional 'transfer' system for English and Japanese. The linguistic core of the system is an extensive case frame analysis of Japanese and English, and of contextual "world knowledge". Text processing of SL input involves the matching of case frames and knowledge representations against lexical information. The result is a structure of semantic and syntactic dependencies. Transfer from SL to TL representations is by pattern matching and frame manipulation. The final generation of TL texts is envisaged as simple linearisation of TL frame structures. The distinctive features of LUTE are the extension of case frame structures to tense, aspect, modality, and semantic implicatures, in part adopting Montague grammar approaches (Naito *et al.* 1985), and the intended integration of 'common-sense' and 'expert' knowledge databases for SL text disambiguation. The system is implemented within a highly sophisticated environment for interactive text processing, screen editing, and integrated dictionary and grammar development. As in other Japanese projects, programs are to be written in LISP (the Maclisp dialect in this case.) The system is being developed initially on a corpus of general scientific articles from *Scientific American* and its Japanese equivalent. There is evidence of considerable ingenuity and expertise in both linguistic and computational aspects of the experiment; LUTE is an example of Japanese skill in integrating the most advanced techniques in a project at the forefront of current research.

18.13 KYOTO UNIVERSITY

There had apparently been some activity at Kyoto in the first decade of MT research (Ch. 7.1), but effectively the major effort began around 1968 with the experimental project under Toshiyuki Sakai. The project developed two small-scale 'syntactic transfer' systems for English–Japanese and Japanese–English translation. Syntactic analysis was on the phrase-structure model, transfer was purely via syntax pattern matching, and there was no semantics. "Distinction between singular and plural form is not considered, and articles are neglected." The rudimentary results are well illustrated by two example translations (Sakai *et al.* 1970): *Passing through long tunnel of border, it was snow country; We cross river that water flow*.

At the present time there are two major MT projects at Kyoto University. The first is the development of a practical operational system for the translation of English article titles into Japanese. The second is a full-scale government-sponsored project for English–Japanese and Japanese–English translation, initially of abstracts. In addition, there have been some small-scale experimental projects in recent years.

The TITRAN system has been designed specifically for the translation of titles of scientific and engineering papers from English into Japanese (Nagao and Tsujii 1980, Nagao *et al.* 1982). The system relies heavily on the restricted grammar and vocabulary of titles. It was found that more than

98% of titles consist of noun phrases only. Therefore, the system has been designed to translate only noun phrases and prepositional phrases; it can deal with infinitive verbs, verbal adjectives ending in *-ing* or *-ed*, but it cannot treat embedded relative clauses containing finite verb forms. The semantics of titles are equally restricted. It was found that nouns are usually specific terminological words of a particular field, and so there is little problem with polysemy. Compounds could be treated without problems as units, and it was found that simple noun phrases could be translated word for word without needing any change in word order. There are six stages of translation as follows:

(1) Dictionary lookup and search for idioms
(2) Parsing of conjunctive phrases
(3) Parsing of simple noun phrases by a transition network parser.
(4) Handling of special structures and semantic disambiguation
(5) Skeleton pattern matching and word order change for Japanese
(6) Synthesis of Japanese title

Semantic disambiguation is limited to recognition of basic case frame relations, i.e. the compatibility of verb participles with particular classes of nouns (only five were found necessary: tool, aspect, physical object, theory, unit). Hence, the system can distinguish between *-ing* forms which may be modifiers of 'tool' nouns (*measuring devices*) and *-ing* forms which govern object nouns (*measuring temperature*). For structural transfer it was found that the variety of patterns was remarkably limited; only 18 different ones have been identified and the vast majority of titles conform to just three of these patterns (N, N+prep+N, N+prep+N+prep+N). However, the Skeleton pattern step does not cover all transfer operations; certain structures have to be treated by special routines (in step 4), such as titles which are prepositional phrases, e.g. *On pattern recognition*. In these cases, the noun phrase is translated independently and the preposition is transposed into a Japanese postposition at the end of the phrase. Finally, it is admitted that certain structures cannot be handled satisfactorily, in particular coordinate structures.

Within its limitations the system has had a satisfying success rate. In the specific area of physics and mathematics the average success rate was as high as 93%; out of 3000 titles there were only 42 rejected (1.4%), primarily because they included finite verb forms, and only 5% were either wrongly translated or could not be understood. Even when extended to the full range of scientific and engineering papers covered in the INSPEC database the average success rate was still 80%, the errors being attributable primarily to inevitable deficiencies in the dictionaries.

The system is now being used on a trial operational basis at the Tsukuba Research Information Processing System (RIPS) of the Agency of Industrial Science and Technology. In a collaborative project with Saarbrücken, the system is being linked to SUSY for an experiment in the translation of titles from and into German (cf. Ch. 13.2, Ammon and Wessoly 1984).

At the same time as Nagao and his group were developing TITRAN, various small-scale MT projects were active. A Japanese–English system for translating computer software manuals investigated the use of case frames for Japanese verbs in a 'lexicon-driven' approach to analysis. There was substantial work on the problems of morphological analysis and dictionary lookup, with of course particular attention to the problems of Japanese character handling in input and output (Nagao & Tsujii 1980). More speculative and tentative was the research by Nishida & Doshita (1982) on an experimental interactive English–Japanese system which investigated the use of a logico-semantic 'interlingua' on the basis of Montague's semantic theory (Montague 1974), and which has been continued by Tomita at Carnegie-Mellon University (Ch. 17.13). The research was part of the general interest at Kyoto on the possibilities of incorporating 'understanding' routines in MT systems; the prototype, written in LISP, was tested on four technical reports and computer manuals. Equally speculative are Nagao's suggestions for a 'learning' MT system: on the basis of example sentences presented to it, the system would develop its own methods of analysis. It would work by "example-guided inference, or machine translation by analogy principle". It is argued that use of the computer for gathering and analysing linguistic data is a more fruitful approach than application of linguistic models and methods: "Linguistic theories change rapidly to and fro, and sometimes a model must be thrown away in a few years. We will rely on the primary data rather than analysed data which may change sometimes because of changes in the theory" This statement, though it recalls the views of earlier MT 'empiricists', may in fact have more to do with the Western bias of theoretical linguistics and the 'failure' to produce models suitable for non-Western languages, cf. Ch. 19.2 below. As just one instance, there is the view of another Kyoto researcher, Tsujii, who from his experience at GETA (Tsujii 1982) while working on a trial English–Japanese system, became convinced that there was no real justification for assuming a 'universal' set of case relations, that it was necessary to establish different types of classification for English and Japanese verbs, and that, therefore, transfer had to be lexicon-driven.

The national MT project of the Japanese government, the Mu-project, began in April 1982 (Nagao 1984, Nakamura *et al.* 1984, Nagao 1985, Nagao *et al.* 1985). The project, called officially "Fast Information Transfer System for Japanese & English Documents in Science and Technology", includes the creation of a Japanese–English terminology databank for science and technology (beginning with electrical engineering), the development of a 'transfer' MT system for Japanese–English and English–Japanese translation of scientific and technical abstracts and an integrated system incorporating both databank and MT system. The Japan Information Center of Science and Technology (JICST) has responsibility for the development of the term bank; the Tsukuba Information Center (RIPS) for the integrated system and for overall evaluation; and the Electrotechnical Laboratory (ETL) in collaboration with Kyoto University for the MT software, the grammars, and the linguistic information for dictionaries.

The method will follow the familiar 'transfer' model (Nagao 1984): series of subgrammars, partial analyses, and 'deep structure' interface representations based on case grammar analyses (as we have seen, the Japanese are in general agreement that the 'case grammar' model is the most suitable for the Japanese language). There will be no attempt to strive for interlinguality in transfer representations and procedures; much of the transfer will be controlled by specific instructions contained in SL and TL dictionary entries ('dictionary rules'), which will take precedence over any general transfer rules, i.e. it is basically a "lexicon-driven machine translation system". The detailed semantic analyses of Japanese and English verbs and their case frames is the responsibility of the Kyoto team; for the scientific and technical vocabulary the JICST term bank is expected to provide appropriate information. It is intended to classify vocabulary by subject fields to assist with polysemy, and it is suggested that a thesaurus might be added in the future.

Although translation in both directions is being planned from the start there will be in fact two independent systems: one for Japanese–English, and one for English–Japanese. "To achieve high-quality translation, there is the possibility that special and different information and mechanisms are required for each translation direction. Japanese analysis grammar, for example, may not necessarily be the same as Japanese generation grammar"; it is thought possible that "one common set of transfer rules for both directions may be feasible. However, to play it safe, we are generating two independent sets of transfer rules at present, because we have still little confidence in this reversibility of the rules." (Nagao 1984). In this respect the project team has learnt from the experience of earlier 'transfer' systems, e.g. GETA and SUSY (cf. Ch. 13.2–3).

The software is to be written in LISP, with which the Kyoto team has 20 years of experience. It includes GRADE, a metalanguage for specifying grammar and dictionary rules and for interactive MT developmental research (Nakamura *et al.* 1984, Nagao *et al.* 1985). GRADE is a powerful grammar writing system (GRammar DEscriber) written in UTILISP (University of Tokyo Interactive LISP), providing a framework for writing programs of analysis, transfer, and synthesis, handling word-specific grammar rules, which are able to treat syntactic and semantic ambiguities, and for writing transduction rules for labelled trees. The conception is very similar to the developments in GETA and Eurotra: tree–tree conversions, specifying conditions, features, partial analyses, and output representations; networks of subgrammars, flexible control, etc.

The goal of the project is to achieve with four years a practical working system for "the batch translation of abstracts at JICST, etc., for collective post-editing, and an on-line conversational mode for writing research papers in English via machine translation". It is assumed that post-editing will be essential for the foreseeable future; and the total system configuration remains uncertain, partly because until now the Japanese have had no practical experience at all of operational MT systems.

18.14 OTHER JAPANESE PROJECTS

There are and have been many other MT projects in Japan. For example there was at Kyushu University a small-scale 'transfer' Japanese–English system for translating texts on transistors which included analysis of case relations (Shudo 1974). Elsewhere it is known that research continues at Kyushu University (based on dependency grammar) and that many new projects have been established in recent years: at the Tokyo Institute of Technology under H. Tanaka, at the Electrotechnical Laboratory under S. Ishizaki (a system based on Schank's MOPTRANS theory, cf. Ch. 15.2), at the National Electric Company, at Toyohashi University of Technology, and at the computer manufacturers Toshiba, Oki, Mitsubishi, and IBM-Japan (Nishida 1985). No doubt recent interest in the possibilities of AI will encourage more projects to be set up in the near future.

19

Present developments and future prospects

19.1 THE GENERAL SCENE IN THE 1980s

When the Commission of the European Communities announced the installation of Systran in their translation service, it marked the end of MT's quiet period in the scientific and technical doldrums. MT emerged from 'academic' obscurity into public view, and further technological advances brought it on to the market place.

In the 1960s MT was primarily the concern of university linguists and computer engineers. Commercial interests were not absent, but they did not flourish. The dramatic miniaturisation and the increasing sophistication of computer equipment have changed the picture in the 1980s. Now MT is also the concern of translators and of those selling translation aids and systems. Academic interests remain, but are now not dominant.

In the 1970s MT activity was concentrated on two main areas. Firstly, progressive improvements were being made to systems of the 'direct translation' type; the most important being Systran. The second main area was the development of 'indirect' approaches, initially the interlingual systems at CETA and LRC and the ambitious Soviet 'meaning-text' model, and then the development of the advanced transfer approaches (TAUM, GETA, SUSY). These emerged as the most realistic and feasible foundation for MT systems of the 'second generation' (where the 'first generation' was considered to be the direct approach favoured in the previous decade). At the same time, the 1970s saw the beginning of semantics-based approaches, primarily associated with AI, and the development of commercial interactive systems.

In the 1980s these lines have continued to be investigated and developed. There is now a variety of MT systems which almost defies any neat classification. It is still often legitimate to apply the labels of the 1960s: practical vs. theoretical, empirical vs. perfectionist, direct vs. indirect, interlingual and transfer. But now there are new labels and new perspectives: interactive vs. fully automatic, 'try-anything' systems vs. 'restricted language' systems, mainframe systems vs. microcomputer or word-processor systems, AI-based systems vs. linguistics-oriented systems.

In overall MT design strategy it is clear that, while the transfer approach has now been adopted by most (linguistically) advanced systems, the 'direct' approach is still attractive as a well-tested strategy, and the interlingual approach continues to appeal to the idealists and 'perfectionists'. It may be noted, however, that occasionally these familiar categories no longer seem completely appropriate: Systran has features of a 'transfer' approach in a basically 'direct' design; and the differences between the 'interlingual' and the 'transfer' approach have become blurred in Logos, Eurotra, and METAL, for example.

For large scale systems there is now a broad measure of agreement in basic design: the flexible transfer strategy of GETA and SUSY is to be found in its essentials in the Eurotra project and in the newer Kyoto project. There is now a sound foundation of well-tested linguistic and computational techniques of analysis, transfer, and synthesis. The systems represent a continuation of the earlier 'indirect' systems (MIT, CETA, LRC, TAUM). At the same time, there are revivals of older approaches. There are again, for example, projects with 'empirical' approaches (the statistical and contextual models in the Soviet Union); and there are word-centred or lexicon-driven approaches (as in a number of AI systems).

In the past decade, however, the innovation with the most immediate impact has been the emergence of the interactive systems (ALPS, Weidner, etc.); as Vauquois (1976) forecast, one of the most fruitful way, forward in MT research has been the development of on-line interrogation and editing techniques; there are now a number of systems available, more will no doubt appear in the next few years, and nearly all systems at present under development, whether designed for mainframe or microcomputer, envisage some kind of interactive component.

Finally, there remain attractions in 'restricted language' systems. Most of the earlier systems were designed primarily for particular subject areas (chemistry, mathematics, etc.); the most successful recent example has been METEO for meteorological reports. Alternatively, systems are limited to language which computer programs can handle relatively easily (TITUS, Smart).

All these various types of MT systems have each their own places and functions. The MT field is a mixture of practice and research. Practical operational systems apply well tested methods, both in large scale systems for mainframe computers (e.g. Systran and PAHO) and in smaller systems for microcomputers (e.g. Weidner and ALPS). Experimental systems test new ideas, such as AI methods, new parsers, logico-semantic representations. Some innovatory approaches are to be found in the sophisticated and complex linguistics-oriented 'transfer' systems (GETA, Eurotra,

Kyoto); others are to be found in the smaller scale AI-inspired knowledge-based systems (Yale, LUTE and ATLAS); and others in the new interlingual approaches (DLT, Rosetta). From these projects will no doubt emerge the techniques of future fully automatic systems.

It is evident that the earlier divisions between pragmatists (e.g. IBM, Georgetown) and perfectionists (e.g. MIT, Berkeley) remain to the present. Now the pragmatists are mainly the designers of interactive systems, and the perfectionists are among those who experiment with AI approaches.

This opposition of practicality and idealism is a sign of health. MT is not just a special sort of data processing, just another application of computers. This lesson was learnt in the early days of MT when computer engineers found that translation was rather more than manipulating a dictionary. Nor is MT just another branch of linguistics, of computational linguistics, or of artificial intelligence. It is not an 'academic' quest for theories of language or for models of human intellectual behaviour. The primary stimulus for MT research has been the urgent needs of scientists, engineers, technologists, economists, administrators, etc., to cope with an ever increasing volume of materials in foreign languages. In the 1950s and 1960s most demand was for access to scientific literature (in the United States, mainly from Russian); now the demand is for technical, legal, commercial, and administrative translations prompted by the 'linguistic equality' of the European Communities and the biculturalism of Canada, by the needs of multinational companies and the exigencies of global telecommunications.

MT is a marriage of practical needs and theoretical idealism. Wilks referred to MT as a 'testbed' for AI theories. MT has been and continues to be a test for linguistic theories, although linguists have been reluctant to acknowledge the fact. MT provides a touchstone for the realism of theory; small scale models applied to carefully selected or specially composed texts are no proof, large scale application to actual texts outside the laboratory are the real test. As yet, the more sophisticated approaches (of GETA, Eurotra, and AI systems) have not demonstrated their capabilities; only the earlier cruder 'direct' systems and the interactive systems have shown their practicality.

19.2 LINGUISTIC PROBLEMS AND METHODS

MT research is a mixture of solid achievement and speculative experiment. There are now few problems with morphological analysis and with dictionary searching routines. There is broad agreement along MT researchers on general strategies for these processes, and the same techniques are found repeatedly in one system after another. This has been true since the mid-1960s and it is surprising, therefore, that there seem still to be no standard programming 'packages' available (Damerau 1976).

Syntactic analysis techniques are likewise well tested and relatively efficient. There is now a wide variety of computational techniques and aids to choose from (cf. King 1983): context free parsers, ATN parsers, tree transducers, charts, etc. There are, of course, still disagreements about the relative merits of different parsing strategies: bottom-up vs. top-down, etc. (Ch. 3). A more recent issue is the question of production systems vs. procedural systems (Rosner 1983, Johnson 1983): production systems are sets of unordered generalised rewrite rules, which may be applied as appropriate to input strings or trees (as in Q-systems and charts, cf. 9.14–15 above); procedural systems by contrast specify sequences of rewriting rules (e.g. ATN parsers), they represent a deterministic approach to parsing. As yet, choice of syntactic analysis strategies would seem to be largely a matter of individual preferences (Johnson 1983).

Two recent developments in formal linguistics may well influence future developments in parsing, since both deny the need for transformational rules. One is the theory of 'lexical–functional grammar' (e.g. Bresnan 1982), in which relationships between semantically related surface structures are handled by lexical rules. Thus, whereas in the standard transformational approach (Chomsky 1965) active and passive forms are derived from the same underlying 'deep' phrase structure, in lexical–functional theory the equation is expressed through correlations of functional structures assigned to the active and passive verb forms, i.e. that the object of the active form of a verb has the same thematic function as the subject of the verb's passive form. In this way language-specific features are removed from the syntactic (transformational) component into the lexicon. As a parser the model supports a lexicon-driven approach.

The other development is the theory of 'generalised phrase structure grammar' by Gazdar and others (1985). Chomsky claimed to have proved that phrase structure grammars (and hence all context-free grammars) were mathematically inadequate for describing natural language sentence structures. Gazdar argues that Chomsky imposed unnecessary constraints on the formal properties of phrase structure grammars, in particular by excluding the use of complex symbols. Gazdar proposes formalisms which capture the generalisations and generative power of transformations without going outside the limitations of context-free grammar.

While syntax and parsing are thoroughly researched and well founded, the greatest problems remain, as they always have been, in the area of semantics. The use of semantic features for resolving certain types of syntactic ambiguity and the use of case frame analyses are now well established in very many systems of all kinds. The problems arise whenever information is required from outside the sentence being analysed. Pronominal reference is one area of difficulty; in practical systems a simple rule of taking the most recent noun phrase as the antecedent may work by and large, and corrections can be made during post-editing. Satisfactory treatment, however, clearly often requires 'real world' knowledge. Likewise, very many problems of lexical ambiguity and of TL lexical selection demand some 'understanding' of texts. Much can be achieved with restrictions of systems to particular sublanguages, but unfortunately few actual texts fall neatly into one particular subject field; most refer to other areas and disciplines.

There has been considerable activity in linguistics in all these areas. The work on sublanguages arose directly from problems of MT and related spheres of computational linguistics, e.g. Kittredge & Lehrberger (1982), both members at one time of the TAUM group, and Sager (1981) of the Pennsylvania group. There has been a growing substantial interest by linguists in recent years in discourse analysis and text structures (e.g. Halliday & Hasan 1976, van Dijk 1977, 1980, de Beaugrande & Dressler 1981). Petr Sgall of the Prague group has made particular study of topic–comment structures and presupposition, both traditional specialities of Czech linguists (Ch. 13.5 above). Although this linguistics research has aroused considerable interest there is little evidence yet of its direct effects on MT research.

It is an embarrassing fact for those who believe there can only be better quality MT with more linguistically sophisticated systems that the most successful operational MT systems so far (based essentially on the 'direct translation' approach) owe almost nothing to linguistic theory, or rather to be precise, to syntactic theory. What is the reason for this apparent 'failure' of syntactic theory to provide or suggest models appropriate to MT? One may be the distinction between 'competence' and 'perfomance'. Linguistic theory (largely inspired by Chomsky's theoretical position) has concentrated on the formal definition of language systems and has generally neglected the investigation of language behaviour in social contexts; it has pursued the goal of 'scientific' rigour, idealisation, and abstraction without checking its hypotheses and theoretical models against empirical observations of actual linguistic usage. It is paradoxical that the primary impetus for the formalisation of grammars which made the automation of linguistic processes appear feasible should have itself encouraged the dissociation of theory and practical reality which has led to be adoption of unrealisable models.

The influence of linguistic theory in the past is to be seen in the strict separation of stages of analysis (morphological, syntactic, semantic), the adoption of the 'filtering' approach. This rigidity was found to be a major cause of the failures of the 'interlingual' systems (Ch. 10). It was also a mistake, as Ljudskanov (1968) pointed out, to assume that translation processes necessarily took place at the 'deepest' levels of analysis; surface information was often sufficient, and was usually needed in any case. As we have seen, the newer linguistics-oriented systems have abandoned filtering, retain surface information and mix semantic, syntactic and lexical information in representations and procedures (GETA, Eurotra, METAL). These systems are no longer implementations of any particular linguistic theories; they are independent MT models, albeit founded on linguistics approaches. As such, they are still essentially developments of syntax-based MT strategies, and have problems whenever analysis has to go beyond sentence boundaries and whenever disambiguation needs to take account of 'real world' knowledge. Nevertheless, these systems have such a high degree of flexibility that there is no reason to doubt their capacity to incorporate new methods of analysis, including AI methods, without detrimental effects on existing successful procedures.

19.3 ARTIFICIAL INTELLIGENCE AND MT

For AI researchers, the difficulties and past 'failures' of linguistics-oriented MT point to the need for AI semantics-based approaches: semantic parsers, preference semantics, knowledge databases, inference routines, expert systems, and the rest of the AI techniques.

There is no denying the basic AI argument that at some stage translation involves the 'understanding' of a SL text in order to convey its 'meaning' in a TL text. For AI researchers this means that texts must be given semantic or 'conceptual' representations (independent of particular languages), that parsing must be based on semantic criteria, that 'knowledge' of the world must be called upon to interpret relationships and resolve ambiguities, etc. The result is an impressive battery of AI techniques, some of which have been already described (Ch. 15 above).

The concept of knowledge databases as sources of information necessary for disambiguation and inference mechanisms has considerable attractions. Many of the newer MT projects intend to incorporate such data in their systems. However, there have been no estimations of the size or complexity required for the knowledge base of a MT system. Therefore, despite assurances from AI researchers, there are many MT researchers who doubt the feasibility of such approaches in large scale systems.

The degree of understanding required for translation is, in any case, still an open question. Does the translator of a biochemistry document need to be a biochemist? He must have some knowledge, it is true, but does he need to 'understand' as fully as the biochemist? It is surely evident that much translation can take place at a fairly superficial level (Slocum 1984a, Ljudskanov 1968). If this were not so, then 'word-for-word' translations would not convey any meaning at all. For practical MT purposes, it has yet to be shown that complete understanding in the AI sense is necessary. It is therefore not surprising that many MT projects still aim to translate at lexical and phrase structure levels (e.g. the Kyoto projects, Ch. 18.7).

When considering the applicability of AI methods to MT, there need be no commitment to AI philosophy. That is to say, it does not matter whether we believe that AI programs map texts onto 'universal' conceptual representations or whether we take these 'representations' as just useful computer data structures and nothing more. What matters is whether the programs work, i.e. produce paraphrases, answer questions, translate. It may be dangerous, as Weizenbaum (1976) argues, to imagine that the machine really 'understands' and that it is simulating the way we as humans understand, since this has social and moral implications. But there is no need to see the computer as anything other than a symbol manipulator.

The most successful application of AI methods has been the development of expert systems, i.e. knowledge bases incorporating the 'lore' of experts in a particular field (e.g. medical diagnosis or geology) and an 'inference engine' to work out conclusions from data submitted by users. Most rules are conditional and probablistic ('if X and Y are true then Z is likely with a probablility of p'). An important feature is the ability of the computer to describe the steps leading to a conclusion or explain the logical reasoning being pursued, thus enabling the user to assess the validity of the output.

What could be the role of expert systems in MT? The most obvious one would be to assist in SL text disambiguation (as proposed for the GETA, SALAT, TRANSLATOR, DLT, and LUTE systems). MT methods of semantic analysis have tended to apply 'selection restrictions' and measures of semantic compatibility (Ch. 3.6). An expert-system approach would be less rigid, more probabilistic, more inferential — more, it would be hoped, like a human translator. The idea is certainly attractive, but the complexities of codifying the knowledge of an expert translator would appear to be particularly daunting.

Most AI systems have been experimental projects on highly restricted domains. The results in many cases seem promising, but there is no guarantee that if extended to larger scale system the methods would still work. AI researchers are confident: "Knowledge-based machine translation . . . has been implemented in a pilot system" which "established the technical feasibility of KBMT . . . Newer and more robust semantic-based parsing techniques and better natural language generators argue in favor of converting the KBMT approach from a laboratory exercise to production-quality translation systems in the very near future" (Carbonell & Tomita 1985). There were similar pronouncements by MT researchers in the 1950s. The history of MT has numerous examples of methods which promised much at first but proved disappointing failures.

Such exaggerations should not be allowed to disguise the real promise of AI techniques. There is no doubt that AI methods of semantic analysis will become standard components of MT systems in the future. But they will be components; AI approaches are in themselves not the whole solution. In the 1960s there was a tendency for a number of MT groups to concentrate on a single approach (particularly in syntax). The lesson of the 1970s was that integrated flexible approaches were needed. A number of AI researchers are recognising that efficient parsing cannot be exclusively semantics-based, and that some use of syntactic information must be made (Lytinen 1985). Similar conclusions were reached much earlier by the Grenoble and Saarbrücken groups, and flexibility of this nature has been built into the Eurotra system.

In this respect, it should be noted that a number of AI researchers have developed 'lexicon-driven' systems. A example is the 'word-expert' parser of Small (1983), where each word has associated with it (in the lexicon) a set of predictions about preceding and succeeding lexical items and creates tentative 'concept structures' (or frames). Even word endings such as the plural *-s* invoke predictions. Although similar techniques have been applied in many AI experiments (e.g. the Yale group), this is the most extensive exploration. It may be noted in passing that both the word-expert approach of Small and the lexical–functional theory of Bresnan (above) are examples of the recent revival of 'lexis-oriented' grammars (which is also to be seen in the adoption by a number of MT systems of 'lexicon-driven' methods of analysis and synthesis, in general philosophy similar to some systems of the 1960s.)

There are now many MT groups already applying AI techniques; and many recent projects are to investigate the possibilities in greater depth. American researchers have been impressed by the achievements of AI techniques, and the same is true for many European MT researchers. A particular stimulus in Japan has been the launch of the 'Fifth Generation Computer Systems' project in October 1981 by the Japanese Ministry of International Trade and Industry. The project has political and social motives, to give Japan a leading, perhaps dominant, role in the future world economy. The Japanese see information technology as the key. "The goal is to develop computers for the 1990s and beyond — *intelligent* computers that will be able to converse with humans in natural language and understand speech and pictures . . . that can learn, associate, make inferences, make decisions . . ." (Feigenbaum & McCorduck 1984). MT has a central role in the project, as one of the "basic application systems" along with "consultation systems, intelligent programming systems, and an intelligent VLSI-CAD system." The aim is a multilingual system with a vocabulary of 100,000 words, guaranteeing "a 90% accuracy, with the remaining 10% to be processed through intervention by man, and with total costs . . . at 30% or lower than those of translation by man" (Moto-Oka 1983).

In many respects, these immediate objectives are not unrealistic — the Eurotra project has similar aims and they are expected to be achievable with present MT expertise in linguistics oriented approaches and with present computer technology (Ch. 14.2 above). However, more distant objectives of the Fifth Generation project seem more utopian. Yasuo Kato, general manager of systems research at the Nippon Electric Corporation, one of the consortium backing the project, predicts that "in 20 years you will have (an interpreting) machine that you can put in your pocket. The system will recognise your voice, translate what you say, and read it out in another language." (quoted in *Business Week*, Sept.16, 1985).

There is no obligation to accept such prognostications when acknowledging the future impact of AI in MT systems. A more sober assessment would predict a gradual integration of AI approaches in MT systems, leading to definite (perhaps highly significant) improvements over the next twenty years, but with the ultimate completely automatic system still a distant goal.

19.4 MT QUALITY AND REVISION

The goal of the MT 'perfectionists' of the 1960s was fully automatic high quality translation. While it may be true that some AI-inspired researchers are still aiming for FAHQT, this goal has long been abandoned by the great majority of those working in the MT field. It is recognised that revision is normal and expected for all translations, whether done by humans or by computers. Debates about what is meant by 'high quality' or 'fully automatic' are largely irrelevant. What matters is whether the MT output is satisfactory for its intended use (revised or not) and whether the operation is cost-effective. The question of translation quality is entirely relative to the needs of recipients, as Bar-Hillel (1971) acknowledged some years after his influential FAHQT pronouncements (Ch. 8.3). There can be valid uses of poor quality output in unedited form if it is produced quickly, cheaply, and is not intended for publication. If better quality is required then collaboration of man and machine is essential. As we have seen, this means in practice either post-edited or interactive MT.

What is meant by good quality MT output? It is a surprisingly elusive concept. Judgments of quality are primarily subjective. MT output is ranked lower than human translation generally because MT systems still make gross grammatical 'mistakes', select the wrong words and produce stylistic barbarisms. Objective criteria are difficult to establish. Van Slype (1982) has attempted to assess the value of different yardsticks: intelligibility (of output text, e.g. via readability scales, cloze tests), fidelity (to SL original, e.g. via measures of information transfer), acceptability (to recipient of translation), time spent in revision (post-editing), number of 'errors' corrected, and type. Costing of MT in comparison with human translation requires careful accounting of all stages of the translation processes from receipt of SL text to final despatch of revised TL version. Evaluation of MT is made that much more difficult by the lack of any objective measures of human translation. As Van Slype (1982) comments, human translation has never been the subject of quality controls of the kind common in industrial enterprises. It has only been evaluated 'objectively' since comparisons began to be made with MT output.

There is now considerable practical experience of post-editing 'raw' MT output. Reports of 'professional' MT revisers have been presented at the annual series of Aslib conferences (e.g. Lawson 1982, 1985). The work rate of post-editors depends largely on their attitude to mechanisation and word processors, and on their motivation; translators are trained to aim for high quality products, they find it difficult initially to accept low quality MT with equanimity. Translation is a creative activity; many find MT revision inhibiting: it is "not an aid, but a hindrance, because it limits their freedom of expression" (Wagner 1985). Others, however, rise to the challenge. Such differences in attitude can easily account for the wide ranges in productivity which have been reported, from 5 pages a day to 25 pages or more a day. But the amount of revision is clearly very much dependent on the quality and difficulty of the original text. Nevertheless, it is the conviction of many translation services that MT with post-editing is a viable economic proposition. The experience of translation bureaux such as ITT, which has installed the Weidner system, is generally favourable: they claim increased productivity with no degradation of quality (Magnusson-Murray 1985).

Initially post-editors tend to be overzealous in their correction of MT texts, changing not only grammatical and lexical mistakes but also altering the style of texts. They have to learn to edit without complete rewriting. Some become very fast: the idea of 'rapid post-editing' has developed (e.g. in the translation service of the Commission of the European Communities) in recognition that not all users want 'purple prose' versions. There is now a growing realisation that for many recipients stylistic refinements are not necessary; it appears that on the whole users are more content with low quality texts than translators and post-editors. There would seem to be a growing market for rapidly produced low quality translation, which the advent of MT has opened up. There is undoubtedly a considerable latent demand for texts to be translated for information purposes which would otherwise not be translated at all. But, of course, there is a natural fear by many translators that standards will be lowered and have a consequent detrimental impact on their professional image and social standing.

19.5 FUTURE PROSPECTS

Taube expressed the fears of an earlier generation about the insidious mechanistic and dehumanising influence of the computer (Ch. 8.7). Weizenbaum (1976) has expressed the continuing fears of a later generation. It is not surprising that many translators should have similiar fears about the potential influence of MT.

Technical advances in on-line interactive facilities may well dispel such fears. There is no need to assume that computerisation means either that translators will be no longer needed or that the translator will be a slave to a machine. There is ample evidence to show that there will always be a demand for the high quality product which only the human translator can achieve; not only in the translation of literary works where sensitivity to cultural and linguistic nuances is crucial, but also in such areas as diplomatic and legal translation where meticulous accuracy is of paramount importance.

The most likely development in the near future is a translator's workstation, on the lines envisaged by Melby (Ch. 17.10), and exemplified by the recent SUSANNAH project at Saarbrücken (Ch. 13.2). A workstation would combine a word processor, access to machine aids (not only dictionaries but other reference materials), a multi-level interactive MT system (of the ALPS kind), and a fully automatic MT system. The translator would select whichever method might be the most appropriate for a text to be translated. The technology is already available, and translators are likely to be attracted by a 'translating machine' which they can control.

It is for such reasons that interactive MT systems can be expected to remain popular for a long time. There is also no sign that fully automatic systems will be able in the near future to resolve the semantic problems that prevent good quality output; interactive disambiguation and stylistic improvement will continue to offer an obvious solution, and one which satisfies the professional integrity of the translator.

At the same time, it is unlikely that the fully automatic systems which are now operative or under development will disappear in the near or even distant future. Large scale systems on mainframe computers will continue to retain a place in the larger translation services and in service bureaux. Systran is already available through bureaux to smaller translation agencies and individual clients. Free-lance translators already have access over public telecommunication networks to remote term banks (e.g. EURODICAUTOM). Remote access to mainframe MT systems is surely the next stage.

By then, it is to be hoped or expected that 'direct' systems such as Systran will be superseded by more sophisticated 'transfer' systems like Eurotra. There are signs already of quality degradation in Systran (at least in the Russian–English version, Ch. 12.1); and there are good grounds for optimism that transfer systems (Eurotra, METAL, Kyoto) will produce significantly better quality output, even though the high quality anticipated by AI researchers may not be forthcoming in the near future.

Many of the interactive systems (ALPS, Weidner, Logos) are already available on microcomputers (mainly Wang and IBM PC). With progressive miniaturisation there is the future prospect of even larger translation program packages for personal computers, perhaps approaching the size and complexity of the present mainframe systems. Eventually perhaps, there will be genuine hand-held 'personal translators', which would be so useful for businessmen, travellers, and students, and which ought to be substantially more satisfactory than the rudimentary 'phrase dictionary' types introduced abortively in the late 1970s by Nixdorf, Craig, and other manufacturers (Smith 1984). In the more immediate future there is most likely the development of programs which combine the writing and composing of business correspondence and simultaneous translation; initially they will be 'restricted language' interactive systems on the lines suggested by the researchers at UMIST and Carnegie-Mellon (Ch. 17.13), but later no doubt there will be systems with almost unrestricted input.

In the immediate future, a major problem still to be solved is that of cheap input to MT systems. The need for optical character readers has been recognised from the earliest days, and yet there are still no inexpensive machines capable of reading a wide variety of typefaces and fonts (Roman and non-Roman). Until they appear the costs of all types of MT will remain relatively high. Voice input is, of course, often mentioned as a future possibility; but the problems of phonetic analysis and transcription, for more than highly restricted vocabularies, are almost equal to the problems of 'high-quality' semantic analysis.

Development of MT systems is no longer an exclusively 'academic' pursuit; it is in the hands of commercial companies (and as a consequence, much technical information is unavailable): Siemens, Philips, Fujitsu, Hitachi, Weidner, etc. But more importantly for the future, it is increasingly in the hands of translators themselves: as post-editors they provide feedback for system improvements (e.g. in the CEC Systran service, Ch. 14) and they can influence directly the direction of commercial MT development. It can be argued that one of the failures of earlier MT research was the neglect of what translators actually did and what they actually wanted from computer systems (Masterman 1979).

The centres of MT research since the mid-1960s have been in Europe (predominantly France, Germany, and the Soviet Union), Japan, Canada, and the United States. The pattern reflects the general concentration of scientific research in the major industrialised nations. It is not then surprising that there has apparently been no MT research in South America, Africa, and India. But there have also been other omissions: Australia and Scandinavia (with the exception of the Danish contribution to Eurotra), Poland, and East Germany. There is evidence of some activity in China again since the 1950s (cf. 15.5), although little is known of what has been achieved; and interest is growing in the Middle East, where it can be expected that MT projects will be established in the future. A model for the future might be the international collaboration of the Eurotra project; the political complexities of funding the research teams have been daunting, but if the project proves successful there will surely be others to come.

Although in comparison with the 1960s the range of languages involved in MT has greatly expanded, there are still notable gaps. The earlier neglect of Spanish (Ch. 8.11) has been rectified by Systran, PAHO, and a number of interactive systems; but there is still a relative neglect of Arabic, Portuguese, and (since the mid-1960s) Italian. Some major languages have yet to be treated in MT systems; in particular, the languages of India and Africa (e.g. Hindustani, Bengali, Punjabi, Swahili) and most Southeast Asian languages (Vietnamese was a short-lived exception). On the other hand even some European languages have not yet been tackled in MT systems: Polish, Swedish, Greek. Involvement in the Eurotra project will entail MT research at some future date on some of these 'neglected' languages: Portuguese, Italian, Greek, and Danish. For other languages, however, it would seem that what is required is some economic or political incentive; for good or ill, international understanding and cooperation have not in the past been sufficient motivations for financing substantial MT projects.

Advances in computer technology and programming have made possible the proliferation of MT projects. Whereas until the mid-1970s MT research demanded large scale computer facilities, it is now possible for anyone with a microcomputer to experiment. There is evidence of this happening already, and it will no doubt increase. In the past, MT programming was almost exclusively in assembly code for specific machines; now increasingly, MT programs are written in high level languages (at present, the most popular are LISP, Prolog, and Pascal) and this itself will encourage more interest by many who otherwise have no opportunity to do MT research. It is notable that many AI projects have involved small numbers of researchers, often no more than two or three.

While small projects have made valuable contributions and will no doubt continue to do so in the future, it is equally indisputable that major advances in MT will probably come primarily from the larger projects of the size of GETA, Eurotra, Kyoto, and so forth. Only these have the capacity to test new linguistic and AI techniques on a sufficiently large scale. The lesson from the past ought to be clear enough: the complexity of MT derives from the complexity of language and the huge variety of text types. Small scale projects often seem initially of great promise, but there are frequently disappointing results when methods are tested on larger systems. The history of MT reveals how difficult it is to achieve success: of the many projects in the past thirty years, only a handful have resulted in operational systems. However, much has been learned and there is genuine and well-founded optimism for future progress.

19.6 GENERATIONS AND PERIODS

In computer science it is common practice to refer to generations of computers: vacuum tube computers, transistorised computers, integrated circuit computers, and very large-scale integrated computers (VLSI). In the anticipated 'fifth generation', the basic serial von Neumann design of computers until now is expected to be replaced by parallel architectures, new memory organisations, and new programming languages.

There has been an inclination among MT researchers to refer also to generations of systems. For some the first generation is represented by the simple word-for-word systems, the second generation added syntactic analysis and the third incorporated semantics of some kind (Locke 1975, Toma 1977). For others, the first generation is represented by the 'direct translation' systems, the second by the 'indirect' systems and the third by systems based on AI approaches (Vauquois 1976, Hutchins 1978). As a result Systran, for example, is sometimes classified as a 'third generation' system because it incorporates some semantic analysis, and sometimes as a 'first generation' system because it adopts the direct translation approach. In addition, however, there is no place in either classification for the interactive systems, unless they are regarded as 'transitional' stages between generations, as does Melby (1980) with the Brigham Young system, or as 'hybrid' forms — i.e. CULT would belong to the first generation as an interactive 'direct' system.

It may be more appropriate to see the development of MT in terms of evolutionary periods. The first period extended from the end of the Second World War until the mid-1950s (the Georgetown-IBM demonstration and the MIT conference in 1956). The second period, which lasted until the ALPAC report in the mid-1960s, was characterised by vast US governmental and military support, great enthusiasm, and considerable disappointments. The third period was MT's 'quiet' period when research concentrated on 'indirect' systems and when the first operational systems became well established. The fourth period began in the mid-1970s with the interest of the Commission of the European Communities in the possibilities of MT (Systran), the first public MT system (METEO), the reorganisation of MT activity in the Soviet Union, and shortly afterwards, the appearance of commercial systems, increasing research on AI approaches, and the revival of Japanese interest.

The periods are roughly decades, and so it is tempting to believe that a new decade is now beginning. If so, it may possibly be marked by a burst of activity associated with the Japanese 'fifth generation' project and by a resurgence of MT research activity in the United States, for which there are already signs (conferences at Georgetown and Colgate University in 1985, and the foundation of a new specialist journal *Computers and Translation*). Whether entering a new period or not, the future of MT is secure: it satisfies a genuine urgent need, it is the subject of worldwide research and development, and it is becoming a commercial product like other technical aids and office equipment; the application of the computer to translation is a reality, for many it is already as much a part of life as the computer itself.

Chronological table of main projects and systems

Dates	Location	Name	Directors researchers	Method	Languages	Section
49–60	U. Washington		Reifler	dir	RE,(GE,CE)	4.1
50–60	RAND Corp.		Harper	dir	RE	4.4
			Hays			
51–65	MIT		Bar-Hillel	tr	GE	4.7
			Yngve		(F,A,C,Fin)	
52–63	Georgetown U.	GAT	Dostert	dir	RE	4.3
			Zarechnak		RE	
		–SERNA	Toma			
		–SLC	Brown		FE	
54–64	Harvard U.		Oettinger	dir	RE	4.9
			Kuno		(JE)	
54–67	CLRU		Masterman	int	E,I,L	5.2
55–59	Birkbeck C.		Booth	dir	FE,GE	5.1
55–67	Ramo-W.		Swanson	dir	RE	4.6
			Garvin			
55–62	U. Michigan		Koutsoudas	dir	RE	4.5
55–64?	ITVMT Moscow		Panov	dir		6.1
			Bel'skaya	dir	ER	
			Nikolaeva		RE	
55–66	MIAN Moscow		Lyapunov			6.2
			Kulagina	dir	FR	
			Moloshnaya	tr	ER	
55–65?	Inst. Ling.		Reformatskii		FR	6.3
	Moscow		Mel'chuk	(int)	(HR)	
57–?	1st Moscow		Revzin		(E,F,S,R)	6.5
	State Ped. Inst.		Rozentsveig			
57–66	Prague		Sgall	(int)	ECz	6.10
58–67?	Leningrad		Andreev	int	mult	6.4
			Zasorina	dir	RE	
58–70	ETL Tokyo	Yamato	Wada, Tadenuma	dir	EJ,(JE)	7.1
58–64	IBM	Mark I,II	King	dir	RE,(FE,CE)	4.2
58–64	UC Berkeley		Lamb	(dir)	RE,(CE)	4.10
58–72	Wayne State U.		Josselson	dir	RE	4.12
58–68	LRC Texas		Lehmann, Tosh	tr	GE(RE,F,S,J)	4.11
59–66	Milan		Ceccato	int	RE,(I,G,L)	5.3
59–63	NBS		Rhodes	dir	RE	4.8
59–66	NPL			dir	RE	5.4
61–71	U. Grenoble	CETA	Vauquois	int	RF,(GF,JF)	5.5
63–77	Patent Off.		Vasilevskii	tr,rst	ER	11.5
	Moscow					
64–	Latsec/WTC	Systran	Toma	dir	RE	12.1
					EF,FE,EI,&c.	14.1
64–76	Bonn	LIMAS	Hoppe	int	EG,GE	10.4
65–81	U. Montreal	TAUM(-AV)	Kittredge	tr	EF	13.1
		METEO		dir,rst	EF	
65–76	Moscow	MTM	Mel'chuk	int	ER	10.2
66–76	Leningrad		Fitialov	tr	ER	11.5
67–	Saarbrücken	SUSY	Maas	tr	RG	13.2
			Luckhardt		E,F,J,Esp	

continued next page

Chronological table of main projects and systems (contd.)

Dates	Location	Name	Directors researchers	Method	Languages	Section
67–75	CETIS Ispra	EURATOM	Perschke	tr	RE	11.1
67–75	UC Berkeley	POLA	Wang	tr	CE	11.2
69–78	Logos Corp.	LOGOS	Scott	dir	EV, etc.	12.2
69–	Hong Kong	CULT	Loh	IA,dir	CE	17.9
70–74	Stanford U.		Wilks	AI	EF	15.1
70–75	LRC Texas	METAL	Lehmann Stachowitz	int	GE,(RE)	10.3
70–79	Brigham Y. U.	ITS	Lytle	IA,int	Emult	17.10
70–	Paris	TITUS	Ducrot	rst	E,F,G,S	17.3
71–	U. Grenoble	GETA -ARIANE	Vauquois Boitet	tr	RF,(E,G, C,J,P,Mal)	13.3
73–	U. Heidelberg	SALAT		int	E,F,G	16.1
74–	Moscow	AMPAR	Marchuk	dir	ER	18.4
		NERPA	Marchuk	dir	GR	18.5
		FRAP		tr	FR	18.6
75–	Leningrad		Piotrowski	dir,rst	ER,JR	18.2
76–	PAHO	SPANAM	Vasconcellos	dir	SE	12.4
		ENGSPAN	Leon	dir	ES	
76–	Prague		Kirschner	tr	ECz	13.5
77–	Chicago	Weidner		IA,dir	A,E,F,G I,J,P,S	17.12
77–	New York	Smart	Smart	IA,rst	EF	17.4
78–	CEC	Eurotra	Perschke	tr	mult	14.2
78–	LRC Texas	METAL	Lehmann Slocum	tr	GE	13.4
78–82	Yale		Carbonell	AI	ER,ES	15.2
		MOPTRANS	Lytinen	AI	SE,FE	
79–	BSO Utrecht	DLT	Witkam	int	(Esp)	16.3
80–	Provo (Utah)	ALPS		IA	EF,EG,EI,ES	17.11
80–	Kyoto	TITRAN	Nagao	dir,rst	EJ	18.13
		Mu	Nagao	tr	EJ,JE	
81–	Hitachi	ATHENE		tr	EJ,JE	18.10
81–	Fujitsu	ATLAS		AI,IA	JE,JG	18.11
81–	Osaka			tr	EJ,JE	18.9
81–	NTT	LUTE	Nomura	AI	JE,EJ	18.12
82–	Logos Corp.	Logos		tr	GE,(EG)	13.6
83–	Colgate U.	TRANSLATOR	Tucker	AI	E,S,R,J	15.7

Abbreviations

Methods:- dir=direct, int=interlingual, tr=transfer, IA=interactive, rst=restricted language, AI=artificial intelligence.

Languages:- C=Chinese, Cz=Czech, E=English, Esp=Esperanto, F=French, Fln=Finnish, G=German, H=Hungarian, I=Italian, J=Japanese, L=Latin, Mal=Malayan, mult=multilingual, P=Portuguese, R=Russian, S=Spanish, V=Vietnamese

Bibliography

Abraham, S. & Kiefer, F. (1966): *A theory of structural semantics*. The Hague: Mouton.

Agricola, E. (1967): Aktuelle theoretisch-linguistische Probleme der automatischen Sprachübersetzung. *Sprache im Technischen Zeitalter* **23**, 284–298.

Albani, E., Ceccato, S. & Maretti, E. (1961): Classifications, rules, and code of an operational grammar for mechanical translation. In: Kent (1961), 693–753.

ALPAC (1966): *Language and machines: computers in translation and linguistics*. A report by the Automatic Language Processing Advisory Committee, Division of Behavioral Sciences, National Academy of Sciences, National Research Council. Washington, D.C.: National Academy of Sciences — National Research Council.

Alt, F. & Rhodes, I. (1961): Recognition of clauses and phrases in machine translation of languages. In: NPL (1962), 126–142.

Ammon, R. von & Wessoly, R. (1984-85): Das Evaluationskonzept des automatischen Uebersetzungsprojekts SUSY-DJT (Deutsch-Japanische Titelübersetzung). *Multilingua* **3**(4), 189–195; & **4**(1), 27–33.

Andreev, N. D. (1961): Basic directions of work at the Experimental Laboratory of Machine Translation. In: Kent (1961), 687–691.

Andreev, N. D. (1964): Linguistic aspects of translation. In: *Proceedings of the Ninth International Congress of Linguists, Cambridge, Mass., August 27–31, 1962* (The Hague: Mouton), 625–634.

Andreev, N. (1967): The intermediary language as the focal point of machine translation. In: Booth (1967), 1–29.

Appelo, L. & Schenk, A. (1985); Linguistic problems in the machine translation project Rosetta. In: Dehaan, G. & Zonneveld, W., eds. *Formal parameters of generative grammar I: yearbook 1985*. (Dordrecht: ICG Printing), 11–16

Apresyan, Yu. D., Mel'chuk, I. A. & Zholkovsky, A. K. (1969): Semantics and lexicography: towards a new type of unilingual dictionary. In: Kiefer, F. ed. *Studies in syntax and semantics* (Dordrecht: Reidel), 1–33.

Arnold, D. & Johnson, R. (1984): Robust processing in machine translation. Paper presented at International Seminar on Machine Translation, February 1984, Cranfield, England.

Arnold, D., Jaspaert, L. & Des Tombe, L. (1984): Eurotra linguistic specifications. 134p.

Aslib (1981): Machine aids for translators. *Aslib Proceedings* **33**(7), 265–323.

Augarten, S. (1984): *Bit by bit: an illustrated history of computers.* London: Allen & Unwin.

Bachut, D. & Verastegui, N. (1984): Software tools for the environment of a computer aided translation system. Paper presented at Coling-84, Stanford Univ., July 1984. Grenoble: GETA.

Bar-Hillel, Y. (1951): The state of machine translation in 1951. *American Documentation* **2**, 229–237. Repr. in: Bar-Hillel (1964), 153–165.

Bar-Hillel, Y. (1953): Machine translation.*Computers and Automation* 2(5), 1–6.

Bar-Hillel, Y. (1955): Idioms. In: Locke & Booth (1955), 183–193.

Bar-Hillel, Y. (1959): Report on the state of machine translation in the United States and Great Britain. Technical report, 15 February 1959. Jerusalem: Hebrew Univ.

Bar-Hillel, Y. (1960): The present status of automatic translation of languages. *Advances in Computers* **1**, 91–163.

Bar-Hillel, Y. (1964): *Language and information.* Reading, Mass.: Addison-Wesley.

Bar-Hillel, Y. (1966): Four lectures on algebraic linguistics and machine translation. In: NATO (1966), 1–26.

Bar-Hillel, Y. (1971): Some reflections on the present outlook for high-quality machine translation. In: Lehmann & Stachowitz (1971), 73–76.

Batori, I. (1969): Disambiguating verbs with multiple meaning in the MT-system of IBM Germany. *Review of the Institute of Applied Linguistics* **5**, 5–16.

Baudot, J. *et al.* (1977): Projet Aviation. Rapport d'étape mai 1977. Montréal: TAUM.

Beaugrande, R. A. de & Dressler, W. U. (1981): *Introduction to text linguistics.* London: Longman.

Becher, J. J. (1962): *Zur mechanischen Sprachübersetzung: allgemeine Verschlüsselung der Sprache. Ein Programmierungsversuch aus der Jahre 1661.* Stuttgart: Kohlhammer.

Beesley, K. (1982): Letter to the author, 14 January 1982.

Bel'skaya, I. K. (1957): Machine translation of languages. *Research* **10**(10), 383–389.

Bel'skaya, I. K. (1960): Machine translation methods and their application to an Anglo-Russian scheme. In: Unesco (1960), 199–217.

Billmeier, R. (1982): Zu den linguistischen Grundlagen von SYSTRAN. *Multilingua* **1**(2), 83–96.

Blois, J. *et al.* (1968): *Problèmes de la traduction automatique.* Alabama: Univ. P.

Bloomfield, L. (1933): *Language*. London: Allen & Unwin.

Boden, M. (1977): *Artificial intelligence and natural man*. Hassocks (Sussex, UK): Harvester P.

Boitet, C. (1976): Méthodes sémantiques en traduction automatique. *T.A. Informations* 1976, no. 1, 3–42.

Boitet, C. (1978): Where does GETA stand at the beginning of 1977? In: CEC (1977), 88–120.

Boitet, C. (1982): Traduction automatisée au GETA: principes, applications, evaluations et exemples. Grenoble: GETA.

Boitet, C. (1983): Le logiciel ARIANE 78.5 du G.E.T.A.: principes généraux, applications actuelles et études. Communication présentée au 5ème congrès national sur l'information et la documentation, Grenoble, juin 1983. Grenoble: GETA.

Boitet, C. & Nedobejkine, N. (1981): Recent developments in Russian–French machine translation at Grenoble. *Linguistics* **19**(3/4), 199–271.

Boitet, C. & Nedobejkine, N. (1983): L'informatique au service de la linguistique: illustration sur le développement d'un atelier de traduction automatisée. Communication présentée au Colloque de Metz, juin 1983. Grenoble: GETA.

Boitet, C., Guillaume, P. & Quezel-Ambrunaz, M. (1985): A case study in software evolution: from ARIANE-78.4 to ARIANE-85. In: Nirenburg (1985), 27–58.

Boitet, C. & Gerber, R. (1984): Expert systems and other new techniques in MT systems. Paper presented at Coling-84, Stanford Univ., July 1984. Grenoble: GETA.

Booth, A. D. (1948): Proposals for the establishment of a centre for the construction and use of an electronic computer; February 12, 1948. (Rockefeller Foundation Archives).

Booth, A. D. (1953): Mechanical translation.*Computers and Automation* **2**(4), 6–8.

Booth, A. D. & Booth, K. H. V. (1953): *Automatic digital calculators*. London: Butterworth.

Booth, A. D. (1955): Storage devices. In: Locke & Booth (1955), 119–123.

Booth, A. D. (1955a): Use of a computing machine as a mechanical dictionary. *Nature* **176**(4481), 565.

Booth, A. D. & Locke, W. N. (1955): Historical introduction. In: Locke & Booth (1955), 1–14

Booth, A. D. (1956): Present objectives of MT research in the United Kingdom. *Babel* **2**(3), 108–110.

Booth, A. D. (1956a): Influence of context on translation. In: Cherry, C. ed. *Information theory: papers read at a symposium . . . Royal Institution . . . 1955* (London: Butterworth), 181–183.

Booth, A. D. (1958): Translating machines. *International Social Science Bulletin* 10, 55–62.

Booth, A. D., Brandwood, L. & Cleave, J. P. (1958): *Mechanical resolution of linguistic problems*. London: Butterworth.

Booth, A. D. (1963): "Invisible lunatic". *Nature* **200**(4905), 392–393.

Booth, A. D. (1965): Mechanical resolution of linguistic problems. In: Kent, A. & Taulbee, O. E. eds. *Electronic information handling* (Washington, D.C.: Spartan Books), 41–50.

Booth, A. D. (1967) ed.: *Machine translation*. Amsterdam: North-Holland.

Booth, A. D. (1980): Computers in the University of London, 1945–1962. In: Metropolis, N., Howlett, J., and Rota, G-C., eds. *A history of computing in the twentieth century: a collection of essays* (New York: Academic Press), 551–561.

Booth, A. D. (1985): Letter, and cassette tape, to the author, 16 May 1985.

Booth, K. H. V. (1958): *Programming for an automatic digital calculator*. London: Butterworth.

Booth, K. H. V. (1967): Machine aided translation with a post-editor. In: Booth (1967), 51–76.

Booth, K. (1970): Statistical parsing by computer. *Pensiero e Linguaggio* **1**, 107–110.

Booth, K., Brown, C. A. & Stock, C. (1971): English-French translation on a computer. *Pensiero e Linguaggio* **2**, 231–238.

Bostad, D. A. (1982): Quality control procedures in modification of the Air Force Russian–English MT system. In: Lawson (1982), 129–133.

Bourbeau, L. (1981): Linguistic documentation of the computerized translation chain of the TAUM-AVIATION system. Montréal: TAUM.

Bourbeau, L. (1983): La traduction automatique à l'Université de Montréal de 1965 à 1981: bibliographie. Ottawa: Bureau des Traductions.

Bowers, D. M. & Fisk, M. B. (1965): The World's Fair machine translator. *Computer Design*, April 1965, 16–29.

Brandwood, L. (1956): Mechanical translation of French. *Mechanical Translation* **3**(2), 52–61.

Brandwood, L. (1958): Some problems in the mechanical translation of German. *Mechanical Translation* **5**(2), 60–66.

Bresnan, J. (1982) ed.: *The mental representation of grammatical relations*. Cambridge, Mass.: MIT Press.

Brockhaus, K. (1971) *Automatische Übersetzung: Untersuchungen am Beispiel der Sprachen Englisch und Deutsch*. Braunschweig: Vieweg.

Brown, A. F. R. (1958): Language translation. *Journal of the Association for Computing Machinery* **5**(1), 1–8.

Brown, A. F. R. (1966): Automatic translation of languages. In: NATO (1966), 27–54.

Brown, G. P. (1974): Some problems in German to English machine translation. Interim scientific report (MAC-TR-142). Cambridge, Mass.: MIT Dept. Electrical Engineering. (AD/A-003-002).

Bruderer, H. E. (1978): *Handbuch der maschinellen und maschinenunterstützten Sprachübersetzung*. München: Verlag Dokumentation.

Bruderer, H. E. (1982) ed.: *Automatische Sprachübersetzung*. Darmstadt: Wissenschaftliche Buchgesellschaft.

Byrne, C. E., Scott, B. E. & Binh, T. N. 1970: Demonstration of Logos I system for English–Vietnamese machine translation. Final technical report, Aug 1970 (RADC-TR-70-170). Griffiss AFB: RADC. (AD874612).

Carbonell, J. G., Cullingford, R. E. & Gershman, A. V. (1981): Steps toward knowledge-based machine translation. *IEEE Transactions on Pattern Analysis and Machine Intelligence* **3**(4), 376–392.

Carbonell, J. G. & Tomita, M. (1985): New approaches to machine translation. In: Nirenburg (1985), 59–74.

Carroll, J. B. (1966): An experiment in evaluating the quality of translations. *Mechanical Translation* **9**(3/4), 55–66.

CEC (1976): Plan of action for the improvement of the transfer of information between European languages (COM(76)705 final). Brussels: Commission of the European Communities. 23 December 1976.

CEC (1977): *Overcoming the language barrier.* Third European Congress on Information Systems and Networks, Luxembourg, May 1977. 2 vols. München: Verlag Dokumentation.

Ceccato, S. & Maretti, E. (1956): Suggestions for mechanical translation. In: Cherry, C. ed. *Information theory: papers read at a symposium . . . Royal Institution . . . 1955* (London, Butterworth), 171–180.

Ceccato, S. (1961): *Linguistic analysis and programming for mechanical translation.* Technical report RADC-TR-60-18. Milan: Feltrinelli.

Ceccato, S. & Zonta, B. (1962): Human translation and translation by machine I. In: NPL (1962), 222–246.

Ceccato, S. (1966): Automatic translation of languages. In: NATO (1966), 55–108.

Ceccato, S. (1967): Correlational analysis and mechanical translation. In: Booth (1967), 77–135.

Chai, D. T. (1967): Chinese–English machine translation. *Law and Computer Technology* **1**(8), 10–16.

Chaloupka, B. (1976): Excerpt from Mr. Bedrich Chaloupka's presentation on Xonics MT system. In: FBIS (1976), 37–38.

Chandioux, J. (1976): METEO: un système opérationnel pour la traduction automatique des bulletins météorologiques destinés au grand public. *Meta* **21**, 127–133.

Chandioux, J. (1976a): Leibniz — a multilingual system. In: FBIS (1976), 25.

Chandioux, J. (1977): Histoire de la traduction automatique au Canada. *Meta* **22**, 54–56.

Chandioux, J. & Guérard, M.F. (1981): Météo: un système à l'épreuve du temps. *Meta* **26**(1), 17–22.

Charney, E. K. (1962): On the semantic interpretation of linguistic entities that function structurally. In: NPL (1962), 544–556.

Chauché, J. (1975) Les systemes A.T.E.F. et C.E.T.A. *T.A. Informations* 1975, no. 2, 27–38.

Chaumier, J. *et al.* (1977): Evaluation of the SYSTRAN automatic translation system. Report no. 5: Synthesis of the economic and qualitative evaluations. Study carried out (for the) Commission of the European Communities. Paris: Bureau Marcel van Dijk.

Chevalier, M., Dansereau, J. & Poulin, G. (1978): TAUM-METEO: description du système, janvier 1978. Montréal: TAUM.
Chomsky, N. (1957): *Syntactic structures.* The Hague: Mouton.
Chomsky, N. (1965): *Aspects of the theory of syntax.* Cambridge, Mass.: MIT Press.
Chomsky, N. (1975): *The logical structure of linguistic theory.* Chicago: Univ.Chicago P.
Cleave, J. P. & Zacharov, B. (1955): Language translation by electronics. *Wireless World* **61**, 433–435
Cleave, J. P. (1957): A type of program for mechanical translation. *Mechanical Translation* **4**(3), 54–58.
CLRU (1956): Report on research. *Mechanical Translation* **3**(2), 36–37.
CLRU (1959):*Essays on and in machine translation by the Cambridge Language Research Unit.*Cambridge: CLRU.
Colmerauer, A. (1971): Les systèmes-Q ou un formalisme pour analyser et synthétiser des phrases sur ordinateur. In: TAUM (1971), 1–45.
Corbé, M. (1960): La machine à traduire francaise aura bientôt trente ans. *Automatisme* **5**(3), 87–91.
Corbé, M. & Tabory, R. (1962): Introduction to an automatic English syntax (by fragmentation). In: NPL (1962), 617–652.
Couturat, L. & Leau, L. (1903): *Histoire de la langue universelle.* Paris: Hachette.
Crawford, T. D. (1976): Project BABEL: machine translation with English as the target language. In: Jones, A. & Churchhouse, R.F. eds. *The computer in literary and linguistic studies* (Cardiff, Univ. Wales P.), 223–229.
Cresswell, M. J. (1973): *Logics and languages.* London: Methuen.
Cullingford, R. E. & Onyshkevych, B. A. (1985): Lexicon-driven machine translation. In: Nirenburg (1985), 75–115.
Damerau, F. (1976): Automated language processing. *Annual Review of Information Science and Technology* **5**, 107–161.
Danik, A. (1984): The ALPS computer assisted translation system. *British Computer Society, Natural Language Translation Specialist Group Newsletter* **14**, 5–14.
Delavenay, E. (1960): *An introduction to machine translation.* London: Thames and Hudson.
Delavenay, E. (1960a): Bibliographie de la traduction automatique. s-Gravenhage: Mouton.
Des Tombe, L. *et al.* (1985): A preliminary linguistic framework for EUROTRA, June 1985. In: Nirenburg (1985), 283–288.
Dodd, S. C. (1955): Model English. In: Locke & Booth (1955), 165–173.
Domonkos, E. (1962): Report on the algorithm for the mechanical translation from English into Rumanian. Sofia: Academy of the Rumanian People's Republic, Commission for Mathematical Linguistics.
Dostert, L. E. (1955): The Georgetown-IBM experiment. In: Locke & Booth (1955), 124–135.

Dostert, L. E. (1957): Brief history of machine translation research. In: Dostert (1957a), 3–10.

Dostert, L. E. (1957a) ed.: *Report of the Eighth Annual Round Table Meeting on Linguistics and Language Studies: research on machine translation.* Washington, D.C.: Georgetown Univ. P.

Dostert, L. E. (1963): Machine translation and automatic language data processing. In: Howerton, P. W. & Weeks, D. C. eds. *Vistas in information handling, vol.1: The augmentation of man's intellect by machine* (Washington, D.C.: Spartan Books), 92–110.

Ducrot, J. M. (1973): Le système TITUS II. *A.N.R.T. Information et Documentation* **4**, 3–40.

Dupuis, L. (1966): Un système morphologique, compris entre les facilités de la compilation, les recherches syntaxiques et l'adaptation à de futurs programmes de T.A. In: NATO (1966), 109–121.

Edmundson, H. P. & Hays, D. G. (1958): Research methodology for machine translation. *Mechanical Translation* **5**(1), 8–15.

Edmundson, H. P. (1961) ed.: *Proceedings of the National Symposium on Machine Translation, held at the University of California, Los Angeles, February 2–5, 1960.* London: Prentice-Hall.

Eggers, H. *et al.* (1969): *Elektronische Syntaxanalyse der deutschen Gegenwartssprache.* Tübingen: Niemeyer.

Eggers, H. (1981): Das Lemmatisierungssystem SALEM des Sonderforschungsbereichs 90 'Elektronische Sprachforschung' in Saarbrücken. *ALLC Bulletin* **9**(2), 9–15.

Elliston, J.S.G. (1979): Computer aided translation: a business viewpoint. In: Snell (1979), 149–158.

Fähnrich, H. (1970): Zur Gestaltung der maschinellen Uebersetzung aus der georgischen Sprache ins Deutsche. *Zeitschrift für Phonetik, Sprachwissenschaft und Kommunikationsforschung* **23**(5), 475–495.

FBIS (1976): FBIS Seminar on Machine Translation, ed. by D.G.Hays and J.Mathias. *American Journal of Computational Linguistics* microfiche 46. "Summary proceedings of a seminar held at Rosslyn, Virginia, on 8–9 May 1976, organized . . . for the U.S. Government Foreign Broadcast Information Service."

Feigenbaum, E. A. & McCorduck, P. (1984): *The fifth generation: artificial inteligence and Japan's challenge to the world.* London: Joseph.

Fillmore, C. J. (1968): The case for case. In: Bach, E. & Harms, R. T. eds. *Universals in linguistic theory* (New York: Holt, Rinehart and Winston), 1–88.

Fodor, J. A. & Katz, J. J. (1964) eds.: *The structure of language.* Englewood Cliffs, N.J.: Prentice-Hall.

Foust, W. D. & Walker, J. R. (1962): A preliminary structural transfer system. In: NPL (1962), 196–206.

Freigang, K. H. (1981): Erfahrungen bei der Anpassung eines Mü-Systems an eine neue Sprache bzw. einen neuen Texttyp. *Sprache und Datenverarbeitung* **5**(1/2), 29–32.

Fries, C. C. (1952): *The structure of English.* New York: Harcourt Brace.

Garvin, P. L. (1957): Linguistic analysis and translation analysis. In: Dostert (1957a), 19–38.

Garvin, P. L. (1961): Syntactic retrieval. In: Edmundson (1961), 288–292.

Garvin, P. L. (1962): Automatic linguistic analysis — a heuristic problem. In: NPL (1962), 656–669.

Garvin, P. L. (1963): Syntax in machine translation. In: Garvin, P. L. ed. *Natural language and the computer* (New York: McGraw-Hill), 223–232.

Garvin, P. L. (1967): Machine translation — fact or fancy? *Datamation* **13**(4), 29–31.

Garvin (1967a): The Georgetown-IBM experiment of 1954: an evaluation in retrospect. In: *Papers in Linguistics in Honor of Leon Dostert* (The Hague: Mouton), 46–56. Repr.in: Garvin (1972), 51–64.

Garvin, P. L. (1967b): The fulcrum syntactic analyzer for Russian. In: Grenoble (1967) 10pp.

Garvin, P. L. (1968): Machine translation today: the fulcrum approach and heuristics *Lingua* **21**, 162–182. Repr. in: Garvin (1972), 90–113.

Garvin, P. L. (1972): *On machine translation: selected papers*. The Hague: Mouton.

Garvin, P. L. (1980): The fulcrum approach — twelve years later. *International Forum on Information and Documentation* **5**(2), 27–29.

Gazdar, G., Klein, E., Pullum, G., & Sag, I. (1985) *Generalized phrase structure grammar*. Oxford: Blackwell.

Gerber, R. & Boitet, C. (1985): On the design of expert systems grafted on MT systems. In: Nirenburg (1985), 116–134.

Gervais, A. (1980): Evaluation du système pilote de traduction automatique TAUM-AVIATION. Ottawa: Bureau des Traductions.

Gesellschaft für Mathematik und Datenverarbeitung GmbH. (1977): Prüftexte zur Erprobung des maschinellen Uebersetzungssystems SYSTRAN (Russisch–Englisch) GRAMMATIK. Bonn: GMD.

Giuliano, V.E. & Oettinger, A.G. (1960): Research on automatic translation at the Harvard Computation Laboratory. In: Unesco (1960), 163–183.

Giuliano, V.E. (1961): A formula finder for the automatic synthesis of translation algorithms. *Mechanical Translation* **6**, 11–24.

Glasersfeld, E. von, Perschke, S. & Samet, E. (1962): Human translation and translation by machine II. In: NPL (1962), 508–528.

Glasersfeld, E. von & Pisani, P. P. (1970): The multistore parser for hierarchical syntactic structures. *Communications of the ACM* **13**(2), 74–82.

Gode, A. (1955): The signal system in Interlingua — a factor in mechanical translation. *Mechanical Translation* **2**(3), 55–60.

Goshawke, W. (1977): SLUNT (Spoken Languages Universal Numeric Translation). In: CEC (1977), 661–675.

Grishman, R. (1976): A survey of syntactic analysis procedures for natural language. *American Journal of Computational Linguistics* microfiche 47.

Grenoble (1967): *2ième Conference Internationale sur la Traitement Automatique des Langues, Grenoble 23–25 août 1967.* Grenoble: CETA.

Gross, M. (1966): On the equivalence of models of language used in the fields of mechanical translation and information retrieval. In: NATO (1966), 123–137.

Gross, M. & Lentin, A. (1967): *Introduction to formal grammars.* New York: Springer.

Habermann, F. W. A. (1984): Application of SYSTRAN for translation of nuclear technology texts at the Nuclear Centre of Karlsruhe. Paper presented at International Seminar on Machine translation, February 1984, Cranfield, England.

Hajičova, E. & Kirschner, Z. (1981): Automatic translation from English to Czech. *Prague Bulletin of Mathematical Linguistics* **35**, 55–65.

Hajičova, E. & Sgall, P. (1981): Towards automatic understanding of technical texts *Prague Bulletin of Mathematical Lingistics* **36**, 5–23.

Halliday, M. A. K. (1956): The linguistic basis of a mechanical thesaurus. *Mechanical Translation* **3**(3), 81–88.

Halliday, M. A. K. (1973): *Explorations in the functions of language.* London: Arnold.

Halliday, M. A. K. & Hasan, R. (1976): *Cohesion in English.* London: Longman.

Halliday, M. A. K. (1985): *An introduction to functional grammar.* London: Arnold.

Harper, K. E. (1956): Contextual analysis in word-for-word MT. *Mechanical Translation* **3**(2), 40–41.

Harper, K. E. & Hays, D. G. (1960): The use of machines in the construction of a grammar and computer program for structural analysis. In: Unesco (1960), 188–193.

Harper, K. (1961): Soviet research in machine translation. In: Edmundson (1961), 2–12.

Harper, K. E. (1963): Machine translation. In: *Current trends in linguistics. vol.1: Soviet and East European linguistics* (The Hague: Mouton), 133–142.

Harris, Z. S. (1957): Cooccurrence and transformation in linguistic structure *Language* **33**, 283–340. Repr. in: Fodor & Katz (1964), 155-210; and in: Householder (1972), 151–185.

Hauenschild, C., Huckert, E. & Maier, R. (1979): SALAT: machine translation via semantic representation. In: Bäuerle, R. *et al.,* eds. *Semantics from different points of view* (Berlin: Springer), 324–352.

Hawes, R. E. (1985): Logos: the intelligent translation system. In: Lawson (1985), 131–139.

Hays, D. G. (1960): Dependency theory: a formalism and some observations *Language* **40**, 511–525.

Hays, D. G. (1961): Linguistic research at the RAND Corporation. In: Edmundson (1961), 13–25.

Hays, D. G. (1963): Research procedures in machine translation. In:

Garvin, P. L. ed. *Natural language and the computer* (New York: McGraw-Hill), 183–214.

Hays, D. G. (1964): Dependency theory: a formalism and some observations. *Language* **40**, 511–525. Repr. in: Householder (1972), 223–240.

Hays, D. G. (1967): Computational linguistics: research in progress at the RAND Corporation. *T.A. Informations* 1967, pt.1, 15–20.

Henisz-Dostert, B. (1979): Users' evaluation of machine translation. In: Henisz-Dostert *et al.* (1979), 147–244.

Henisz-Dostert, B., Macdonald, R. R. & Zarechnak, M. (1979): *Machine translation.* The Hague: Mouton.

Hockett, C. F. (1967): *Language, mathematics and linguistics.* The Hague: Mouton.

Hockett, C. F. (1968): *The state of the art.* The Hague: Mouton.

Hodges, A. (1983): *Alan Turing: the enigma of intelligence.* London: Burnett Books.

Hofmann, T. R. (1971): REF-Bug. In TAUM (1971a).

Holmstrom, J. E. (1951): Report on interlingual scientific and technical dictionaries. Paris: Unesco, 1951. (Unesco Publication 884.)

Hoppe, A. (1966): Eine Formelgrammatik als Brücke der maschinellen Sprachübersetzung. *Beiträge zur Linguistik und Informationsverarbeitung* **8**, 19–29.

Hoppe, A. (1967): L'explication automatique du facteur semantiquc 'appartenance' apparaissant dans le "Zuwendsatz" allemand et la traduction automatique de ce facteur: de l'allemand vers l'anglais et de l'anglais vers l'allemand. In: Grenoble (1967) 27pp.

Hoppe, A. (1984): Communicative grammar and machine-assisted text contents analysis. *International Classification* **11**(1), 9–12.

Horecky, J. (1982) ed.: *COLING 82: proceedings of the Ninth International Conference on Computational Linguistics, Prague, July 5–10, 1982.* Amsterdam: North-Holland.

Hornby, A. S. (1963): *Advanced learner's dictionary of current English.* Oxford: Oxford Univ. P.

Householder, F. W. (1972) ed.: *Syntactic theory 1: structuralist.* Harmondsworth: Penguin.

Huang, X. (1984): The generation of Chinese sentences from semantic representations of English sentences. Paper presented at International Seminar on Machine Translation, February 1984, Cranfield, England.

Huang, X. (1985): Machine translation in the SDCG formalism. In: Nirenburg (1985), 135–144.

Hundt, M. G. (1982): Working with the Weidner machine-aided translation system. In: Lawson (1982), 45–51.

Hutchins, W. J. (1978): Machine translation and machine-aided translation. *Journal of Documentation* **34**(2), 119–159.

Hutchins, W. J. (1979): Linguistic models in machine translation. *UEA Papers in Linguistics* **9**, 29–52.

Hutchins, W. J. (1982): The evolution of machine translation systems. In: Lawson (1982), 21–37.

Iida, H., Ogura, K. & Nomura, H. (1984): A case analysis method cooperating with ATNG and its application to machine translation. *Proceedings of COLING 84* (Stanford Univ.), 154–158.

Iordanskaya, I. K. (1973): Tentative lexicographic definitions for a group of Russian words denoting emotions. In: Kiefer, F. ed. *Trends in Soviet theoretical linguistics* (Dordrecht: Reidel), 389–410.

Isabelle, P. *et al.* (1978): TAUM-AVIATION: description d'un système de traduction automatisée des manuels d'entretien en aéronautique. Presented at COLING 78. Montreal: TAUM.

Isabelle, P. (1984): Machine translation at the TAUM group. Paper presented at the Tutorial on Machine Translation, Lugano, April 1984.

Isabelle, P. & Bourbeau, L. (1984): TAUM-AVIATION: its technical features and some experimental results. To appear in: *Computational Linguistics.*

Ishihara, K. *et al.* (1985): Hitachi's research and development in knowledge engineering. Paper to be presented at AICA, Oct 1986.

Janda, J. W., Rothkegel, A. & Zimmermann, H. (1970): Dokumentation eines Programms zur Analyse russischer Sätze. *Beiträge zur Linguistik und Informationsverarbeitung* **19**, 7–39, and **20**, 7–31.

Janiotis, A. & Josselson, H. H. (1962): Multiple meaning in machine translation. In: NPL (1962), 406–414.

Jelinek, J. & Hawgood, J. (1984): Automatic integrated dictionary systems. Paper presented at International Seminar on Machine Translation, February 1984, Cranfield, England.

Jespersen, O. (1937): *Analytic syntax.* Copenhagen: Munksgaard.

Johnson, R. (1983): Parsing with transition networks. In: King (1983), 59–72.

Johnson, R. & Whitelock, P. (1985): Machine translation as an expert task. In: Nirenburg (1985), 145–153.

Jordan, S. R., Brown, A. F. R. & Hutton, F. C. (1977): Computerized Russian translation at ORNL. *Journal of the American Society for Information Science* **28**, 26–33.

Josselson, H. H. (1961): Research in machine translation. In: Edmundson (1961), 160–172.

Josselson, H. H. (1971): Automatic translation of languages since 1960: a linguist's view. *Advances in Computers* **11**, 1–58. Repr. in: Bruderer (1982), 122–191.

Josselson, H. H. (1972): Fourteen year summary of the work of the Wayne State University machine translation project. In: Fourteenth annual report on Research in computer-aided translation Russian–English, Wayne State University, April 1972 (Detroit: Wayne State Univ.), 124–140.

Kaplan, A. (1955): An experimental study of ambiguity and context. *Mechanical Translation* **2**(2), 39–46.

Kaplan, R. M. (1973): A general syntactic processor. In: Rustin (1973), 193–241.

Kay, M. (1973): Automatic translation of natural languages. *Daedalus* **102**, 217–230. Repr. in: Bruderer (1982), 209–225.

Kay, M. (1973a): The MIND system. In: Rustin (1973), 155–188.

Kent, A. (1960–61), ed.: *Information retrieval and machine translation*. 2 vols. New York: Interscience.

Kent, A. (1960a): Machine literature searching and translation: an analytical review. In: Kent (1960–61), 13–236.

Kertesz, F. (1974): How to cope with the foreign-language problem: experience gained at a multidisciplinary laboratory. *Journal of the American Society for Information Science* **25**, 86–104.

Kiefer, F. (1964): Mathematical linguistics and machine translation in the Computing Centre of the Hungarian Academy of Sciences. *Computational Linguistics* **2**, 203–211.

King, G. W., Brown, G. W. & Ridenour, L. N. (1953): Photographic techniques for information storage. *Proceedings of the I.R.E.* **41**, 1421–1428.

King, G. W. (1956): Stochastic methods of mechanical translation. *Mechanical translation* **3**(2), 38–39.

King, G. W. (1958): A thesaurus-lattice approach to the structure of language and communication with words. Report on the work of the Cambridge Language Research Unit for the National Science Foundation, July 1958.

King, G. W. (1959): Final report on computer set AN/GSQ-16(XW-1). Vol.1: The photoscopic memory system. (RADC-TR-59-110). Yorktown Heights, N.Y.: IBM Research Center.

King, G. W. (1961): Functions required of a translation system. In: Edmundson (1961), 53–61.

King, G. W. & Chang, H. W. (1963): Machine translation of Chinese. *Scientific American* **208**, 124–135.

King, G. W. (1963): Letter (replying to A. G. Oettinger). *Scientific American* **209**, 8–9.

King, M. (1981): EUROTRA — a European system for machine translation. *Lebende Sprachen* **26**, 12–14.

King, M. (1982): EUROTRA: an attempt to achieve multilingual MT. In: Lawson (1982), 139–147.

King, M. & Perschke, S. (1982): EUROTRA and its objectives. *Multilingua* **1**(1), 27–32.

King, M. (1983) ed.: *Parsing natural language*. London: Academic Press.

King, M. (1983a): Transformational parsing. In: King (1983), 19–34.

Kingscott, G. (1984): ALPS moves to improve European sales for computer-aided translation. *Language Monthly* **14**, 27–29.

Kirschner, Z. (1984): On a dependency analysis of English for automatic translation. In: Sgall, P. ed. *Contributions to functional syntax, semantics, and language comprehension* (Amsterdam: Benjamins), 335–358.

Kiselev, A. N. (1984): The utilisation of the structural type-based routines as a homograph resolution method in the AMPAR system. *International Forum on Information and Documentation* **9**(2), 31–35.

Kittredge, R. I. (1972): The Montreal MT prototype. *Cahiers Linguistiques d'Ottawa* **2**, 69–81.

Kittredge, R. I. (1981): The development of automated translation systems in Canada. *Lebende Sprachen* **26**(3), 100–103.

Kittredge, R. & Lehrberger, J. (1982) eds.: *Sublanguage: studies of language in restricted semantic domains*. Berlin: de Gruyter.

Klein, W. (1971): Eine kommentierte Bibliographie zur Computerlinguistik. *Linguistische Berichte* **11**, 101–134.

Klima, E. S. (1964): Negation in English. In: Fodor & Katz (1964), 246–323.

Knowles, F. E. (1979): Error analysis of Systran output. In: Snell (1979), 109–133.

Konečna, D., Novák, P. & Sgall, P. (1966): Machine translation in Prague. *Prague Studies in Mathematical Linguistics* **1**, 185–193.

Kotov, R. G., Marchuk, Yu. N., & Nelyubin, L. L. (1983): Mashinnyi perevod v nachale 80-kh godov. *Voprosy Yazykoznaniya* **32**(1), 31–38.

Koutsoudas, A. & Korfhage, R. (1956): Mechanical translation and the problem of multiple meaning. *Mechanical Translation* **3**(2), 46–51.

Koutsoudas, A. & Machol, R. (1956): Mechanical translation work at the University of Michigan. *Mechanical Translation* **3**(2), 34 & 41.

Koutsoudas, A. & Humecky, A. (1957): Ambiguity of syntactic function resolved by linear context. *Word* **13**(3), 403–414.

Koutsoudas, A. (1961): Machine translation at the University of Michigan. In: Kent (1961), 765–770.

Kowalski, R. (1985): The origins of logic programming. *Byte* **10(8),** 192–193.

Krauwer, S. & Des Tombe, L. (1984): Reflections on transfer in machine translation. *Contrastes* A4 (Jan 1984), 69–80.

Kravets, L. G., Vasilevskaya, A. L. & Dubitskaya, A. M. (1967): Eksperimental'naya sistema avtomaticheskogo perevoda publikatsii iz amerikanskogo patentnogo ezhenedel'nika "Official Gazette". *Nauchno-Tekhnicheskaya Informatsiya*, Ser. 2, **1**, 35–40.

Kulagina, O. S., Martynova, A. I. & Nikolaeva, T. M. (1961): Mechanical translation at the Academy of Sciences of the USSR. In: Kent (1961), 867–879.

Kulagina, O. S. & Mel'chuk, I. A. (1967): Automatic translation: some theoretical aspects and the design of a translation system. In: Booth (1967), 137–171.

Kulagina, O. S., Mel'chuk, I. A. & Erastov, K. O. (1971): Ob odnoi vozmozhnoi sisteme mashinnogo perevoda. (Predvaritel'ye Publikatsii, vyp.21) Moskva: Institut Russkogo Yazyka SSSR.

Kulagina, O. S. (1976): History and present state of machine translation. *Cybernetics* **6**, 937–944.

Kuno, S. (1962): A preliminary approach to Japanese-English automatic translation. In: NPL (1962), 8–23.

Kuno, S. & Oettinger, A. G. (1963a): Multiple-path syntactic analyzer. In: *Information Processing 1962: proceedings of IFIP Congress 62* (Amsterdam: North-Holland), 306–311.

Kuno, S. & Oettinger, A. G. (1963b): Syntactic structure and ambiguity of English. In: *Proceedings AFIPS 1963 Fall Joint Computer Conference* (New York: Spartan Books), 24, 397–418.

Kuno, S. (1965): The predictive analyzer and a path elimination technique. *Communications of the ACM* **8**(7), 453–462.

Kuno, S. (1966): The augmented predictive analyzer for context-free languages — its relative efficiency. *Communications of the ACM* **9**(11), 810–823.

Kunze, J. (1966): Theoretische Probleme der automatischen Uebersetzung. *Zeitschrift für Mathematische Logik und Grundlagen der Mathematik* **12**(1/2), 85-130.

Kunze, J. (1975): *Abhängigkeitsgrammatik.* (Studia grammatica 12). Berlin: Akademie-Verlag.

Lamb, S. M. (1961): MT research at the University of California, Berkeley. In: Edmundson (1961), 140–154.

Lamb, S. M. & Jacobsen, W. H. (1961): A high-speed large-capacity dictionary system. *Mechanical Translation* **6**, 76–107.

Lamb, S. M. (1962): On the mechanization of syntactic analysis. In: NPL (1962), 674–684.

Lamb, S. M. (1965): The nature of the machine translation problem. *Journal of Verbal Learning and Verbal Behavior* **4**, 196-210.

Lamb, S. M. (1966): *Outline of stratificational grammar.* Washington, D.C.: Georgetown Univ.P.

Lamb, S. M. (1973): Stratificational linguistics as a basis for machine translation. In: Makkai, A. & Lockwood, D. G. eds. *Readings in stratificational linguistics* (Alabama, Univ. Alabama P.), 34–59.

Landsbergen, J. (1981): Adaptation of Montague grammar to the requirements of parsing. In: Groenendijk, J. A. G. *et al.* eds. *Formal methods in the study of language* (Amsterdam: Mathematical Centre), 399–419.

Landsbergen, J. (1982): Machine translation based on logically isomorphic Montague grammars. In: Horecky (1982), 175–181.

Large, A. (1985): *The artificial language movement.* Oxford: Blackwell.

Laurian, J. M. (1984): Systran et Eurotra: la traduction automatique à la Commission des Communautés Européennes. *Contrastes*, Hors serie A4, 11–42.

Lawson, V. (1982) ed.: *Practical experience of machine translation: proceedings of a conference, London, 5–6 November 1981.* Amsterdam: North-Holland.

Lawson, V. (1983): Machine translation. In: Picken, C. ed. *The translator's handbook* (London: Aslib), 81–88.

Lawson, V. (1984): Users of machine translation system report increased output. *Language Monthly* **11**, 6–10.

Lawson, V. (1985) ed.: *Tools for the trade, Translating and the computer 5: proceedings of a conference . . . 10–11 November 1983.* London: Aslib.

Leavitt, A. W., Dehaven, R. C. & Giese, G. W. (1972): SYSTRAN machine translation evaluation. Final technical report (RADC-72-293). Griffiss AFB: RADC. (AD753676).

Lehmann, W. P. (1965): An experiment in machine translation. *The Graduate Journal* 7(1), 111–131.

Lehmann, W. P., Stachowitz, R. & Tosh, L. W. (1970): Research in German-English machine translation on syntactic level. 2 vols. Austin, Texas: Linguistics Research Center.

Lehmann, W. P. & Stachowitz, R. A. (1971–75): Development of German–English machine translation system. Final (annual) report(s), Feb. 1970–June 1974 (RADC-TR-72-47, RADC-TR-72-74, RADC-TR-73-260, RADC-TR-73-309, RADC-TR-75-2) Austin, Tex.: Linguistics Research Center. (AD740631, AD743319, AD769704, AD774564, AD-A008525)

Lehmann, W. P. & Stachowitz, R. (1971): Feasibility study on fully automatic high quality translation. (RADC-TR-71-295). 2 vols. Griffiss AFB: Rome Air Development Center. (Appendix of papers by seminar participants.)

Lehmann, W. P. & Stachowitz, R. A. (1972): Machine translation in Western Europe: a survey. *Current Trends in Linguistics, vol.9: Linguistics in Western Europe* (The Hague: Mouton), 688–701. Repr. in: Bruderer (1982), 226–242.

Lehmann, W. P. & Stachowitz, R. (1972a): Normalization of natural language for information retrieval. Final technical report (AFOSR-TR-72-0480). Austin, Tex.: Linguistics Research Center. (AD737740).

Lehrberger, J. (1982): Automatic translation and the concept of sublanguage. In: Kittredge & Lehrberger (1982), 81–106.

Leon, M. (1984): Development of English–Spanish machine translation. Paper presented at International Seminar on Machine Translation, February 1984, Cranfield, England.

Levison, M. (1962): The mechanical analysis of language. In: NPL (1962), 562–574.

Lippmann, E.O. (1971): An approach to computer-aided translation. *IEEE Transactions on Engineering Writing and Speech* **14**(1), 10–33.

Ljudskanov, A. (1966): La traduction automatique dans la République Populaire Bulgare. *T.A. Informations* 1966, pt.2, 96–103.

Ljudskanov, A. (1968): Is the generally accepted strategy of machine translation research optimal? *Mechanical Translation* **11**(1/2), 14–21.

Ljudskanov, A. (1972): *Mensch und Maschine als Uebersetzer*. München: Hueber.

Locke, W. N. & Booth, A. D. (1955) eds.: *Machine translation of languages.* Cambridge, Mass.: MIT Press.

Locke, W. N. & Yngve, V. H. (1958): Research in translation by machine at M.I.T. In: *Proceedings of the Eighth International Congress of Linguists* (Oslo: Univ.P.), 510–514.

Locke, W. N. (1975): Machine translation. In: Kent, A. *et al.* eds. *Encyclopedia of Library and Information Science* (New York: Dekker), vol. 16, 414–444.

Lockwood, D. G. (1972): *Introduction to stratificational linguistics*. New York: Harcourt Brace Jovanovich.

Loh, S. C. & Kong, L. (1977): Computer translation of Chinese scientific journals. In: CEC (1977), 631–645.

Loh, S. C. & Kong, L. (1979): An interactive on-line machine translation system (Chinese into English). In: Snell (1979), 135–148.

Loh, S. C., Hung, H-S. & Kong, L. (1979): A dual language translator. In: Ager, D. E. *et al.* eds. *Advances in computer-aided literary and lingustic research* (Birmingham: Aston Univ.), 107–115.

Loh, S. C., Kong, L. & Hung, H-S. (1984): A new dictionary structure for bi-directional MT system. Paper presented at International Seminar on Machine Translation, February 1984, Cranfield, England.

Lonsdale, D. (1984): Notes on interactive translation. Paper presented at International Seminar on Machine Translation, February 1984, Cranfield, England.

Loomis, W. F. (1951): Memorandum to Warren Weaver on Mechanical translation, summarizing results of letters of inquiry sent in November 1950. (Rockefeller Foundation Archives)

Luckhardt, H. D. (1976): Technische Beschreibung des Saarbrücker Uebersetzungssystems SUSY, Teil i: Programmablauf und Dateibeschreibung (Linguistische Arbeiten 21). Saarbrücken: Univ. des Saarlandes.

Luckhardt, H. D. & Maas, H. D. (1976): Transfer und Synthese in der Saarbrücker maschinellen Uebersetzung. (Linguistische Arbeiten 18). Saarbrücken: Univ. des Saarlandes.

Luckhardt, H. D. (1982): SUSY: capabilities and range of application. *Multilingua* **1**(4), 213–219.

Luckhardt, H.D, Maas, H.D. & Thiel, M. (1984): The SUSY-E machine translation system. Saarbrücken: Univ.des Saarlandes. To appear in *Computational Linguistics*.

Lukjanow, A. (1961): Report on some principles of the unified transfer system. In: Edmundson (1961), 88–120.

Lytinen, S. L. & Schank, R. (1982): Representation and translation. *Text* **2**(1/3), 83–111.

Lytinen, S. L. (1985): Integrating syntax and semantics. In: Nirenburg (1985), 167–178.

Lytle, E. G. (1974): *A grammar of subordinate structures in English*. The Hague: Mouton.

Lytle, E. G. *et al.* (1975): Junction grammar as a base for natural language processing. *American Journal of Computational Linguistics* microfiche 26.

Lytle, E. G. (1980): Junction grammar: theory and application. In: *The Sixth LACUS Forum* (Columbia, S.Carolina: Hornbeam P.), 305–343.

McCorduck, P. (1979): *Machines who think*. San Francisco: Freeman.

McCulloch, W. S. & Pitts, W. (1943): A logical calculus of the ideas immanent in nervous activity. *Bulletin of Mathematical Biophysics* **5**, 115–133.

McDaniel, J. & Whelan, B. (1962): The grammatical interpretation of Russian inflected forms using a stem dictionary. In: NPL (1962), 364–377.

McDaniel, J. *et al.* (1967): Translation of Russian scientific texts into English by computer. A final report. Teddington: National Physical Laboratory, Autonomics Division.

McDaniel, J. *et al.* (1967a): Machine translation at the National Physical Laboratory, Teddington, Middlesex, England. In: Booth (1967), 229–266.

McDaniel, J. *et al.* (1967b): An evaluation of the usefulness of machine translations produced at the National Physical Laboratory, Teddington, with a summary of the translation methods. In: Grenoble (1967). 18pp.

Macdonald, N. (1954): Language translation by machine — a report of the first successful trial. *Computers and Automation* **3**(2), 6–10.

Macdonald, N. (1960): The photoscopic language translator. *Computers and Automation* **9**(8), 6–8.

Macdonald, R. R. (1963): General report 1952–1963 (Georgetown University Occasional Papers in Machine Translation, no. 30) Washington, D.C.: Georgetown Univ.

McDonald, D. D. (1985): Recovering the speaker's decisions during mechanical translation. In: Nirenburg (1985), 183–199.

Maas, H. D. (1977): The Saarbrücken automatic translation system (SUSY). In: CEC (1977), 585–592.

Maas, H. D. (1977a): Ergebnisse der Satzanalyse und transformationelle Synthese im Saarbrücker Uebersetzungssystem SUSY (Linguistische Arbeiten 24). Saarbrücken: Univ. des Saarlandes.

Maas, H. D. (1978): Das Saarbrücker Uebersetzungssystem SUSY. *Sprache und Datenverarbeitung* **2**(1), 43–61.

Maas, H. D. (1981): SUSY I und SUSY II: verschiedene Analysestrategien in der Maschinellen Uebersetzung. *Sprache und Datenverarbeitung* **5**(1/2), 9–15.

Macklovitch, E. (1984): Recent Canadian experience in machine translation. Paper presented at International Seminar on Machine Translation, February 1984, Cranfield, England.

Magnusson-Murray, U. (1985): Operational experience of a machine translation service. In: Lawson (1985), 171–180.

Maier, R. (1978): Zur Struktur des Uebersetzungssystems SALAT. In: Conte, M. E. *et al.* eds. *Wortstellung und Bedeutung: Akten des 12. Linguistischen Kolloquiums Pavia 1977* (Tübingen: Niemeyer), vol. 1, 249–268.

Marchuk, Y. N., Tikhomirov, B. D. & Shcherbin, V. I. (1975): Ein System zur maschinellen Uebersetzung aus dem Englischen ins Russische. German transl. (of Sistema mashinnogo perevoda s angliiskogo yazyka na russkii) in: Bruderer (1982), 319–336.

Marchuk, Y. N. (1977): Machine translation in the All-Union Translation Centre. In: CEC (1977), 623–624.

Marchuk, Y. N. (1979): The contextological dictionary: use in programmed language teaching. *Computers and the Humanities* **13**, 277–281.

Marchuk, Y. N. (1984): Machine translation in the USSR. *International Forum on Information and Documentation* **9**(2), 3–8.

Marchuk, Y. N. (1984a): Machine translation in the USSR. Paper intended for International Seminar on machine Translation, February 1984, Cranfield.

Marshall, J. (1947): Letter to Professor Ivor A. Richards, September 3, 1947. (Rockefeller Foundation Archives).

Martem'yanov, Y. S. (1977): Eliminating formal constraints of language. In: CEC (1977), 625–627.

Masterman, M. (1956): The potentialities of a mechanical thesaurus. (ML 1). Cambridge: CLRU.

Masterman, M. (1957): The thesaurus in syntax and semantics. *Mechanical Translation* **4**(1/2), 35–43.

Masterman, M., Needham, R. M. & Sparck Jones, K. (1959): The analogy between mechanical translation and library retrieval. In: *Proceedings of the International Conference on Scientific Information, Washington, D.C., November 16–21, 1958* (Washington, D.C.: National Academy of Sciences), 917–935.

Masterman, M. & Kay, M. (1960): Mechanical pidgin translation. (ML133). Cambridge: CLRU.

Masterman, M. (1961): Translation. *Proceedings of the Aristotelian Society*, 1961, 169–216.

Masterman, M. (1962): Semantic message detection for machine translation, using an interlingua. In: NPL (1962), 438–474.

Masterman, M. (1967): Mechanical pidgin translation. In: Booth (1967), 195–227.

Masterman, M. (1967a): Machine-aided computer translation from English into French using an on-line system to manipulate a bi-lingual conceptual dictionary or thesaurus. In: Grenoble (1967).22pp.

Masterman, M. (1970): Cambridge Language Research Unit (CLRU). In: Kent, A. & Lancour, H. eds. *Encyclopedia of library and information science* (New York: Dekker), vol. 4, 33–50.

Masterman, M. (1979): The essential skills to be acquired for machine translation. In: Snell (1979), 159–180.

Masterman, M. (1980): Final report of study contract TR-29 on the automatic annotation of the Systran system. Luxembourg: CEC.

Masterman, M. (1982): The limits of innovation in machine translation. In: Lawson (1982), 163–186.

Matthews, G. H. & Rogovin, S. (1958): German sentence recognition. *Mechanical Translation* **5**(3), 114–120.

Matthews, G. H. (1962): Analysis by synthesis of sentences of natural languages. In: NPL (1962), 532–540.

Meile, P. (1962): On problems of address in an automatic dictionary of French. In: NPL (1962), 379–399.

Melby, A. K. (1980a): A comparative look at junction grammar. In: *The Sixth LACUS Forum* (Columbia, S. Carolina: Hornbeam P.), 344–352.

Melby, A. K. (1980b): Design and implementation of a computer-assisted translation system. *British Computer Society, Natural Language Translation Specialist Group Newsletter* **9**, 7–19.

Melby, A. K. (1982): Multi-level translation aids in a distributed system. In: Horecky (1982), 215–220.

Melby, A. K. (1983): Computer-assisted translation systems: the standard design and a multi-level design. Paper presented at Conference on Applied Natural Language Processing, February 1983, Santa Monica, California.

Melby, A. K. (1984): Machine translation with post editing versus a three-level integrated translator aid system. Paper presented at International Seminar on Machine Translation, February 1984, Cranfield, England.

Mel'chuk, I. A. (1963): Machine translation and linguistics. In: Akhmanova, O. S. *et al. Exact methods in linguistic research* (Berkeley: Univ. California P.), 44–79.

Mel'chuk, I. A. & Ravich, D. (1967): *Avtomaticheskii perevod 1949–1963: kritiko-bibliograficheskii spravochnik*. Moskva: Institut Yazykoznaniya.

Mel'chuk, I. A. & Zholkovskii, A. K. (1970): Towards a functioning 'meaning-text' model of language. *Linguistics* **57**, 10–47.

Mel'chuk, I. A. (1973): Towards a linguistic 'meaning<—>text' model. In: Kiefer, F. ed. *Trends in Soviet theoretical linguistics* (Dordrecht: Reidel), 33–57.

Mel'chuk, I. A. & Ravich, R. D. (1978): *Traduction automatique. 1964–1970. Automatic translation*. Montréal: Univ. de Montréal, Dép. de Linguistique et Philologie. (In Russian).

Mel'chuk, I. A. (1981): Meaning-text models: a recent trend in Soviet linguistics. *Annual Review of Anthropology* **10**, 27–62.

Mersel, J. (1961): Research in machine translation at Ramo-Wooldridge. In: Edmundson (1961), 26–38.

Micklesen, L. W. (1958): Russian–English MT. In: *American contributions to the Fourth International Congress of Slavicists, Moscow, September 1958* ('s-Gravenhage: Mouton), 1–21. Repr. in: University of Washington (1960).

Micklesen, L. W. (1960): Lexicography. In: University of Washington (1960), 71–87.

Micklesen, L. W. (1960a): MT operational analysis. In: University of Washington (1960), 93–184.

Micklesen, L. W. & Wall, R. E. (1961): Logical programming research in the University of Washington machine translation project. In: Kent (1961), 853–866.

Micklesen, L. W. (1962): Source-language specification with table lookup and high-capacity dictionary. In: NPL (1962), 318–340.

Miller, G. A. & Beebe-Center, J. G. (1958): Some psychological methods for evaluating the quality of translations. *Mechanical Translation* **3**, 73–80.

Moisil, G. C. (1960): De la traduction automatique preliminaire. *Limba Romina* **9**(1), 3–10.

Montague, R. M. (1974): *Formal philosophy*, ed. R. H. Thomason. New Haven, Conn.: Yale Univ. P.

Moto-Oka, T. (1983): Overview and introduction to the Fifth Generation. In: *The Fifth Generation Computer Project: state of the art report* (Oxford: Pergamon), 5–16.

Mounin, G. (1962): Ceccato et l'Ecole Opérationnelle Italienne. *Traduction Automatique* **3**(3), 92–95.

Mounin, G. (1964): *La machine à traduire*. The Hague: Mouton.

Moyne, J. A. (1962): Georgetown automatic translation: general information and operation manual. Washington, D.C.: Georgetown Univ. Machine Translation Research.

Mukhin, I. S. (1956): An experiment on the machine translation of languages carried out on the BESM. *Proceedings of the Institute of Electrical Engineers* 103B (suppl.3), 463–471.

Mukhin, I. S. (1963): *On some problems of mechanical translation*. Moscow: Institute of Exact Mechanics and Computing Technique.

Nagao, M. & Tsujii, J-I. (1980): Some topics of language processing for machine translation. *International Forum on Information and Documentation* **5**(2), 32–37.

Nagao, M. & Tsujii, J. (1980a): Untersuchungen über Daten und Hilfsmittel zur Analyse der japanischen Sprache. *Sprache und Datenverarbeitung* **4**(2), 129–138.

Nagao, M. (1982): A survey of natural language processing and machine translation in Japan. In: Kitagawa, T. ed. *Computer science & technologies 1982* (Tokyo: OHM), 64–70.

Nagao, M. *et al.* (1982): An English Japanese machine translation system of the titles of scientific and engineering papers. In: Horecky (1982), 245–252.

Nagao, M. (1984): Outline of the machine translation project of the Japanese government. *International Forum on Information and Documentation* **9**(2), 12–17.

Nagao, M. (1985): Structural transformation in the generation stage of Mu Japanese to English machine translation system. In: Nirenburg (1985), 200–223.

Nagao, M. *et al.* (1985): Machine translation system from Japanese into English: Mu-JE. To appear in: *Computational Linguistics*.

Naito, S., Shimazu, A. & Nomura, H. (1985): Classification of modality function and its application to Japanese language analysis. Paper presented at ACL conference, Chicago, July 1985.

Nakamura, J-I., Tsujii, J-I. & Nagao, M. (1984): Grammar writing system (GRADE) of Mu-machine translation project and its characteristics. Paper presented at Coling 84.

NATO (1966): *Automatic translation of languages: papers presented at NATO Summer School held in Venice, July 1962*. Oxford: Pergamon P.

NBS (1957): Syntax patterns in English studied by electronic computer. *Computers and Automation* **6**(7), 15–17 & 32.

Needham, R. M. & Joyce, T. (1958): The thesaurus approach to information retrieval. *American Documentation* **9**(3), 192–197.

Nikolaeva, T.N. (1958): Soviet developments in machine translation: Russian sentence analysis. *Mechanical Translation* **5**(2), 51–59.

Nirenburg, S. (1985) ed.: *Proceedings of the Conference on Theoretical and methodological issues in machine translation of natural languages, Colgate University . . . August 14–16 1985*. Hamilton, N.Y.: Colgate Univ.

Nirenburg, S. (1985a) ed.: Special section on machine translation of natural languages. *SIGART Newsletter* **92**, 128–144.

Nirenburg, S., Raskin, V. & Tucker, A. (1985): Interlingua design for TRANSLATOR. In: Nirenburg (1985), 224–244.

Nishida, T. & Doshita, S. (1982): An English–Japanese machine translation system based on formal semantics of natural language. In: Horecky (1982), 277–282.

Nishida, F. & Takamatsu, S. (1982): Japanese–English translation through internal expressions. In: Horecky (1982), 271–276.

Nishida, T. (1985): Machine translation: Japanese perspectives. Paper presented at Translating and the Computer, 7th International conference on translating, London, 14–15 November 1985.

Nishimura, H. (1970): The development of a machine translation system. *Researches of the Electrotechnical Laboratory*, no. 705.

Nitta, Y. *et al.* (1982): A heuristic approach to English-into-Japanese machine translation. In: Horecky (1982), 283–288.

Nitta, Y. *et al.* (1984): A proper treatment of syntax and semantics in machine translation. Paper presented at Coling 84.

Nomura, H. (1983): Towards the high ability machine translation. Paper presented at Eurotra Joint Japanese–European Workshop, November 1983, Brussels.

NPL (1962): *1961 International Conference on Machine Translation of Languages and Applied Language Analysis: proceedings of the conference held at the National Physical Laboratory, Teddington, Middlesex, on 5th, 6th, 7th and 8th September*. 2 vols. London: HMSO.

Nündel, S. *et al.* (1969): *Automatische Sprachübersetzung Russisch-Deutsch*. Berlin: Akademie-Vlg.

Oettinger, A. G. (1955): The design of an automatic Russian–English technical dictionary. In: Locke & Booth (1955), 47–65.

Oettinger, A. G. (1958): A survey of Soviet work on automatic translation. *Mechanical Translation* **5**(3), 101–110.

Oettinger, A. G. *et al.* (1959): Linguistic and machine methods for compiling and updating the Harvard automatic dictionary. In: *Proceedings of the International Conference on Scientific Information, Washington,*

D.C., November 16–21, 1958 (Washington, D.C.: National Academy of Sciences), 951–973.

Oettinger, A. G. (1960): *Automatic language translation: lexical and technical aspects, with particular reference to Russian.* Cambridge, Mass.: Harvard Univ. P.

Oettinger, A. G. & Sherry, M. E. (1961): Current research on automatic translation at Harvard University and predictive syntactic analysis. In: Edmundson (1961), 173–182.

Oettinger, A. G. (1963): The state of the art of automatic language translation: an appraisal. *Beiträge zur Sprachkunde und Informationsverarbeitung* **2**, 17–32. Repr. in: Bruderer (1982), 7–19.

Ogden, C. K. (1968): *Basic English international second language.* New York: Harcourt Brace.

Okajima, A. *et al.* (1983): Lexicon structure for machine translation — an example from English-into-Japanese translation ATHENE. Paper presented at ICTP 83.

Orr, D. B. & Small, V. H. (1967): Comprehensibility of machine-aided translations of Russian scientific documents. *Mechanical Translation* **10**(1/2), 1–10.

Oswald, V. A. & Fletcher, S. L. (1951): Proposals for the mechanical resolution of German syntax patterns. *Modern Language Forum* **36**(3/4), 1–24.

Oswald, V. A. & Lawson, R. H. (1953): An idioglossary for mechanical translation. *Modern Language Forum* 38(3/4), 1–11.

Oswald, V. A. (1957): Lexical problems in machine translation: the rationale of the idioglossary technique. In: Dostert (1957a), 63–69.

Oubine, I. I. & Tikhomirov, B. D. (1982): Machine translation systems and computer dictionaries in the information service: ways of their development and operation. In: Horecky (1982), 289–294.

Pacak, M. (1961): Morphology in terms of mechanical translation. In: Kent (1961), 881–885.

Pacak, M. (1966): Computational morphology. *T.A. Informations* 1966, pt. 1, 25–36.

Pacak, M. (1967): Homographs: classification and identification. *Etudes de Linguistique Appliquée* **5**, 89–105.

Panov, D. Y. (1956): On the problem of mechanical translation. *Mechanical Translation* **3**(2), 42–43.

Panov, D. Y. (1960): *Automatic translation.* Translated . . . by R. Kisch. London: Pergamon.

Panov, D. Y. (1960a): Machine translation and the human being. *Impact of Science on Society* **10**, 16–25.

Papp, F. (1964): Mathematical and applied linguistics at the University of Debrecen. *Computational Linguistics* **2**, 213–218.

Papp, F. (1966): *Mathematical linguistics in the Soviet Union.* The Hague: Mouton.

Parker-Rhodes, A. F. (1956): Computer operations required for mechanical translation. *Proceedings of the Institute of Electrical Engineers* 103B (suppl.3), 453–455.

Parker-Rhodes, A. F. (1961): A lattice model of syntactic description. (M.L.147). Cambridge: CLRU.

Parker-Rhodes, A. F. (1962): A new model of syntactic description. In: NPL (1962), 26–80.

Parker-Rhodes, A. F. R. (1966): Syntax. In: NATO (1966), 167–203.

Pendergraft, E. D. (1967): Translating languages. In: Borko, H. ed. *Automated language processing* (New York: Wiley), 291–323.

Perschke, S. (1968): Machine translation — the second phase of development. *Endeavour* **27**, 97–100.

Perschke, S. (1969): The use of machine translation in documentation. In: *1968 Meeting of European librarians working in the nuclear field* (Luxembourg: Centre for Information and Documentation), 75–88.

Perschke, S. (1970): Machine translation: a necessary component of an international information system. In: *Handling of nuclear information: proceedings of the symposium . . . Vienna, 1970* (Vienna: International Atomic Energy Agency), 291–304.

Perschke, S. (1970a): Possibilities of further development of automatic language translation. *Pensiero e Linguaggio in Operazioni* **1**, 83–93.

Perschke, S. *et al.* (1974): Les travaux du CETIS dans le domaine de l'informatique documentaire. *Documentaliste* (numero special), 47–57.

Petrick, S. R. (1971): Syntactic analysis for transformational grammars. In: Lehmann & Stachowitz (1971), 325–342.

Pfafflin, S. M. (1965): Evaluation of machine translation by reading comprehension tests and subjective judgments. *Mechanical Translation* **8**, 2–8.

Pigott, I. M. (1979): Theoretical options and practical limitations of using semantics to solve problems of natural language analysis and machine translation. In: MacCafferty, M. & Gray, K. eds. *The analysis of meaning: Informatics 5, proceedings of a conference . . .* (London: Aslib), 239–268.

Pigott, I. M. (1981): How does Systran translate? *British Computer Society, Natural Language Translation Specialist Group Newsletter* no. 10, 21–42.

Pigott, I. M. (1983): Systran: a key to overcoming language barriers in Europe. *Multingua* **2**(3), 149–156.

Pigott, I. M. (1983a): SYSTRAN machine translation at the EC Commission: present status and history, July 1983. *Terminologie Bulletin* **44**, 23–29.

Pigott, I. M. (1984): The difficulty of developing logical algorithms for the machine translation of natural language. *Terminologie Bulletin* **45**, 7–19.

Piotrovskii, R. G. (1980): Machine translation in the Research Group on Speech Statistics: theory, results and outlook. *International Forum on Information and Documentation* **5**(2), 9–11.

Plath, W. J. (1967): Multiple-path analysis and automatic translation. In: Booth (1967), 267–315.

Prager, W. (1948): Letter to Warren Weaver, March 15, 1948. (Rockefeller Foundation Archives.)

Price, J. D. (1969): Abstract of the development of a theoretical basis for machine aids for translation from Hebrew to English. Ph.D. dissertation, Dropsie College, Philadelphia.

Pyne, J. A. (1957): Some ideas on inter-structural syntax. In: Dostert (1957), 143–149.

Quine, W. V. (1960): *Word and object.* Cambridge, Mass.: MIT Press.

Ramo-Wooldridge (1958): Experimental machine translation of Russian to English. A project progress report, 15 December 1958. Los Angeles, Cal.: Ramo-Wooldridge.

Ramo-Wooldridge (1961): Machine translation studies of semantic techniques. Final report, February 22, 1961. (AF30(602)–2036). Canoga Park, Cal.: Ramo-Wooldridge.

Reid, R.B. (1949): Letter to Warren Weaver, 27 December 1949. (Rockefeller Foundation Archives.)

Reifler, E. (1950): Studies in mechanical translation, no. 1, MT. Mimeo, Jan. 10, 1950. Seattle: Univ. Washington.

Reifler, E. (1954): The first conference on mechanical translation. *Mechanical Translation* **1**(2), 23–32.

Reifler, E. (1955): The mechanical determination of meaning. In: Locke & Booth (1955), 136–164.

Reifler, E. (1955a): Mechanical determination of the constituents of German substantive compounds. *Mechanical Translation* **2**(1), 3–14.

Reifler, E. (1958): The machine translation project at the University of Washington, Seattle, Washington, U.S.A. In: *Proceedings of the Eighth International Congress of Linguists* (Oslo: Univ. P.), 514–518.

Reifler, E. (1960): MT linguistics and MT lexicography. In: University of Washington (1960), 59–65.

Reifler, E. (1961a): Current research at the University of Washington. In: Edmundson (1961), 155–159.

Reifler, E. (1961b): The machine translation project at the University of Washington, Seattle, Washington: outline of the project. *Mechanical Translation* **6**, 25–32.

Reifler, E. (1961c): MT linguistics and MT lexicography at the University of Washington. In: Kent (1961), 841–852.

Reifler, E. (1967): Chinese–English machine translation: its lexicographic and linguistic problems. In: Booth (1967), 317–428.

Reynolds, A. C. (1954): The conference on mechanical translation held at M.I.T., June 17–20, 1952. *Mechanical Translation* **1**(3), 47–55.

Rhodes, I. (1959): A new approach to the mechanical syntactic analysis of Russian. Washington, D.C.: National Bureau of Standards.

Rhodes, I. (1961): A new approach to the mechanical syntactic analysis of Russian. *Mechanical Translation* **6**, 33–50.

Rhodes, I. (1961a): The National Bureau of Standards method of syntactic integration. In: Edmundson (1961), 39–44.

Rhodes, I. & Alt, F. L. (1962): Hindsight technique in machine translation of natural languages. *Journal of Research of the National Bureau of Standards* **66B**(2), 47–51.

Rhodes, I. (1966): Syntactic integration carried out mechanically. In: NATO (1966), 205–209.

Rhodes, I. (1967): The importance of the glossary storage in machine translation. In: Booth (1967), 429–449.

Rich, E. (1983): *Artificial intelligence.* New York: McGraw-Hill.

Richards, I. A. (1943): *Basic English and its uses.* London: Kegan Paul, Trench, Trubner.

Richards, I. A. & Gibson, C. M. (1952–58): *English through pictures.* 2 pts. New York: Cardinal.

Richens, R. H. & Booth, A. D. (1955): Some methods of mechanized translation. In: Locke & Booth (1955), 24–46.

Richens, R. H. (1956a): Preprogramming for mechanical translation. *Mechanical Translation* **3**(1), 20–25.

Richens, R. H. (1956b): A general programme for mechanical translation between any two languages via an algebraic interlingua. (ML5). Cambridge: CLRU.

Richens, R. H. (1956c): The thirteen steps. (ML15). Cambridge: CLRU.

Richens, R. H. (1984): Letter to the author, 13 May 1984.

Roberts, A. H. & Zarechnak, M. (1974): Mechanical translation. *Current Trends in Linguistics, vol.12: Linguistics and Adjacent Arts and Sciences* (The Hague: Mouton), 2825–2870. Repr. in: Bruderer (1982), 262–298.

Rolling, L. (1978): Computer-aided translation today and tomorrow. Paper presented at FID Congress, Edinburgh, September 1978.

Rosner, M. (1983): Production systems. In: King (1983), 35–58.

Rozentsveig, V. Y. (1958): The work on machine translation in the Soviet Union: Fourth International Congress of Slavicists reports, Sept. 1958. *Mechanical Translation* **5**(3), 95–100.

Rozencveig, V. Ju. (1974), ed.: *Machine translation and applied linguistics.* 2 vols. Frankfurt a.M.: Athenaion Vlg.

Ruffino, J. R. (1982): Coping with machine translation. In: Lawson (1982), 57–60.

Rustin, R. (1973) ed.: *Natural language processing. Courant Computer Science Symposium no. 8, 20–21 December 1971.* New York: Algorithmics P.

Sager, N. (1981): *Natural language information processing: a computer grammar of English and its applications.* Reading, Mass.: Addison-Wesley.

Sakai, I. (1962): Syntax in universal translation. In: NPL (1962), 594–608.

Sakai, T., Sugita, S. & Watanabe, A. (1970): Mechanical translation from Japanese into English. *Information Processing in Japan* **10**, 32–39. Repr. in: Bruderer (1982), 109–121.

Sakamoto, Y. (1970): Automatic language processing system in natural language dictionary for machine translation. *Research of the Electrotechnical Laboratory* no. 707.

Sammet, J. E. (1969): *Programming languages: history and fundamentals.* Englewood Cliffs, N.J.: Prentice-Hall.

Satterthwait, A. C. (1965): Sentence-for-sentence translation: an example. *Mechanical Translation* **8**(2), 14–38.

Sawai, S. *et al.* (1982): Knowledge representation and machine translation. In: Horecky (1982), 351–356.

Schank, R. (1973): Identification of conceptualizations underlying natural language. In: Schank & Colby (1973), 187–247.

Schank, R. & Colby, K. M. (1973) eds. *Computer models of thought and language.* San Francisco: Freeman.

Schank, R. (1975), ed.: *Conceptual information processing.* Amsterdam: North-Holland.

Schirmer, B. (1969): Erfahrungen bei der Entwicklung eines maschinellen Uebersetzungssystems (Englisch–Deutsch). *IBM-Nachrichten* **19**, 600–605. Repr. in: Bruderer (1982), 71–90.

Schweisthal, K. G. (1967): Semantically governed machine translation of BE-clauses with adverbs and prepositional phrases. In: Grenoble (1967). 11pp.

Sereda, S. P. (1982): Practical experience of machine translation. In: Lawson (1982), 119–125.

Sgall, P. & Hajičová, E. (1966): Computational linguistics in Czechoslovakia. *Beiträge zur Linguistik und Informationsverarbeitung* **8**, 65–74.

Sgall, P., Hajičová, E. & Benešová, E. (1973): *Topic, focus and generative semantics.* Kronberg: Scriptor Vlg.

Shalyapina, Z. M. (1980): Automatic translation as a model of the human translation activity. *International Forum on Information and Documentation* **5**(2), 18–23.

Shannon, C. & Weaver, W. (1949): *The mathematical theory of communication.* Urbana: Univ. Illinois P.

Sheridan, P. (1955): Research in language translation on the IBM type 701. *IBM Technical Newsletter* **9**, 5–24.

Sherry, M. E. (1962): The identification of nested structures in predictive syntactic analysis. In: NPL (1962), 144–155.

Shillan, D. (1967): Segmenting natural language by articulatory features. In: Grenoble (1967). 11pp.

Shiner, G. (1958): The USAF automatic language translator, Mark I. *IRE National Convention Record* 1958, 296–301.

Shudo, K. (1974): On machine translation from Japanese into English for a technical field. *Information Processing in Japan* **14**, 44–50.

Simmons, R. F. (1973): Semantic networks: their computation and use for understanding English sentences. In: Schank & Colby (1973), 63–113.

Sinaiko, H. W. (1971): Letter: Translating by computer. *Science* **174**, 1182–4.

Sinaiko, H. W. & Klare, G. R. (1972): Further experiments in language translation: readability of computer translations. *ITL (Review of Institute of Applied Linguistics, Louvain)* **15**, 1–29.

Sinaiko, H. W & Klare, G. R. (1973): Further experiments in language translation: a second evaluation of the readability of computer translations. *ITL* **19**, 29–52.

Sipöczy, G. (1964): Some semantic aspects of the machine translation from Russian into Hungarian. *Computational Linguistics* **2,** 159–177.

Slocum, J. (1980): An experiment in machine translation. In: *18th Annual Meeting of the Association for Computational Linguistics and Parasession on Topics in Interactive Discourse, June 1980, Univ. of Pennsylvania* (Menlo Park, Cal.: SRI International), 163–167.

Slocum, J. (1982): A status report on the LRC machine translation system. (Working Paper LRC-82-3; December 1982). Austin, Texas: LRC.

Slocum, J. (1984): METAL: the LRC machine translation system. (Working Paper LRC-84-2; April 1984). Austin, Texas: LRC.

Slocum, J. (1984a): Machine translation: its history, current status, and future prospects. In: *COLING 84: proceedings of the Tenth International Conference on Computational Linguistics* (Stanford University), 546–561.

Small, S. (1983): Parsing as cooperative distributed inference: understanding through memory interactions. In: King (1983), 247–276.

Smart, J. M. (1985): Letter to the author, July 23, 1985.

Smith, R. N. (1984): On personal translation. In: Frawley, W. ed. *Translation: literary, linguistic, and philosophical perspectives* (Newark: Univ. Delaware P.), 150–158.

Smoke, W. & Dubinsky, E. (1961): A program for the machine translation of natural languages. *Mechanical Translation* **6**, 2–10.

Snell, B. M. (1979) ed.: *Translating and the computer: proceedings of a seminar, London, 14th November 1978.* Amsterdam: North-Holland.

Sparck Jones, K. (1962): Mechanised semantic classification. In: NPL (1962), 418–433.

Sparck Jones, K. (1965): Experiments in semantic classification. *Mechanical Translation* **8**, 97–112.

Stachowitz, R. (1971): Requirements for machine translation: problems, solutions, prospects. In: Lehmann & Stachowitz (1971), 409–532.

Staples, C. O. (1983): The Logos Intelligent Translation System. Waltham, Mass.: Logos Corporation. Presented at Joint Conference on Artificial Intelligence, Karlsruhe, West Germany, August 10, 1983.

Stewart, G. (1975): Le langage de programmation REZO. Montréal: TAUM.

Stout, T. M. (1954): Computing machines for language translation. *Mechanical Translation* **1**(3), 41–46.

Straub, J. R. & Rogers, C. A. (1979): Computer analysis of Basic English as a first step in machine translation. *Progress in Cybernetics* **5**, 491–494.

Streiff, A. A. (1985): New developments in TITUS 4. In: Lawson (1985), 185–192.

Szanser, A. J. (1966): Machine translation research at the National Physical Laboratory, Teddington. *The Incorporated Linguist* **5**(4), 102–109.

Szanser, A. J. (1967): Machine translation — the evaluation of an experiment. *The Incorporated Linguist* **6**(4), 90–95.

Takahashi, S. *et al.* (1960): English–Japanese machine translation. In: Unesco (1960), 194–199.

Taube, M. (1961): *Computers and common sense: the myth of thinking machines*. New York: Columbia Univ. P.

TAUM (1971): TAUM 71. Projet de Traduction Automatique de l'Université de Montréal. Rapport, janvier 1971. Montréal: TAUM. (microfiche).

TAUM (1971a): Etudes en linguistique appliquée à la traduction automatique: été 1971. Montréal: TAUM.

TAUM (1973a): TAUM 73. Projet de Traduction Automatique de l'Université de Montréal. Rapport de janvier 1973. Montréal: TAUM.

TAUM (1973b): Le système de traduction automatique de l'Université de Montréal (T.A.U.M.). *Meta* **18**(1/2), 277–289.

Tesnière, L. (1959): *Eléments de syntaxe structurale*. Paris: Klincksieck.

Thiel, M. (1981): Die Systemarchitektur von SUSY unter benutzerspezifischem Aspekt. *Sprache und Datenverarbeitung* **5**(1/2), 20–25.

Thomas, R. B. (1957): The use of SEAC in syntactic analysis. In: Dostert (1957a), 151–161.

Thouin, B. (1982): The METEO system. In: Lawson (1982), 39–44.

Tikhomirov, B.D. (1984): Some specific features of software and technology in the AMPAR and NERPA systems of machine translation. *International Forum on Information and Documentation* **9**(2), 9–11.

Toma, P. (1959): SERNA system (Georgetown University, Machine Translation Programming Paper 1; General Analysis Technique, Russian–English). Washington, D.C.: Georgetown Univ. Institute of Languages and Linguistics.

Toma, P., Kozlik, I. A. & Perwin, D. G. (1970): SYSTRAN machine translation system. Final technical report, Sept. 1970 (RADC-TR-70-168). Griffiss AFB: RADC. (AD875290).

Toma,P., Kozlik, I. A. & Perwin, D. G. (1972): Optimization of SYSTRAN system. Final technical report, Oct. 70–Oct. 1971 (RADC-TR-72-73). Griffis AFB: RADC. (AD743315).

Toma, P., Kozlik, I. A. & Perwin, D. G. (1973): Optimization of SYSTRAN system. Final technical report, Jan. 1972–Mar. 1973 (RADC-TR-73-155). Griffiss AFB: RADC. (AD777850).

Toma, P. (1974): Computer translation: in its own right. In: *Kommunikationsforschung und Phonetik* (Hamburg: Buske), 155–164.

Toma, P. *et al.* (1974): Some semantic considerations in Russian–English machine translation. Final report, Feb. 1973–May 1974 (RADC-TR-74-189). Griffiss AFB: RADC. (AD787671).

Toma, P. (1976a): An operational machine translation system. In: Brislin, R.W. ed. *Translation: applications and research* (New York: Gardner P.), 247–259.

Toma, P. (1976b): SYSTRAN. In: FBIS (1976), 40–45.

Toma, P. (1977): SYSTRAN — ein maschinelles Uebersetzungssystem der 3. Generation. *Sprache und Datenverarbeitung* **1**(1), 38–46.

Toma, P. (1977a): Systran as a multilingual machine translation system. In: CEC (1977), 569–581.

Toma, P. (1984): Presentation given at International Seminar on Machine Translation, February 1984, Cranfield, England.

Tomita, M. (1985): Feasibility study of personal/interactive machine translation systems. In: Nirenburg (1985), 289–297.

Tosh, W. (1965): *Syntactic translation.* The Hague: Mouton.

Tosh, L. W. (1968): Initial results of syntactic translation at the Linguistics Research Center. *Lingua* **42**, 96–116.

Tosh, L. W. (1969): Translation model with semantic capability. *Linguistics* **55**, 56–69.

Tosh, L. W. (1970): Stratificational grammar and interlingual mapping for automatic translation. In: *Actes du Xe Congrès International des Linguistes, Bucarest, 28 août–2 septembre 1967* (Bucurest: Ed. Acad. Rép. Soc. de Roumanie), 4, 1049–1060.

Troyanskii, P. P. (1959): *Perevodnaya mashina P. P. Troyanskogo*: sbornik materialov . . . predlozhennoi P. P. Troyanskim v 1933 g. (Ed. I. K. Bel'skaya, L. N. Korolev, D. Y. Panov.) Moskva: Izd. Akad. Nauk SSSR.

Tschira, K. E. (1985): Looking back at a year of German–English MT with Logos. In: Lawson (1985), 215–235.

Tsujii, J.-I. (1980): Computer und semantische Repräsentation. *Sprache und Datenverarbeitung* **4**(2), 142–152.

Tsujii, J.-I. (1982): The transfer phase in an English–Japanese translation system. In: Horecky (1982), 383–390.

Tucker, A.B. (1984): A perspective on machine translation: theory and practice. *Communications of the ACM* **27**(4), 322–329.

Tucker, A. B. & Nirenburg, S. (1984): Machine translation: a contemporary view. *Annual Review of Information Science and Technology* **19**, 129–160.

Turing, A. M. (1948): Intelligent machinery. In: Meltzer, B. & Michie, D. eds. *Machine Intelligence* 5 (Edinburgh: Univ. P.), 1969, 3–23.

Turing, A. M. (1950): Computing machinery and intelligence. *Mind* **59**, 433–460. Repr. in: Feigenbaum, E. A. & Feldman, J. eds. *Computers and thought* (New York: McGraw-Hill), 11–35.

Ullrich, E. H. (1956): Comments on paper by Parker-Rhodes (1956). *Proceedings of the Institute of Electrical Engineers* 103B (suppl. 3), 474.

Unesco (1960): *Information processing: proceedings of the International Conference on Information processing, Unesco, Paris, 15–20 June 1959.* Paris: Unesco.

U.S. House of Representatives (1960): Research on mechanical translation. Report of the Committee on Science and Astronautics, U.S. House of Representatives, Eighty-sixth Congress, Second Session, House report 2021, June 28, 1960. Washington: U.S. Government Printing Office.

University of Washington (1960): Linguistic and engineering studies in the automatic translation of scientific Russian. Phase II. Technical report, October 1959. Seattle: Univ. of Washington.

Valle Bracero, A. & Fernández García, J. A. (1982): Traducción automática de títulos de artículos científicos del ruso al castellano. *Revista Espanola de Documentación Cientifica* **5**(3), 231–143.

Van Hoof, H. (1973): *International bibliography of translation.* München: Vlg. Dokumentation.

Van Dijk, T.A. (1977): *Text and context.* London: Longman.

Van Dijk, T.A. (1980): *Macrostructures: an interdisciplinary study of global structures in discourse, interaction, and cognition.* Hillsdale, N.J.: Erlbaum.

Van Slype, G. & Pigott, I. (1979): Description du système de traduction automatique SYSTRAN de la Commission des Communautés Européennes. *Documentaliste* **16**(4), 150–159.

Van Slype, G. (1979a): Deuxième évaluation du système de traduction automatique SYSTRAN anglais–français de la Commission des Communautés Européennes. Rapport final. Bruxelles: Bureau Marcel van Dijk.

Van Slype, G. (1979b): Evaluation of the 1978 version of the SYSTRAN English–French automatic system of the Commission of the European Communities. *The Incorporated Linguist* **18**(3), 86–89.

Van Slype, G. (1982): Conception d'une méthodologie générale d'évaluation de la traduction automatique. *Multilingua* **1**(4), 221–237.

Van Slype, G. (1983): *Better translation for better communication: a survey of the translation market, present and future.* Oxford: Pergamon.

Varga, D. (1967): Towards a new system of automatic analysis. *Computational Linguistics* **6**, 123–136.

Varile, G. B. (1983): Charts: a data structure for parsing. In: King (1983), 73–87.

Vasconcellos, M. (1984): Machine translation at the Pan American Health Organization. *British Computer Society, Natural Language Translation Specialist Group Newsletter* **14**, 17–34.

Vasconcellos, M. (1985): Management of the machine translation environment: interaction of functions at the Pan American Health Organization. In: Lawson (1985), 115–129.

Vasilevskii, A. D. *et al.* (1971): Eksperimental'nyi algoritm avtomaticheskogo perevoda patentnoi dokumentatsii s angliiskogo yazyka na russkii. *Nauchno-Tekhnicheskaya Informatsiya* 1971, Ser. 2, pt. 1, 29–34.

Vauquois, B., Veillon, G. & Veyrunes, J. (1965): Application des grammaires formelles aux modèles linguistiques en traduction automatique. *Kybernetika* **1**(3), 281–189.

Vauquois, B. (1966): Langages artificiels, systèmes formels et traduction automatique. In: NATO (1966), 211–236.

Vauquois, B. (1966a): Présentation du Centre d'Etudes pour la Traduction

Automatique (C.E.T.A.) du Centre National de la Recherche Scientifique. *T.A. Informations* 1966, pt. 1, 1–18.

Vauquois, B. (1969): Traduction automatique et traitement automatique des langues. *Automatisme* **14**(9), 368–372.

Vauquois, B. *et al.* (1970): Une notation des textes hors des contraintes morphologiques et syntaxiques de l'expression. *T.A. Informations* 1970, pt. 1, 1–20.

Vauquois, B. (1971): Modèles pour la traduction automatique. *Mathematiques et Sciences Humaines* **9**(34), 61–70.

Vauquois, B. (1975): *La traduction automatique à Grenoble.* Paris: Dunod.

Vauquois, B. (1976): Automatic translation — a survey of different approaches. *Statistical Methods in Linguistics* (Stockholm), 127–135.

Vauquois, B. (1977): L'évolution des logiciels et des modèles linguistiques pour la traduction automatisée. Grenoble: GETA.

Vauquois, B. & Boitet, C. (1984): Automated translation at GETA. Grenoble: GETA.

Veillon, G., Veyrunes, J. & Vauquois, B. (1967): Un metalangage de grammaires transformationnelles. In: Grenoble (1967). 50pp.

Veillon, G. (1968): Description du langage pivot du système de traduction automatique du C.E.T.A. *T.A. Informations* 1968, pt.1, 8–17.

Wagner, E. (1985): Rapid post-editing of Systran. In: Lawson (1985), 199–213.

Wall, R. E. (1960): The digital data-processing problem of machine translation of Russian to English. In: University of Washington (1960), 357–423.

Wang, W. S. Y., Chan, S. W. & T'sou, B. K. (1973): Chinese linguistics and the computer. *Linguistics* **118**, 89–117.

Wang, W. S. Y. *et al.* (1974): Development of Chinese–English machine translation system. Berkeley: Univ. California.

Wang, W. S. Y. *et al.* (1975): Chinese–English machine translation system. Final technical report, Sept. 72–Aug. 74 (RADC-TR-75-109). Griffiss AFB: RADC.

Wang, W. S. (1976): Chinese–English machine translation, Project on Linguistic Analysis, University of California, Berkeley. In: FBIS (1976), 24.

Wayne State University (1960): Summary of the proceedings of the Wayne State University conference of federally sponsored machine translation workers, held at Princeton Inn, Princeton, New Jersey, July 18–22, 1960. Detroit: Wayne State Univ.

Wayne State University (1968): Research in machine translation Russian–English: ten-year summary report 1958–1968. Detroit: Wayne State Univ.

Weaver, W. (1946): Record of interview with Dr. Andrew D. Booth, June 20, 1946. (Rockefeller Foundation Archives).

Weaver, W. (1947): Letter to Norbert Wiener, March 4, 1947. (Rockefeller Foundation Archives).

Weaver, W. (1948): Letter to Professor J. D. Bernal, 20th May 1948. (Rockefeller Foundation Archives).

Weaver, W. (1949): Translation. Repr. in: Locke & Booth (1955), 15–23.

Weissenborn, J. (1977): The role and form of analysis in machine translation: the automatic analysis of French at Saarbrücken. In: CEC (1977), 593–611.

Weizenbaum, J. (1976): *Computer power and human reason.* San Francisco: Freeman.

Werbow, S. N. (1961): Research on the Texas project. In: Edmundson (1961), 121–125.

Wheeler, P. & Lawson, V. (1982): Computing ahead of the linguists. *Ambassador International* March 1982, 21–22.

Wheeler, P. J. (1984): Changes and improvements to the European Commission's Systran MT system 1976/84. *Terminologie Bulletin* **45**, 25–37.

White, J. S. (1985): Characteristics of the METAL machine translation system at production stage. In: Nirenburg (1985), 359–369.

Whitelock, P. J. & Kilby, K. J. (1983): Linguistic and computational techniques in machine translation system design. Final report, December 1983 (CCL/UMIST report 84/2). Manchester: UMIST.

Wiener, N. (1947): Letter to Warren Weaver, April 30, 1947. (Rockefeller Foundation Archives).

Wilensky, R., Arens, Y. & Chin, D. (1984): Talking to UNIX in English: an overview of UC. *Comunications of the ACM* **27**(6), 574–593.

Wilks, Y.A. (1972): *Grammar, meaning and the machine analysis of language.* London: Routledge & Kegan Paul.

Wilks, Y. (1973a): An artificial intelligence approach to machine translation. In: Schank & Colby (1973), 114–151.

Wilks, Y. (1973b): The Stanford machine translation project. In: Rustin (1973), 243–290.

Wilks, Y. (1975a): An intelligent analyzer and understander of English. *Communications of the ACM* **18**(5), 264–274.

Wilks, Y. (1975b): Preference semantics. In: Keenan, E. ed. *Formal semantics of natural language* (Cambridge: Cambridge Univ. P.), 329–348.

Wilks, Y. (1978): Four generations of machine translation research and prospects for the future. In: Gerver, D. & Sinaiko, H. W. eds. *Language, interpretation and communication* (New York: Plenum), 171–184.

Wilks, Y. (1985): Letter to the author, 10 June 1985.

Wilms, F. J. M. (1981): Von SUSY zu SUSY-BSA: Forderungen an eine anwenderbezogenes Mü-Systems. *Sprache und Datenverarbeitung* **5**(1/2), 38–43.

Winograd, T. (1972): *Understanding natural language.* Edinburgh: Univ. P.

Witkam, A. P. M. (1981): Esperanto as intermediate language in computer networks — faults and remedies. Utrecht: BSO.

Witkam, A. P. M. (1983): Distributed language translation: feasibility study of a multilingual facility for videotex information networks. Utrecht: BSO.

Witkam, A. P. M. (1984): Distributed language translation, another MT system. Paper presented at International Seminar on Machine Translation, February 1984, Cranfield, England.

Wood, R. & Wright, L. (1985): More may not be better — a discussion note on CAT dictionaries. *Language Monthly* **19**, 6.

Woods, W. (1970): Transition network grammars for natural language analysis. *Communications of the ACM* **13**, 591–606.

Woods, W. (1973): An experimental parsing system for transition network grammars. In: Rustin (1973), 111–154.

Yamada, S. (1964): Segmentation et analyse syntaxique de la phrase japonaise en traduction automatique (système et grammaire). *Traduction Automatique* **5**(4), 102–111.

Yngve, V. H. (1955): Syntax and the problem of multiple meaning. In: Locke & Booth (1955), 208–226.

Yngve, V. H. (1955a): Sentence-for-sentence translation. *Mechanical Translation* **2**, 29–37.

Yngve, V. H. (1957): A framework for syntactic translation. *Mechanical Translation* **4**(3), 59–65.

Yngve, V. H. (1958): A programming language for mechanical translation. *Mechanical Translation* **5**(1), 25–41.

Yngve, V. H. (1960): A model and a hypothesis for language structure *Proceedings of the American Philosophical Society* **104**, 444–467

Yngve, V. H. (1960a): The COMIT system for mechanical translation. In: Unesco (1960), 183–187.

Yngve, V. H. (1961): MT at the Massachusetts Institute of Technology. In: Edmundson (1961), 126–132.

Yngve, V. H. (1964): Implications of mechanical translation research. *Proceedings of the American Philosophical Society* **108**, 275–281. Repr. in: Bruderer (1982), 33–47.

Yngve, V. H. (1967): MT at M.I.T. 1965. In: Booth (1967), 451–523.

Yngve, V. H. (1979): Addendum to Yngve (1964) in: Bruderer (1982), 47–49.

Zarechnak, M. M. (1957): Types of Russian sentences. In: Dostert (1957a), 135–141.

Zarechnak, M. (1959): Three levels of linguistic analysis in machine translation. *Journal of the Association for Computing Machinery* **6**(1), 24–32.

Zarechnak, M. & Brown, A. F. R. (1961): Current research at Georgetown University. In: Edmundson (1961), 63–87.

Zarechnak, M. (1962): A fourth level of linguistic analysis. In: NPL (1962), 160–171.

Zarechnak, M. (1976): Russian–English system, Georgetown University. In: FBIS (1976), 51.

Zarechnak, M. (1979): The history of machine translation. In: Henisz-Dostert, B. *et al.* (1979), 1–87.

Zholkovskii, A. K., Leont'eva, N. N., & Martem'yanov, Y. S. (1961): On the basic use of meaning in machine translation. In: Rozentsveig (1974), 115–141.

Zint, I. (1967): Ueber den gegenwärtigen Stand der automatischen Sprachbearbeitung. *Beiträge zur Linguistik und Informationsverarbeitung* **12**, 36–55.

Zubov, A. V. (1984): Machine translation viewed as generation of text with a pre-defined contents. *International Forum on Information and Documentation* **9**(2), 36–38.

Index